MW00440166

Charity's Children
The Long Days and Nights of the Iron Men

James Ciaravella, MD, FACS

Dr. C's Designs
Shreveport, Louisiana

Charity's Children: The Long Days and Nights of the Iron Men
Copyright © 2021 by James Ciaravella, MD, FACS

Dr. C's Designs
6030 Line Ave., Suite 500
Shreveport, LA 71106
www.westernmirrors.com

Cover concept by Dr. James Ciaravella
Cover and book design by Cypress House

Cover photograph of Charity Hospital by Jack Beech Industrial Photography courtesy of Tulane University Special Collections, Tulane University, New Orleans

Additional photographs in the text are from the author's collection or courtesy of Dr. Mathis Becker, Dr. Bill Browder, Dr. Larry Cohen, Dr. Martin Evans, Dr. Donald Palmisano, Mary Jane Ridgeway, Dr. Jane Todd, and Captain Tim Ursin

Publisher's Cataloging-in-Publication Data

Names:	Ciaravella, James M., author.
Title:	Charity's children : the long days and nights of the iron men / James Ciaravella, MD, FACS.
Description:	First edition.	Shreveport, Louisiana : Dr. C's Designs, [2021]	Includes glossary of medical terms, bibliographical references and index of physicians and other important people.
Identifiers:	ISBN: 978-1-7361549-2-2 (hardcover)	978-1-7361549-0-8 (paperback)	978-1-7361549-1-5 (epub)	LCCN: 2021901192
Subjects:	LCSH: Ciaravella, James M.	Heart surgeons--United States--Biography.	Surgeons--United States--Biography.	Physicians--United States--Biography.	Charity Hospital (New Orleans, La.)--History.	Heart--Surgery--United States--History.
Classification:	LCC: RD27.35.C53 C43 2021	DDC: 617.092--dc23

Printed in the USA

2 4 6 8 9 7 5 3 1

First edition

Dedication

To Len, who, though the kitchen closed at 10 o'clock on those nights I did emergency hearts, always managed to leave a plate in the warming drawer. The Iron Men who came before me. The thousands of patients who trusted us with their lives, and last but not least, the big Gray Lady herself—may she always stand as a monument to what was.

Contents

Foreword

Dr. Jim Ciaravella, a distinguished cardiothoracic surgeon, now retired, has authored *Charity's Children: The Long Days and Nights of the Iron Men* based on his experiences in surgical training at that storied institution in New Orleans. Charity Hospital, once one of the outstanding and largest training and teaching centers in the world, still stands, abandoned following the devastating Hurricane Katrina in 2005. Charity served the people of Louisiana and served as the primary teaching facility for two exceptional and proud medical schools, Tulane University and Louisiana State University.

Dr. Ciaravella recalls anecdotal experiences in detail: "Charity Hospital of Louisiana was an institution, a way of life, it was a culture, and it had soul," he wrote. He described the empathy and gentleness of the young surgeons as well as their proficiency in technical skills. "Every patient received the same level of care, despite their background," he stated. He continued, "I do know that I did train under Iron Men… they sure did teach us how to operate." The term "Iron Men" reflected hard work, long hours day and night, and the mental and physical strain of the vigorous training program commonly recognized as "chronic resident fatigue."

New Orleans has a long and distinguished history in surgical and medical education. The roots of that history evolved from the original Charity Hospital of 1832 and the Medical College of Louisiana founded in 1834, and represents an evolution in pursuit of excellence, marked by austerity but enriched by romanticism and tradition. During the formative years, survival engendered, even encoded, a certain strength and resilience during storms, hurricanes, floods, pestilence, epidemics, and war.

Despite natural disasters, New Orleans had a population of 58,000 in 1834, and a new 540-bed Charity Hospital had been erected just two years earlier, in 1832, on Common Street, now Tulane Avenue, on the site of the present abandoned structure. The Medical College of Louisiana was established by the state of Louisiana in 1834, and was led by Dr. Thomas Hunt of

Charleston, S.C., and Dr. Warren Stone of New York. In 1845, the state legislature authorized creation of a university, and an Act of 1847 provided that the medical college become the Department of Medicine of The University of Louisiana. By 1850, the capacity of Charity Hospital was over 1,000 beds, making it one of the largest hospitals in the world. Of the 15,000 or so patients admitted yearly, most were immigrants or foreign born by a ratio of greater than 5:1. New Orleans was the fourth largest city in the United States, the largest in the South, and vied with New York as the nation's leading port.

The training of surgeons became structured and formalized, first by Theodore Kocher—also the first surgeon to win a Nobel Prize—and others in Europe. Later, surgical training was optimized by William Stewart Halsted, first chairman of surgery at Johns Hopkins University. The development of surgical house-officer programs into surgical residency programs occurred at Tulane under the chairmanships of Rudolph Matas and Alton Ochsner. Dr. Matas is universally recognized as the "Father of Modern Vascular Surgery." Dr. Ochsner founded the Ochsner Clinic and subsequent Ochsner Medical Center.

In 1881, Paul Tulane, a wealthy philanthropist in Princeton, New Jersey, who had made a fortune in New Orleans, decided to establish an independent university in New Orleans, some sixty years after he conceived the idea. As a result, the Board of Administration of the Tulane Educational Fund was organized and took control over the University of Louisiana. On June 4, 1884, Act No. 43 created the Tulane University of Louisiana.

Dr. Ciaravella's experiences reflect an exciting, golden time in the progress of medicine and surgery. Many advances resulted from progress in the space program, with miniaturization and other electrophysical advances that improved pacemakers and monitoring devices for intensive care units. Organ transplantation evolved, and xenotransplantation was explored.

Minimally invasive surgery evolved, and special units for teaching it were introduced. An increasing number of women in surgery has been a significant advance, such that the number of women surgeons is now essentially the same as number of men.

Robert L. Hewitt, M.D.
Chairman of the Department of Surgery of Tulane
University School of Medicine, 1998–2006; Emeritus Professor, 2006

Preface

The patient on the table was a twenty-five-year-old man with his chest open. He was born with a condition preventing normal blood flow to the lower half of his body, coarctation of the aorta. I was a second-year surgical resident holding a stainless steel metal retractor keeping the lungs out of the surgeon's visual field.

Dr. Theodore Drapanas, chairman of the Tulane Medical School Department of Surgery, had put two vascular clamps on the aorta above and below the narrowed area. Using a pair of surgical scissors he precisely cut out the narrowed segment, the coarctation.

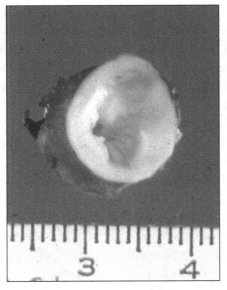

Resected coarctation of the aorta.

We were now looking into two open ends of the patient's aorta. The only thing keeping him from bleeding profusely were those clamps placed in an expert fashion. The anatomy was perfect. It was clean. There were no wasted motions. There was no blood loss.

Deftly, he sewed the two cut ends together with the special suture material. Again, no wasted motion, each stitch placed exactly where he wanted it to be. When finished, he released the clamps sequentially, allowing no air into his body. Normal blood flow was now restored to the lower part of his body for the first time since he had been born. He was cured. Watching that case changed my life and my direction.

On a routine physical exam, my father, a general surgeon, had discovered that the patient had no pulses in his feet and the diagnosis was made. The patient didn't know he had it and it had never been diagnosed until then.

He had referred the patient to Dr. Drapanas for surgical correction and Drapanas had invited me to scrub in on the case.

Nine years prior as an undergraduate student my senior year at Tulane, I had worked three days a week at the medical school with one of the attending thoracic surgeons, Dr. Glenn Kokame. I assisted him with cancer research using high pressure oxygen to the tissues, hyperbaric oxygenation. In the small room behind the Veterans Administration Hospital that housed the hyperbaric chamber, he showed me how to do "cut downs," a procedure in which an incision is made over a blood vessel so a tube can be placed in the vessel to give medicine, fluids or blood.

One day the door opened and one of the chief residents, Dr. Rudy Weichert, was standing in the doorway with the afternoon sun behind him. His white coat glowed from rim light. His name was stitched in red and underneath it read Tulane Department of Surgery. It was almost like a vision. I wanted one of those. I wanted to be a Tulane Surgery Resident.

I now knew I wanted to do that coarctation operation. I knew most of my life I would be a physician. When I entered Tulane Medical School I knew I would be a surgeon. I now knew that I wanted to be a thoracic and cardiac surgeon. Before I ended my career, I would do that operation on a forty-year-old woman and I would do it on newborn infants and many ages in between.

Weichert, Kokame, my father, and many more were all products of Charity Hospital. They were all Charity's children. The staff physicians, the interns and residents as well as any patient who had ever been born there, treated there or died there would be a child of Charity. I would be trained in the shadow of giants such as Dr. Rudolph Matas and Dr. Alton Ochsner and directly under two full-time chairmen and two acting chairmen. I would be of the influence of Dr. Oscar Creech and trained by Dr. Theodore Drapanas and Alton's son, Dr. John Ochsner.

The first day of my internship Dr. A.D. Smith, my third-year resident, took me aside and laid down the law. You may not finish this program. We'll know pretty quickly whether you have it or not. You will screw up and when you do I'm going to let you have it. If you do finish it you might be an Iron Man.

I would learn that I would have to operate until the last case was finished. I could do any case I wanted, but would have to be able to handle the complications of that procedure. I would have to bend but not break, stay the course and take what is given out to me, good or bad. I would have to take whatever was thrown at me by the resident above, the grateful or ungrateful patient, or the round-the-clock surgeries I had to perform.

Many days I would see the sun rise and set from the twelfth-floor operating room windows. One of my colleagues did a straight surgery internship followed by two years of surgery residency. She had not realized how physically and mentally strong she had to be to complete the program. There was virtually no rest.

I didn't realize until after I had retired what a stressful occupation I had chosen. As a house officer you were not supposed to show that you could break or sometimes even be emotionally involved.

This story is about the training of an "Iron Man" at Charity Hospital of Louisiana from my internship in 1968 to 1977, my last year as chief resident on the Tulane Surgical Service.

When meeting other physicians for the first time in social settings, they often ask, "Where did you train?" They don't ask, "Who did you train under?" I trained on the Tulane Service at Charity Hospital and I was "of" Creech, Drapanas and two different Ochsners.

No story about the Charity Hospital of Louisiana can be about one individual. It was born of many lives and gave birth to many lives, figuratively and metaphorically. It touched everyone. It was born of need to treat the needy. It was closed by a war yet survived many political battles. At any one time in its modern history it was staffed by those who had served in two different wars or were going to serve in a third. And many times its patients looked like they had been involved in one.

Although damaged by a Betsy in 1965, it rallied to treat victims. Each time it would come back stronger and better equipped to carry on its purpose, treat the ill and infirmed. Ultimately, politics and a Katrina would be too much and would close its doors to its original purpose. Plans are to have it reborn to serve those that served it, that is, if now a viral storm doesn't end those hopes and plans.

Initially my goal was to just tell my stories of Charity, my training and how it affected my career and my life. But no surgeon can operate alone in a vacuum. It requires a team. Thus, a saga has been born of many stories from many individuals all touched and trained in one way or another by this great institution.

It is about me and all of the children of Charity. It is about the effect we had on each other and the patients who were treated, saved and we tried to save.

Take a walk back in time when technology did not rule and govern our every move. Although it was a time of "see one, do one, and teach one," it was also a time when hands were laid on a patient and not robots. It was a time of judgment and experience and one-on-one care when modern means of testing and sophisticated exams were not available. Notes were handwritten in charts. Pictures were sketched and people were talked to face to face. Decisions were not made by gatekeepers or insurance companies and the end of the day might not come until the next morning.

It was also a time of war. It was not commonly known, but all medical school graduates were required to serve two years in the military branch of their choice. We also had a choice whether to serve after our internship or try to defer until after our residency.

The main function of the Charity Hospital System in the state of Louisiana was to provide health care to its citizens. This policy began when the first Charity Hospital was founded in 1736 by a gift of funds from a ship builder, Jean Louis. That first hospital was in the French Quarter and was called the Hospital of Saint John (L'Hôpital des Pauvres de la Charité). In 1834 the Daughters of Charity assumed control of the hospital and the Medical

College of Louisiana was formed. This would be the first medical school formed as a free-standing institution not supported by a university. In 1882 the medical school's name was changed following a donation by a very successful businessman and merchant, Paul Tulane.

Two other names of significant benefactors known to every Tulane or LSU student were Dr. Albert Miles and Issac Delgado. Both contributed significant funds to the hospital. The surgical amphitheaters on either wing of the twelfth floor, the operating room floor, bear their names.

This single institution later grew to a state wide system of free hospitals in every corner of the state and its center, a system not seen in any other state in this country. The Charity Hospital that I knew, the sixth one constructed, was opened in 1939 after being planned under the administration of Governor Huey P. Long, the "Kingfish." Acting through his administrator, Dr. Arthur Vidrine, Long maintained complete control over the appointment of attending physicians. This situation came to a head with the firing of Dr. Alton Ochsner, who at the age of thirty-one had been appointed chairman of the Tulane Surgery Department in 1927.

Able to pay or not, patients could be taken care of at seven different state-run hospitals. These hospitals, save one, were staffed by Tulane or LSU residents on a rotational basis. Shreveport's Confederate Memorial (now LSU/Ochsner Health Care) had its own residency training program.

The second purpose was to train the doctors finishing from both Tulane and LSU medical schools and elsewhere, in fields ranging from general medicine and surgery, any medical subspecialty to cardiac and neurosurgery.

Charity was a resident-run hospital. Yes, attending staff from both schools were assigned to every aspect of every specialty at Big Charity. On a day-to-day basis, or more likely, a night-to-night basis, it was the resident who admitted the patient, worked up the patient to determine the best course of treatment, operated on or treated the patient when needed and took care of the patient until discharge.

At every level, from intern to senior resident, which might be the seventh year in my case, the level below answered to the level above. If an intern or first-year resident had a problem he went to his immediate superior. You never went straight to the senior resident and Lord help you if you went to the staff. A second-year resident might be on the only rotation where you answered directly to a staff man. Tulane's LM-4 cancer rotation was such as was the rotation to Baptist Hospital.

Charity's strength was not only in the fact that it had a huge volume of patients seen on an elective as well as emergency basis or in the fact that the residents operated on or treated patients with conditions not seen in other programs.

The most unique feature was that one hospital was shared by two major medical schools. Every twenty-four-hour period was either an LSU (L) or Tulane (T) admit day. Every night, no matter what service was on call a full cadre of residents were available to take care of ANY condition that might come through the doors. Charity was a destination hospital. Patients admitted to Big Charity were not transferred to any other hospital. Any new patient coming to the hospital was assigned a number designating him to be a Tulane or LSU patient, forever. On non-admit nights the other residency program kept a contingent of physicians in the hospital to take care of any problems that might arise on their patients only.

Historically there had always been political jousting between the two medical schools for control of the hospital. This political conflict went back as far as when LSU Medical School was founded in 1931 and continued into the seventies when I was there. There was no doubt that LSU wanted control of the whole system. I heard this from my father as he talked about Board of Administrator's meetings held in the fifties. However, the house staff of each school got along well and there was little bickering among us.

I was a Tulane Medical School student and Tulane surgical resident for a total of eleven years. I have written this book from my perspective as a Tulane resident. That's what I was. Initially, my intent was to relate just my many stories and experiences.

As a surgery resident one has to account for all their procedures and surgeries performed. In order to become board certified or be inducted as a Fellow of the American College of Surgeons, your cases are listed and examined. I didn't know anyone who kept a diary, but you do keep your operative reports or record your cases in a journal. I was able to find the journals of all the cases I operated on from the beginning of my second year of residency through 1977 when I was chief resident. I was then able to use many of these cases as stepping stones to aid in telling this story.

As I started writing about significant events, such as the Howard Johnson's shooting in 1973 or a specific operation that Dr. Drapanas performed, or a senior resident who had a profound impact on me, I found myself reaching out to my peers from that era. I had not spoken to most of them for forty-five years.

Bill Browder and I were chief residents together during the 1976–1977 year. Bill has been most helpful with facts and in stirring my memory. Bill, Jan McClanahan, Larry Hollier, Russell Woo, and Bob Hewitt gave me valuable eyewitness accounts to the Howard Johnson events, as did my good friend Jim Dowling shortly after it happened. Mathis Becker was chief of thoracic when I was a third year. He and I have spent hours corresponding and talking about those days, cases and stories.

Martin Evans was a third-year resident when I was chief resident. I appreciated his reflections of a time when he was assistant clinical director and chief resident. Butch Knoepp has provided many stories and insight of those later years, as well as a history of his father. Bob Thornton, an intern when I was a second-year, shared a comparison of Charity and Grady Hospital. Bill, Martin, Larry Cohen, Jane Todd, my intern when I was a third-year resident and Don Palmisano, have provided numerous photos, along with mine, to augment this story. I am most grateful to my old chiefs, George Barnes, Philip Brewer, Al Guynes, Russell Woo, John Gage and Bill Woolverton whom I was able to find. I appreciated the richness and patina of their stories and am thankful that they even remembered me. Mo Bethea shared insight and stories about Dr. Drapanas.

Mark Drapanas, one of Dr. Drapanas' sons, was most generous in sharing an early history of his late father. These and two dozen more I was able to locate have shared their stories and helped me relive and remember a golden time in medicine.

A bowed surgical cap and mask-covered face and acknowledgement goes out to Jim Dowling, Gary Dotson, Chet Noble, Bob Hanchey, Fred Sandifer, A.D. Smith, Phil Robichaux, Art Axelrod, and Howard Nelson, Iron Men and Charity's children who have passed on.

I'm sure LSU residents who had spent as many years as I did at Charity could relate similar experiences. I was not the only Tulane medical student to go into thoracic and cardiovascular surgery. Several other classmates of mine did select that specialty, but I was the only one from my class to train at Charity in cardiothoracic surgery.

In fact, because of Tulane's rich history in the field of vascular surgery with men like Rudolph Matas, Alton Ochsner, Michael DeBakey and Oscar Creech, many of my classmates did pursue it. My advantage and the reason that I was there a little longer than most was that I was the first Tulane surgery resident to do two full years of clinical cardiac surgery training and no research year. One of my friends jokingly said, "Well, it just took you longer to learn it." Perhaps so, but as you will later read, the rules changed in the middle of my training.

I have devoted a significant space to Dr. Theodore Drapanas, the chairman of the Tulane Department of Surgery from 1968 until his untimely death in 1975. I was fortunate to have Dr. Drapanas during those important operating years when I was a third-year resident and beginning of my cardiothoracic residency. You will also see that Dr. John Ochsner played a significant role in my training.

As Tulane residents we had little to no formal contact with the full-time LSU staff. Dr. Isidore Cohn was chairman of the LSU Department of Surgery during my time at Charity. Larry Hollier, who was an LSU resident and trained under Dr. Cohn, has reviewed the section on Dr. Cohn that I have written.

Larry and I were interns and first-year residents at the same time at Charity. We both entered the Service in the summer of 1970. After completing his general surgery residency, Larry went on to complete a vascular fellowship under Dr. Jesse Thompson in Texas, one of the first formal vascular surgery programs established in this country. He then returned to LSU and started the first vascular program on the LSU service at Charity Hospital and later the Mayo Clinic. Hollier and Bob Batson, another LSU resident and vascular surgeon, formed a strong relationship. Bob was above average height and let's just say that Larry was not. They operated together and when seen at Charity together, they got the nickname "Batman and Robin." At the American College of Surgeons convention in Chicago one year, Hollier found a gallery on Michigan Avenue that sold original cells from movies and posters from TV series and movies. And there it was, a poster of Batman and Robin. Larry (Robin) bought one to give to his partner Batson (Batman).

Dr. Larry Hollier with Batman and Robin poster.

Dr. Rowena Spencer was another special individual, not only with regard to my training and my family, but in the history of pediatric surgery as a specialty in this country.

Drapanas, Spencer and a few other topics are presented at length in special sections I call *lagniappe*. This is a south Louisiana term that means "a little something extra."

The stories you are about to read are true. Although a couple of names have been changed, for the most part, I have used actual physician's names with their permission. Nothing is aimed to embarrass anyone. I have tried to be very honest and transparent about mistakes I have made. We all made them and hopefully we learned by our mistakes.

We were learning under fire. It would serve no purpose to relate errors made by other residents and name them, except in cases that they have given me permission. It has been more than forty years since I left Charity. Unfortunately, as a natural occurrence of life-and death, a fair number of the individuals I trained under or with are gone or their memories are fading. In most instances I didn't find this out until I started doing computer searches on them. In some instances, such as Gary Dotson and Jim Dowling, their widows have given me valuable information, stories and facts. Also, patient's initials only, with a few exceptions are used.

To the medically educated readers and individuals who have been a patient, as we all have, the question will often rise, "Why didn't they just order a ____?" or "perform a ____?", or "give the patient ____?" You must understand that in the sixties and seventies most of the sophisticated diagnostic modalities that we have today were not invented. And, if they were, we didn't have them at Charity.

As a medical student, one of the favorite questions that would be asked was, if you were on a desert island, what medications would you want to have with you. To most the answers were penicillin, morphine, aspirin and perhaps digitalis. After beginning my eight year of training, a Special Fellowship in Cardiac Surgery at the Mayo Clinic, I was exposed to my first CAT scanner. I wanted one on my desert island.

There will never be another Charity Hospital in today's litigious governed world. The idea of residents being mainly in charge of total patient care for a hospital, and learning on them, would be unheard of. Besides, why would a patient have his soul and everything else exposed on a fourteen-bed ward with no privacy? These patients were ours. We took care of them to the best of our ability. They are responsible, in a large part, for whatever successes we have had later in life.

Some of the events and antics may seem a little irreverent. Some things were mainly done to relieve stress. There were some that expressed their stress in a different way. I knew a resident who had diarrhea every Thursday before Dr. Drapanas' walking Grand Rounds.

There were also some third-year residents who broke unwritten rules by going to their fellow third-year's weekly clinic and stealing their patient's charts. They were known to cherry-pick the gallbladders, thyroids, and stomachs ready for surgery out of another resident's shopping cart baskets, call up the patient and admit them in to their service. Most didn't do this. The higher up the ladder you climbed, the closer the relationship was formed with your peers. For all that was done and said there was a camaraderie, a brotherhood that existed. You supported your fellow resident to the best of your ability. That way everyone involved, patients and medical personnel, came out ahead.

In the late sixties, in one of the last lectures Dr. Creech gave in the Delgado amphitheater, he looked about the audience and said, "If I am ever in an accident and need emergency care, you bring me to Charity Hospital and nowhere else." I did the same thing when my son was run over by a car in 1974.

Prologue

It was a cool February day as we waited for the first float of the Mardi Gras parade. Policemen on large black-and-white Harleys had just passed and a fire truck was coming into view. It was an old model with an open cab and brass bell with a rope attached. It was huge with its lights flashing and firemen holding on to the back. It stopped just a few feet from us when I saw the driver look down at my dad, "Hey, Doc, is that your boy? How about a ride?"

My father lifted me up and I sat next to the driver, his patient. I rode along with them for a little while, with my father walking alongside. Occasionally I would ring that big shiny brass bell.

I was born in, grew up in, and trained in New Orleans. My father was one of many out-of-state students who came to Tulane Medical School to get a medical degree. He was the second oldest of six children raised by his immigrant father who was born in the Sicilian mountain town of Alessandria della Rocca. His mother had died when he was twelve from what was thought to be rheumatic fever. Times were tough and many days he did not have enough money to pay for a meal.

When I was an undergraduate student at Tulane he took me to the Richardson Memorial Building on the uptown campus. At that time, and in his, the first two years of medical school were taught there. He showed me the two-story tall amphitheater where he attended lectures. We explored the large room with the flat wooden tables where he dissected cadavers and studied anatomy. He then brought me downstairs to the ground floor "basement" which held a large vat filled with formalin where the cadavers were kept. Leno had been the diener, the man in charge of tending to the cadavers, when my father was in school. He told me about the large glass jar full of gold teeth Leno had accumulated.

Most of my childhood I wanted to be either a fireman or a cowboy. Later, after taking an aptitude test in the ninth grade, my teacher, Vita B. Aime, told me I should be a forest ranger. She said I didn't relate to people well and was a loner. Hell, I was an only child. Despite those early dreams, I think I always knew I would be in medicine.

Some nights after my father got home from his day at the office or in surgery my mother and I would go out with him to make house calls. Afterward, many times, we would wind up in the French Market parked in front of the Morning Call Café getting what I called coffee and donuts, or what is officially known as cafe au lait and beignets. Ah, the beignets, those air-filled puffs of deep-fried dough covered with powdered sugar that seemed to explode when you bit into them getting sugar all over you. The original Morning Call had curbside service. My father would have to roll up the window a little so the metal tray could hook on the glass. The coffee would come in those heavy white mugs, half French Market coffee and half warm milk.

Morning Call Cafe, circa 1950s.

On weekends, sometimes just he and I would make house calls. Early on he taught me how to drive by sitting on his lap and holding on to the steering wheel. At first my feet couldn't reach the pedals. Later, on Sundays, we'd go down to the then-deserted, warehouse district of New Orleans around Tchoupitoulas Street, way before the Convention Center was built, and I would drive.

Most of the time when he was making a house call, I'd wait in the car as he'd carry his black leather bag into a shotgun house in just about every section of New Orleans: Mid City, Gentilly, and the Carrolton area, to name just a few. He knew every street and shortcut, and I never saw him look at a street map.

On the occasions that I would go into the houses with him, I would stay in the front room. He'd go in the back to see the mother, the grandfather, the sick and the dying. Quite often they would offer him a cup of coffee and we'd sit there. "You gonna be a doctor like your daddy?" they'd ask. They'd all ask it. "What do you wanna be when you grow up, a doctor like your daddy?" It was all I ever knew. There really wasn't anything else. As I sit and reminisce about those times and my eyes fill with tears thinking about what was, what medicine was then, how pure and uncomplicated: a stethoscope, a little leather case in his bag that contained those glass ampoules of Cedilanid, Lasix, and other drugs. He would score the neck of them with a little file and snap the top off before drawing up the fluid with a needle and glass syringe.

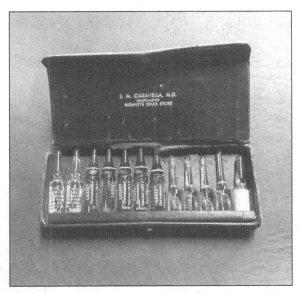

Drug ampoules from Dr. James Ciaravella Sr.'s medicine bag.

There was that long flat metal case with the hinged top that contained the mercury-filled glass tube that he used to take blood pressures with. "Come see me in the office next week." or "I'll stop by and see her in a couple of days." He'd tell them. And then in the car on the way home he'd tell me about them, "You know I delivered all their babies and did a hysterectomy on the mama and took out the son's appendix." I think he knew every procedure, every operation, and hospital admission of every one of the thousands of patients he'd ever seen. Yes, I wanted to be a doctor like my daddy.

My medical school class contained students from all parts of the country. If one wanted to be admitted to Tulane Medical School it was known that undergraduate students from Tulane had a better shot at being admitted than those from elsewhere, if everything else was equal. It also followed that Tulane Medical School graduates were favored when it came time for appointing internships.

My class was the last class admitted by Dr. Harold Cummins. He was a caricature of a medical school professor. He smoked a pipe and wore little wire-rimmed glasses. He was very unassuming and had a quiet demeanor about him. Known as the "father of dermatoglyphics" Cummins was a pioneer in the study of palm and finger prints. With a doctorate in anatomy, he had been head of that department and an associate dean of the medical school.

In order to be admitted to medical school, one had to have good grades and you had to have passed the MEDCAT exam but, in his eyes, the most important qualification for admission to medical school was what he thought of you during his interview. If you had a close family member who was a Tulane Medical school graduate, that didn't hurt you a bit. Four of my classmate's fathers or uncles had been classmates of my fathers. "Why do you want to be a doctor?" he asked. I told him I wanted to help people, to make them better. I had watched my father do it all my life.

I grew up hearing not only about Dr. Cummins but the history of Tulane Medical School. I had read the biography on Dr. Rudolph Matas. How he did the first intrasaccular repair of an arterial aneurysm in 1882, his pioneering work with Yellow Fever, and that he was the first of two New Orleanians who would be president of the American College of Surgeons. He also was the chairman of the Tulane Department of Surgery for thirty years.

I had been told how the Flexner Report published in 1910 listed Tulane Medical School as one of the few Southern schools worthy of development.

I heard that the formal designation of the Tulane Surgical Service at Charity Hospital had been named in 1925 and was still in existence in my day.

I had met Matas' successor, Dr. Alton Ochsner, who had become one of the most daring and fearless surgeons in the South. I knew about his feuds with Huey Long and the letter. The letter he wrote about leaving Tulane because of Long's policies and how Long then dismissed him from the staff of Charity Hospital. This would only lead to Ochsner becoming more recognized in the community and to his founding the Ochsner Clinic.

I had heard about Huey Long being instrumental in the founding of the LSU Medical School in 1931 to serve the students of Louisiana who couldn't afford the more expensive Tulane that catered mainly to out-of-state students. I had grown up hearing about these facts as long as I can remember from a father who devoured history and learning.

Following graduation from medical school, my father had been a resident on the old Independent Service at Charity Hospital. Much later he would be on the Board of Administrators of the whole Charity Hospital System. Our civics class in high school had toured Charity in 1956 and of course they took us down to the morgue. A fresh autopsy was being carried out on one of the tables. As young teenagers we stared wide-eyed with our mouths agape. It was nothing like the frogs we had dissected in biology. These were real dead naked people with their insides hanging out. It was cool.

Charity was more than an eighteen-story building made of steel, concrete, glass, and granite. It was a living entity. It breathed, it died and it bled. Its heart and soul were its emergency and operating rooms. Its abdomen contained unending wards filled and over-filled with patients from all walks of life, all corners of the state, all shapes, sizes and colors.

It spoke English with a Brooklyn accent, Cajun French, Spanish, Lower Ninth Ward jive, and Irish Channel "yat." There were unintelligible screams of pain, birthing mothers' "ooh ee's," children's cries, next-of-kin's sobs, and the sound of the occasional gunshot. Its bowels contained a labyrinth of underground tunnels, dining rooms, and a morgue for the dead.

It was held together by a glue composed of any body fluid one could imagine, patient's blood, pus, baby's tears, doctor's and nurse's sweat, and occasionally a physician's own blood. And on more than one occasion it was patched up with band-aids, miles upon miles of adhesive tape, and even rolls of duct tape. Its eyes could be pinpoint, bloodshot, black and blue, nonreactive, or jaundiced yellow. Ironically, on top of it all was a beach and an indoor playground.

In Mike King's *A Spirit of Charity*, he describes Charity Hospital as "the very definition of an urban hospital dedicated to serving the poor." Lady Liberty's motto, "Give me your tired your poor, your huddled masses," could easily be adapted to a cardboard sign hung on Big Charity's front or back door reading, "Give me your tired, your poor, your injured and dying. Pay or not you're welcome through these portals to enter twenty-four hours a day, seven days a week, this house of caring. We may fail at perfection but excel at attempting to heal." It truly was a "House of God."

Every Friday afternoon at three o'clock you were expected to be present in the library of the surgery department on the eighth floor of the medical school for the Death and Complications conference (D&C). Unless you were scrubbed in emergency surgery, your wife had just delivered your first born or you yourself were a patient in ICU, attendance was mandatory.

That room contained all the publications and personal library of Dr. Rudolph Matas. It also contained a large glass container with the formaldehyde preserved brain of Dr. Matas, a condition for donating his library to Tulane.

When Dr. Lewis Flint became chairman of the department he told Bill Browder to get rid of Matas' brain. Browder then kept the brain on the floor in his office when he was a staff attending. One day Dr. Edward Krementz took the brain and, supposedly, placed it in Matas' crypt in the cemetery. Matas' will be damned. When you're gone, you're gone.

A weekly report was printed called the Bugle. It contained a list of all the cases done for the previous week by the four general surgery services, plastic surgery, and thoracic surgery. The patient's name and age were listed as well as the operation performed and the surgeon. At the back of the Bugle were listed any and all complications and a separate sheet for each death from the preceding week.

If you screwed up and your case was presented and discussed, you took the criticism as a learning experience from the attending. If you were allowed to sit at that table in the reflection of the formaldehyde-filled jar containing Matas' brain, you didn't smile or laugh unless everyone else did. That conference was not for your entertainment, although sometimes you felt it was for the staff's.

Tulane Medical School Surgery Library.

You had better be prepared to discuss or justify any complication and certainly any death. There are three recognized errors in surgery: errors in judgment, errors in technique and patient error. In other words a patient's condition might prevent a good result or contribute to a poor result in his outcome. However, you *never* used that last error as a reason for a death or complication.

When asked why a patient died or suffered a complication, the resident's answer was always "I should have ___." "I didn't ___." or "I could have___" etc. If one of the attendings came to your aid and said, "The patient should have

___ " or "I don't think it would have mattered because if ___ " that was okay and you might be spared the blame. It was *always* your fault.

The mood in that room was always very sober. There were no name cards telling one where to sit, but it was a given that interns should sit on the back row and pretty much your rank went in ascending order toward the head of the table. Drapanas and the staff always sat at the head. When I became a more senior resident I preferred a seat in the middle, still in rifle range, but not always in eye contact.

One of the lightest moments, I believe to occur in that room centered around John Church. John was a medical school classmate of mine and did a plastic surgery residency. Not only did he have a great sense of humor, but he seemed to always have a way of using humor to defuse any situation.

When he was on an out-of-town rotation, a patient came to the ER with a dildo in his rectum. The item was removed, but because it was done in the OR it was listed on the weekly Bugle as a case.

Of course, Dr. Drapanas asked John about the unique foreign body. John, "Well, Dr. Drapanas I didn't know whether to remove it or change the battery."

Dr. Earl Peacock, a plastic surgeon on the staff, had a different take on the cause of things happening. He would always press the resident for an answer as to why a patient had died. Of course he would be told all the medical, scientific, and other reasons leading up to death. Nothing was the right answer. Then he would volunteer it, "Doctor, it was the 'death hormone." Sometimes it was just as good an answer as any.

Whereas everyone was at risk in Friday D&C conference Saturday morning Grand Rounds held in the Delgado amphitheater was designed to feature just two or three cases. These were usually presented by the third year residents and offered the staff, full time and visiting, a time to show their stuff. It was still intimidating to be at the bottom of the pit and having everyone looking down on you.

Grand Rounds, Delgado Amphitheater, Charity Hospital.

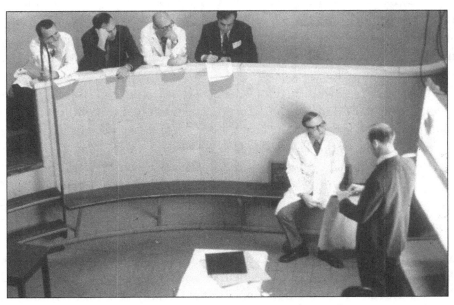

Ruary O'Connell presents to Grand Rounds.

We learned a lot of surgery operating on patients with penetrating trauma. These informally belonged to what we called the "knife-and-gun club."

The Creech Era

In December 1967, during my senior year of medical school, Dr. Oscar Creech, chairman of the Department of Surgery at Tulane, died from complications of reticulum cell sarcoma. Creech was an incredible man as well as a surgeon. After receiving his medical degree from Jefferson Medical College in 1941 he went "looking for action" and began his training at Charity Hospital. Like many physicians, his internship was cut short by World War II. He served as a combat surgeon in the North African and Italian campaigns and he received the Purple Heart for injuries received in combat. He returned to Charity in 1945, initially seeking a residency in Obstetrics and Gynecology.

Because of the flood of other physicians coming out of the service, he was told he would have to wait for a position to open. After encouragement by a friend he began a surgical residency instead. Creech was a natural surgeon and investigator. By the time he had finished his residency, Dr. Michael DeBakey had left Tulane for Baylor University. Recognizing Creech's potential, DeBakey recruited Creech to Baylor. These early days of vascular reconstruction saw Creech on the cutting edge of its development. So much so, that his wife, Dorothy, actually sewed nylon tubes to fashion vascular grafts on her sewing machine at home.

In 1956, Creech returned to Tulane as Henderson Professor and chairman of the Tulane Surgery Department, a position he held until shortly before his death. For the last few months of his life, he had even accepted the position of Dean of the Tulane Medical School.

Besides regional perfusion of carcinomas, Creech's interest in malignant melanoma also involved culturing melanoma cells in the lab in order to achieve a better treatment of this ravaging and highly malignant, but sometimes unpredictable disease. He excelled as a vascular surgeon.

His paper on the definitive surgical treatment of abdominal aortic aneurysms was published as the lead article in the *Annals of Surgery* in 1968. Although his technique of endoaneurysmorrhaphy became the standard surgical procedure for the treatment of these deadly conditions, he always credited Rudolph Matas with the idea.

Philip Brewer, chief cardiac resident in 1969, George Barnes, general surgery chief, and others, to a man, "admired the code of conduct he demanded which implied politeness, consideration for co-workers, and respect for their superiors." They all described an incredible efficiency at the operating table.

He possessed a keen sense of humor and loved to teach. A favorite tool he used in the operating room was to have the medical student use a grease pencil to draw the anatomy of the abdominal aorta and all its branches on a glass partition.

Creech assembled around him a highly capable cadre of notable surgeons. They included Dr. Keith Reemstma who had been born on a Navajo reservation, did a series of successful chimpanzee-to-human kidney transplants and later became chairman of the department of surgery at Columbia University College of Physicians and Surgeons.

Phil Brewer described Reemstma as "a surgical genius masquerading as a nice guy."

Dr. Glen Kokame, growing up in Hawaii, had led an early delinquent life. Upon facing a judge and given the choice of joining the Army or going to jail, needless to say he joined up. He later became the Hawaiian knot-tying champion. After graduating from Tulane Medical School he became a thoracic surgeon and was appointed to the surgery department staff.

I worked with Kokame when I was an undergraduate student and again after my second year of medical school doing cancer research with hyperbaric oxygenation. I accompanied him to staff out-of-town surgery cases and even got to sit in on staff meetings of the surgery Department.

At one of these meetings, Reemstma, Dr. Bob Schramel, a thoracic surgeon on staff who had put in New Orleans' first cardiac pacemaker, and Creech discussed a "patient" they had operated on. One of them owned a racehorse kept at the Fairgrounds that had developed a surgical problem. I don't know what the problem was, but one of the most highly trained and educated teams of non-veterinary surgeons in the South operated on a horse and cured it.

Dr. Edward Krementz became acting chairman following the death of Creech. Krementz was a well-known and respected surgical oncologist and had worked closely with Creech in cancer research and treatment. His interest in the treatment of malignant melanoma involved the aggressive use of regional perfusion with warm blood and chemotherapeutic agents.

With Creech's death Tulane Surgery was left with a great void. There was no question that the corps of residents that finished their training before and during the year of Creech's death was "Creech trained." Barnes felt Creech had gone out of his way to make a position for him in the surgical program. He described Creech as having an incredible efficiency at the operating table. There was no wasted dissection.

When Drapanas took over about a year after Creech's death, some of the more senior residents felt they were disowned by Drapanas. For the most part they were Creech trained. They had been through a limbo phase with a temporary chairman and then Drapanas came. Their views and methodology had been those of Creech. Some had left the program to go in the service or do research at another facility. When they returned after Creech's death not only did they experience a new entity, but a whole new philosophy.

One of the most memorable Creech lectures I was able to attend as a student had more to do with who was in the audience rather than the surgical lesson of the day. Stephen Zax, a surgical intern was rumored to have been dating the beautiful red-headed movie star Jill St. John.

Some doubted this to his face. As bold as Babe Ruth pointing over the wall promising a home run, he assured all that he would produce the starlet. One Saturday, sure enough, the lovely Miss St. John accompanied by the always-tanned Dr. Zax entered the second level of the Delgado Amphitheater. And, of course the timing was such that most were already seated as they made their way down a couple of rows to Creech's lecture. The Boss welcomed her, and the show began.

In the summer of 1967, another very noted movie star would not make it to Charity's back ramp. Jayne Mansfield had just performed at a nightclub in Biloxi and was on her way to New Orleans for another engagement. Before I-10 was built, the only way to do this trip was on Highway 90 or what was known as the Chef Menteur Highway. Through the marshes and fishing camps of the south Louisiana, it wound around Lake Pontchartrain. Her driver was blinded by a fog of mosquito control mist and their 1966 Buick plowed into the back of an eighteen-wheeler. All were killed instantly except for her three children.

Part I
General Surgery Training

Intern, 1968–1969

The intern is not a surgeon, and he will never get to be one unless he first suffers the indignities and long hours required of every first-year house officer. No matter how many years I intended to spend in training or what I wanted to specialize in, there had to be a first year, the beginner's year. That year was known as my internship. For those few graduates finishing medical school who were undecided as to what field of medicine they wanted to practice, a rotating internship would theoretically give them exposure to different specialties. If you wanted to do a surgery residency, the goal was to be accepted to a straight surgery internship and get the most surgical exposure you could. This would allow you to get some surgical experience and give you exposure to the members of the surgical staff. More importantly it gave them exposure to you.

Just because one had been accepted as an intern in the Tulane Surgery program there was no guarantee that he or she, would be accepted as a resident. Unlike many of the other well-known programs, Tulane did not operate on a pyramid system.

At the senior resident level it was possible to have as many as eight positions. As an intern you couldn't fully comprehend, and really, wouldn't even be aware of how this juggling of personnel (doctors) went about. There were straight surgery interns who went into ENT, urology, neurosurgery and orthopedics. There were also surgery interns who realized that Charity Hospital was not the kind of experience they wanted or that perhaps they could get better training in their specialty in a hospital served by a different medical school. Nothing was guaranteed or could be taken for granted. Looking back at it this thing called a Charity Hospital Internship it was analogous to the intensity of an elite military unit's training.

Since all interns served a month in the medical admit room and a month in the emergency room (ER), a straight surgery internship assured you of at least ten months on the surgery wards, but it also gave one the option of doing months on services other than surgery.

Following the internship year each successive year of your residency was named in that order: first-year resident, second-year resident, etc. When you were a Tulane or LSU medical student and if you were allowed to write a note on a progress sheet or sign your history and physical for a patient, you signed your name and after it put the letter "T" or "L" followed by what year student you were. If you were a senior, you signed your name followed by T4. Some us who had been Tulane students and did our residencies at Charity would jokingly refer to ourselves as T6 or T7, etc. Only a few of us could put "T11" and I only knew of one T12—Bill Woolverton, one of my chief residents. After I finished my residency, the designation was changed and residents were called "house officers." You would then be a house officer one, two, or three, etc.

An intern is a physician. He has a diploma stating that he has a medical degree. He can write prescriptions, write orders on a chart, and sew up wounds in the ER and at the discretion of his senior resident, maybe even close the skin after a surgical case. He might get to operate on some hemorrhoids, take out an appendix or do an amputation. But, despite his mother bragging about "her son the doctor" or "her son the surgeon," woe be it unto him if he lets it go to his head.

The intern is at the bottom of the totem pole and most of the time a glorified blood drawer, dressing changer, IV starter and any other number of menial but necessary tasks. He will spend hours in the operating room but will spend most of his time swinging on a Deaver retractor. He will hold so many retractors that first year he will think they are actually part of his arm. No matter what the abdominal case was, there was always room for and a need for an intern to hold the guts out of the way.

The only thing worse than holding a retractor was holding two of them, one in each hand. He would operate through the night, make rounds, and if lucky get a bite to eat before he started all over again. His patients called him "doctor," but more likely by his superiors he would be called "boy."

As interns, we received $325 a month. Normally there was a $100-a-month salary increase from your internship to first-year residency. In the spring of 1969 the Louisiana State Legislature voted an across-the-board raise for all residents and interns at Charity amounting to $300 a month. That meant that I went from an intern making $325 a month to a first-year resident making $625 a month. I was single at the time so that was the good news. It was even better news for married house officers. The bad news was we hardly had any time off to spend it and when you did have a break, you might be too tired to enjoy it.

The formal training year starts July 1 and really doesn't end until you retire. You never stop learning. Over the past four years of medical school I had walked into Charity dozens of times. This time it was different.

General Surgery, Charity

I had taken this walk down these halls, with their granite and marble floors and walls, many times. Having parked at the Tulane Medical School parking lot, it was a familiar journey. However, that July day of 1968 was different in that almost overnight I had traded the short brown lab coat of a Tulane medical student for the long white lab coat of a Charity Hospital intern. On the left side was a colorful patch of the State of Louisiana, and sewn on the pocket in red was INTERN CHARITY HOSPITAL.

State of Louisiana patch from house officer's coat and ID tag.

This coat and others like it would represent your identity for the next year. It and your picture ID tag got you unlimited access to the hospital we called the "Big Free," "Big Charity." or the "Big Gray Womb."

Some thought the coat was like Superman's cape and would make them invincible; they would deal with the reality of that in no uncertain terms. No, you weren't indestructible, far from it, but you had achieved your goal of a medical degree and were part of the house staff of one of the finest, busiest and largest teaching hospitals in the country. Charity was known to be one of the "Big Three." Along with Cook County in Chicago and Los Angeles County General in L.A., all in their heyday had over 3,000 beds. Charity was the second-oldest working hospital in the country, second by only two months to New York's Bellevue Hospital.

Charity's beds were divided among the main hospital that faced Tulane Avenue and was bookended by Tulane and LSU Medical Schools.

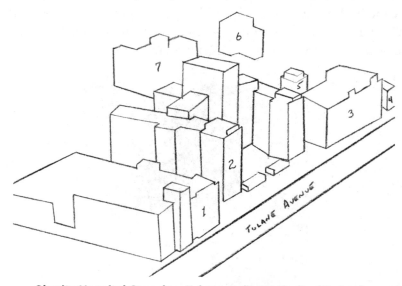

Charity Hospital Complex, Tulane and LSU Medical Schools.

1. Tulane School of Medicine
2. Charity Hospital
3. LSU Medical School
4. Dibert Tuberculosis Hospital
5. Lapeyre-Miltenberger Building
6. Charity Hospital School of Nursing
7. Veterans Administration Hospital

To the hospital's right, next to LSU, facing Claiborne Avenue, was the John Dibert Hospital. Built in 1936, the five floors of this building were devoted solely to the treatment and caring of tuberculosis patients. Behind Charity was the Contagious Disease Building, four more floors of patients with any contagious disease of the day. Although mainly pediatric patients, one could still see older patients suffering from the ravages of polio, their lives still maintained on iron lung machines.

As a medical student we examined diphtheria patients with their characteristic gray "membrane" in the back of their throats. We listened to heart valve murmurs in children with acute rheumatic fever and saw other children with rashes of scarlet fever. As a cardiac surgical resident I would later operate on these same rheumatic fever patients and replace their heart valves. These were diseases medical students who trained at "St. Elsewhere" only read about in books or would see on a missionary trip to a third-world country.

Wedged in between these buildings was the seven-story LM (Lapeyre-Miltenberger) Building.

Lapeyre-Miltenberger Building.

It was originally built as a convalescent home for the poor, funded by a donation from a prominent New Orleanian, Corinne Lapeyre Miltenberger. Tulane and LSU had both designated floors here used for study in various fields of research. On LM-3, Dr. George Burch studied the effects of heat on congestive heart failure patients, and Dr. Grace Goldsmith had a metabolic research unit on LM-6. Tulane's LM-4 cancer research unit was where, in several years, I would do a rotation. Also housed at the L-M building was the first school of physical therapy in the state of Louisiana. This complex of buildings was where I was scheduled to spend the better part of the next five years. Unbeknownst to me at the time, five would turn into seven.

I made my way past the east elevators, a bank of four used primarily by patients, their families and other hospital personal that went only to the first twelve floors. This wing of the hospital, the east side was mainly for Tulane patients. The west side of the hospital, a mirror image of the east, was the LSU side.

Since it was shared by two medical schools, each school had their own identical cardiac, neurosurgery, and general surgery operating rooms on the twelfth floor. Operating and treatment rooms for ear, nose and throat (ENT) specialists occupied the halls connecting the two wings. On either end were the two-story amphitheater operating suites—Miles and Delgado. In the earlier days, these amphitheaters were actually used for surgical demonstrations, however now they were the site of Grand Rounds conferences, patient presentations, Tulane's famous "bull pen" and LSU's version, "the pit."

Bull pen, a teaching modality, or torture, depending on how one looked at it, was brought to Tulane by Dr. Alton Ochsner from the European medical schools. A medical student was assigned a patient and had one hour to examine the patient, take a history and arrive at a diagnosis. He then presented the patient to the professor in charge and hopefully came up with the right diagnosis. The student would then be subject to a line of questioning to justify his conclusions. That line of questioning could resemble the inquisition.

One of the most famous of the Ochsner bullpens is described in Wilds and Harkey's *Alton Ochsner: Surgeon of the South*. Medical student Maurice Sullivan had presented his case, but Ochsner wasn't pleased and became aggressive, backing Sullivan around the floor. "What did you say? Why? Why?" Sullivan kept outlining the symptoms and Ochsner persisted, "Why? Why?"

As Sullivan began to grow pale, Ochsner persisted, "Why did you say that?" Sullivan fainted, and Dr. Mims Gage, Ochsner's close friend and associate, caught him and lowered him into a chair. He then asked, "Who's the next victim?"

Ochsner came back as a visiting professor when I was a student. He was given a white lab coat to wear adorned with a painting of a bull on the back breathing fire.

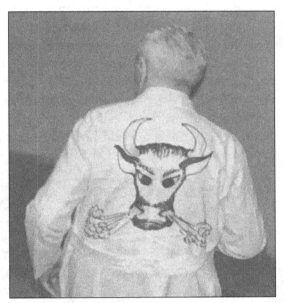

Dr. Alton Ochsner holding bull pen.

My bullpen experience when I was a senior student was anticlimactic. Dr. Robert Ryan was my examiner. When I asked my patient why he had come to the hospital he quickly took his gown off and showed me his back, "I've got a melanoma on my back, Doc. They gonna take it off."

During the time as an undergraduate student when I worked with Glenn Kokame and again after my second year of medical school when I did more hyperbaric oxygen cancer research I had scrubbed with Creech and Krementz on regional perfusions for the treatment of malignant melanoma. That modality of treatment had actually been developed at Tulane by Creech, Krementz, and Ryan. Ryan, a plastic surgeon, was the one who, one night at a cocktail party, first suggested using the then newly developed heart-lung pump to treat melanoma.

Butch Knoepp had a much more dramatic bullpen experience than I. Alton Ochsner was his guest examiner. Butch was the fourth in line of students presenting that day. As he sat on those oaken benches waiting his turn, he said it seemed like an eternity.

Ochsner opened the session by wheeling a stretcher on to the main floor of Delgado amphitheater. With a flourish but no drum roll, he whipped back the sheet on the stretcher revealing a human cadaver. Then, brandishing a scalpel, he made a slashing incision into the cadaver's chest. With a few more cuts, Ochsner withdrew the lung of the deceased. "See that? That's lung cancer. You keep smoking and that's what you'll get." He never passed up the opportunity to tell a fellow physician they were going to get lung cancer if they smoked. I even heard him say that one day.

On the first floor, I passed the large solid oak door that was the entrance to the board room where the directors of Charity met once a month.

**Charity Hospital Board of Administrators, 1960s;
Dr. James Ciaravella Sr. (standing, fifth from right).**

This board not only oversaw the functioning of "Big Charity" but the whole Charity Hospital system of the state of Louisiana. There were state-run hospitals in all four corners of the state: Lallie Kemp in Independence; E.A. Conway in Monroe; Confederate Memorial in Shreveport; and Charity Hospital of Lake Charles. Besides those, there was Huey P. Long in Alexandria and Earl K. Long in Baton Rouge. It might be safe to say that on that day I was the only house officer who knew what was behind that door and maybe the only one who had been in that room. Board members were appointed by the governor; my father had been on the board of directors of Charity Hospital under three separate four-year gubernatorial terms, two under "Uncle" Earl Long and one under John "please hep me" McKeithen.

Under those governors the board had autonomy to run the whole system. This fact was exemplified in a story my father told during a personal meeting with Earl Long concerning a problem the board was having. After my father presented the problem to "The Guvna," Long responded, "Look, damnit, I appointed you guys to do a job. If you can't do it I'll get someone else who can!"

I arrived at the main foyer. This held the front entrance to Charity. Embedded in the marble floor was a large bronze emblem with the state seal of the State of Louisiana on it. On one of the walls was a portrait of Dr. Rudolph Matas, considered the father of vascular surgery and on another a portrait of Sister Stanislaus Malone, the revered past nurse administrator of Charity. There was a bank of four more elevators here. Two were accessible from the lobby and the other two were accessible from the emergency room on the other side of two large oak doors. These four elevators, the fastest in the whole state, went all the way to the eighteenth floor.

The floors above twelve contained rooms for the use of resident staff only. The eighteenth floor housed a full-sized basketball court and a room with a ping pong table. One on the windows up there provided access to the famous "black beach" where I would sometimes have to go hunt for my chief residents. This was actually part of the tar-covered roof of a lower wing of the hospital.

I walked into an empty elevator manned by Eddie, one of the many full-time elevator operators. Although there were push buttons on the shiny brass panel, Eddie operated the elevator by turning a large brass handle. He rarely said anything, but gave me a familiar nod. I leaned against the back wall waiting for the ride to the second-floor auditorium to attend an orientation meeting for all new house staff.

Shortly, another fellow walked into the elevator. I did not recognize him, but I sensed he was another new intern. He had that awkward unsure look about him, not only because of what the year of new responsibilities might hold for him as a new MD, but also being in a strange labyrinth of a hospital and city.

Eddie immediately put his outstretched hand out to stop him from entering. "You have to go to the side elevators."

The new fellow quickly answered, "What do you mean?"

Eddie responded, "This elevator is for doctors."

"I'm a doctor, I'm a doctor," he pleaded excitedly, with a northern accent, getting quite anxious. I tried to hide my smile as Eddie looked back at me to see if I knew him. I didn't but gave Eddie a nod. He let him on, the handle went down, the collapsible grill door shut, and we rose to "hell."

That was my first introduction to Bruce, another new surgical intern. Bruce had trained at one of the noted Canadian medical schools and unfortunately, would become a legend in his own time. He definitely was a "standout" as an intern, but not in the way one wanted to be. I'm not sure he even completed the year.

The orientation lasted a short time. We had already received in the mail our assignments and monthly rotation. Even though I had been accepted as a straight surgery intern, I had elected to spend a month on ENT, three different months of out-of-town surgery, two months of medicine, one being on pulmonary medicine, a month on anesthesia and the other three months on general surgery at Charity.

My first assignment would be Tulane General Surgery Service III. I went to the fourth floor where I met my first-year resident, Gus Wetzel. Each of the four services had two interns, one first-year resident, a third-year resident and a senior or chief resident. A senior resident might be in his fourth year and not be a "chief." The requirements to be chief at Charity usually meant that the individual had spent six months to a year in the research lab or on a cardiothoracic surgery rotation with Dr. Charles Pearce or at the Ochsner Foundation Hospital. The chief resident made out the schedule, did most of the big cases and solved the problems among the residents--or tried to.

The fourth floor contained pre- and mostly post-op surgical patients. There were four wards in the center of the hospital, C400A through D. A and B were Tulane and C and D, LSU. These were fourteen-bed wards. There was a small nursing station in each room, a hall connecting Ward A to Ward B, and off of this short hall was one bathroom and shower for use by the few patients who were ambulatory, and another small room used as a lab.

Although each ward had an assigned number of permanent beds it wasn't unusual after a heavy admit night for there to be rollers with patients on them in between several of the beds. It put a huge strain on the nursing personnel.

When school was in session, medical students would do their patients' blood counts and urinalyses in these small labs, as well as check urine for diabetes. It was a very common sight during our junior year of med school to see students ferrying their microscopes back and forth between Charity and the two schools. These would be used in the ward "labs." At night, just before the 11 p.m. nursing-shift changes, these became the so called "fried chicken rooms." Dinner was eaten there.

There were several windows along one wall and no air conditioning on the wards. The walls were unadorned except for one clock on the wall above bed six. Throughout that year and for most of my residency, I remember that most of the sicker patients on the ward were "under the clock."

The other intern on my service, Gary Dotson, was assigned to E408, a twelve-bed female ward, whereas I was assigned to the male patients. Gary was from Kentucky. His grandfather had been a mule-riding country doctor who Gary would later write a book about during his surgical practice in rural Florida.

I met Gus on the ward where he introduced me to the one Charity Hospital nurse assigned to wards A and B (twenty-eight patients). We made rounds and he presented each patient to me, what their diagnoses were, the procedures they'd had, or what was planned.

For the next twelve months that would be the last time anyone presented a case to me. For the rest of that year I would be the one under the gun. Besides being responsible for my patients on C400A, we also had a few "self-care" patients on other wards.

Patients assigned to these wards had no intravenous fluids and were usually able to take care of themselves. This area was referred to as "bed rest and neglect." More than likely a patient there might have an inguinal hernia, pilonidal cyst, or hemorrhoids, and was waiting to get on the schedule. Post-op patients with a wound infection not requiring any IV fluids, but dressing changes that couldn't be done at home, were also kept there. We had no home health organizations available to us like there are today.

Besides regular pre-op patients, one might also find an Orleans Parish Prison inmate awaiting surgery on these "self-help" wards. As late as the seventies there was no prison ward at Charity, and prisoners were merely handcuffed to their beds. One Orleans Parish prison guard was assigned to the hospital. It was his duty to make rounds on his "patients" and be available to uncuff them so they could go to X-ray, surgery or even just to the bathroom.

I'll never forget during the early part of my internship having a prisoner on that ward waiting for a hernia repair. These were considered first-year or possibly intern cases, depending on how many the first-year had done. Operating room time was at a premium, and these were low-priority cases. Sometimes they were just kept in the hospital to occupy a bed in case it was needed for a more serious case.

I went to see my "prisoner" patient one morning to draw blood and found an empty bed and a set of handcuffs with one open end dangling from the steel bedrail. My patient was nowhere to be found. When the prisoner in the next bed saw the puzzled look on my face, he said, with a smile on his face, "Hey, doc, he decided to check out last night."

"Who let him go?" I asked.

He held up his cuffed arm, "You mean these?" showing me his handcuffs.

"Yes," I said. Whereupon he forcefully hit the edge of his handcuff on the edge of the bed and it popped open.

"I can check out of here anytime I want," he said, "but I got it pretty good." I learned a lot that year.

Each morning there were dressings to be changed, blood to be drawn, IV's to be started, and progress notes to be written. All had to be done before a bite of breakfast and morning surgery, which we were expected to scrub in on. Even though the male patients were mine, Gary and I made rounds together that first morning to get familiar with each other's patients. If he was in surgery or vice versa, and a patient was in trouble on the floor, the free intern could lend assistance.

There were very few orderlies at Charity, so any time your patient was scheduled for an X-ray or a diagnostic procedure, and there were no medical students on hand, it was your job to get them there and back. Besides drawing blood for tests, we usually had to take the tubes of blood to the lab. There was a wooden receptacle on each ward where the tubes of blood, wrapped in an identifying paper slip held in place by a rubber band, were placed to be taken to the lab and tested. However, retrieval of the contents was not always assured in a timely fashion. Many of these duties amounted to "scut" work I had been used to as a medical student. New interns from other medical schools had a major adjustment to these chores.

"Where's the lab?" "What floor is X-ray on?" "Where's the dining room?" "Do I have to draw the blood?" These were just some of the questions I fielded those first few days because I was a "local."

That first day was when I met Jim Dowling (the Fox). Jim was from Ohio. He had been an outstanding high school quarterback from Massillon and was sought after by many Big Ten schools before an automobile accident ended his football career. He had done three years of dental school before deciding to go to medical school. Jim and I and our families would become great friends for many years to come. He was an outstanding surgeon and had a presence about him that exuded confidence. The only defect in Jim's personality centered on the fact that he thought the Big Ten was a superior football conference.

Charity hospital was shaped like the letter "H," which some said stood for "Huey." The central bar was the eighteen-story part. The observation unit on the second floor served for what would later be called a surgical ICU or intensive care unit. Adjacent to it was a medical ICU. This ten-bed unit shared electrical outlets and its electrical supply with the adjacent medical ICU.

According to Louise Dotson, then a nurse on the observation unit, there were times when there were too many patients on ventilators for the amount of electricity and the nurses would have to hand bag (ventilate) patients. At one point it became critical.

An anonymous call was made to the local WDSU-TV station and *The Times-Picayune* newspaper. Reporters showed up at Charity to document the dangerous conditions under which patients were being treated. After the reporters left, hospital administrators lined up the nurses, similar to a firing squad, and threatened to fire them all if they didn't tell who made the call. No one talked and no one was fired—or shot.

Subsequently, a new ICU was built on the seventh floor. There were never enough beds for patients who needed to be in ICU, so a chalk board was hung on the wall. On this board were written the names of patients and the ward numbers of those that were waiting for a bed, sort of a "will call" list. The most critical piece of information written on the board, however, was the name of the resident whose patient it was. The selection process was supposed to be on a first-come first-served basis, unless of course the resident happened to be in disfavor with certain nurses. In that case, allegedly, the eraser came out and a resident's name might be dropped from the board. By the time I was a third-year resident, the ICU was moved to the twelfth floor.

The observation unit was equipped with Engstrom ventilators. These were old units and difficult for the novice to operate. The huge advantage of these units was that they were volume ventilators, as opposed to the other ventilators we had, the Birds, which were pressure respirators. The Engstrom was going to deliver whatever volume of air had been set for it to deliver and not be triggered by high resistance. This fact was significant because of the number of patients we saw with postoperative acute respiratory distress syndrome (ARDS).

We also called it "shock lung." There were many factors that contributed to this condition, the patient's smoking history and fluid resuscitation in the ER or operating room, to name a couple. The Engstroms were gradually replaced by more modern units.

Besides the surgical wards on the fourth floor, there were closed psych units on three, medical wards on five, the lab on six, X-ray on seven, orthopedics on eight, pediatrics on nine, obstetrics-gynecology (ob-gyn) on ten and surgical suites on twelve. There was a doctor's infirmary on six also.

Charity's emergency room area was located on the first floor in the back of the building. It was unique from other hospitals in that trauma was seen in a separate area from medical emergencies such as cardiac events, high blood pressure crises, or patients with diabetic problems. Non-trauma pediatric patients also had their own area.

In the sixties Charity prepared its own IV fluids in a sixth floor lab and dispensed in bottles. IV fluids in disposable plastic bags didn't come around until later. Surgical drapes were reused and sterilized; cloth gowns and surgical gloves were not disposable.

Gloves were cleaned, sterilized, and powered after each use to be reused. The reusable glove situation had been to my advantage when I was a senior student delivering babies during an out-of-town OB rotation. With a splint on a broken finger incurred while playing touch football during a rotation at Lallie Kemp, I was able to have the personnel prepare a set of sterile gloves with one hand size seven and a half and the other eight and a half to fit over the splinted finger. I delivered about twenty babies this way.

Scrub brushes were kept in a metal dispenser above the scrub sinks next to soap dispensers. These were sterilized and reused also. Disposable prepackaged soap-impregnated brushes didn't come out until much later.

Each service had an assigned operating room one day a week. That didn't stop us from putting on extra "to follow" cases on other days if we had them prepped and ready to go. We were on call every fourth night for emergencies, of which there were many. Since Charity was manned by both LSU and Tulane, the admitting days alternated between the two schools. This not only applied to surgery, but to all services.

For instance, any new patient admitted to the hospital on a Tulane day would be given a "T" number, T70-123456. The "70" referred to the year they were admitted. If they ever came into the ER or medical admit room as an emergency, they were treated by the admitting service irrespective of number. If they were dying of cancer or had a complication of a recent surgery, they were admitted to the service that had first seen them and assigned their number. Patients with severe bone infections, osteomyelitis, were admitted by number no matter what service was admitting. These rules, and more, pertaining to the disposition of patients without your school's number were affectionately known as the "monster rules."

In the sixties there were no drugs like Zantac or Tagamet. Peptic ulcer disease was very commonplace and quite often we saw the complications of peptic ulcers such as stomach perforation, intractable pain and most commonly, bleeding. The surgical treatment for these conditions, usually a third-year resident case, was usually removing of half or most of the stomach, a procedure called a gastrectomy. Drainage operations were also done for peptic ulcer disease at the discretion of the surgeon.

Disputes that arose between the house staff of the two schools mainly centered around patients with bleeding ulcers who were admitted on an emergency basis on a night not corresponding to the patients "L" or "T" number. To say that we never removed a stomach on an "L" patient would not be honest, but in general the process worked quite well.

I shared an apartment with one of my medical school classmates, Ron Swartz, at the Ridgelake Apartments in Metairie. If Charity wasn't enough punishment, his next year he went to see what Bellevue was like. He said that Bellevue made Charity look modern. Our apartment was only a short drive from I-10 and then about a ten- to fifteen-minute trip to Charity. At 5:30 in the morning there was no traffic on the interstate other than the Walker-Roemer milk trucks. Although never fully asleep, at six in the morning Charity was waking up.

My first duty was to go to the ward, make rounds, and change dressings. As the first one on the ward, it was usually dark. I hated being the one to turn the lights on and if it turned out there wasn't a lot of blood to be drawn or if I could do a quick uncomplicated dressing change without turning them on, I wouldn't.

One of the first mornings as I eased alongside a patient's bed, my foot hit something. I sensed movement from under the bed. We had sort of become accustomed to seeing rodents scurry along the walls at night. This was bigger. As it turned out the patient's relative had spent the night sleeping on the hard floor under the bed. That was not an infrequent occurrence. Many of our patients were from outside of the New Orleans area. Their relatives couldn't afford a downtown hotel and they had to make do.

Notorious for "camping out" in the wards or under beds were the Roma or Gypsies, even to the point that they would cook modest meals using cans of Stereo as the heat source. I did encounter a few families of them and their "homesteading" was curtailed as best we could.

One of the early duties required of the surgery interns was the sit list for the postoperative hearts. When you were on call and a cardiac operation had been done that day, you had a two-hour shift to sit by the patient's bedside and record vital signs. The patient was kept in the recovery room overnight and every fifteen minutes you charted the patient's blood pressure, pulse rate, amount of chest tube drainage and urinary output.

One of the other dated vital sign modalities of that era was the CVP (central venous pressure) monitor. The process involved taking the manometer, a calibrated foot-long glass tube filled with saline attached to a metal stopcock, and with the stopcock open to the patient, holding it along the side of their chest. It was a very simple unsophisticated means of giving us an idea of what was going on inside the patient's body before the days of more sophisticated tests that would come later.

Intern Cases

There were certain cases that were deemed "intern cases," depending on the experience of the first-year resident, such as most hernias, pilonidal cysts, hemorrhoids, and amputations, to name a few. You don't necessarily remember all the "cases" you did. Anything done in the operating room (OR) was a case. You may also have done something in a treatment room, at the patient's bedside or the ER that was important to you as far as experience was concerned. If it was your "first," unless it was dictated, just put it in your memory/experience bank and hold it there for later. It was all part of the learning process.

Such was one I had in the ER when I was an intern. An elderly diabetic lady came in with a markedly swollen left thigh. An examination of her thigh revealed the three classic signs of an infection. It had warmth (calor), reddish undertone (rubor) and even in her clouded mental state she was in pain (dolor). I had been taught these signs from my general surgeon father since my childhood.

Her thigh needed to be opened. I had a tray set up and was ready to prep the leg after a little 1 percent xylocaine local anesthetic. Phil Robichaux (Chaux) was one of the third-year residents who happened to be on call. I presented the case to him. He came into the room and put both of his hands on her huge left thigh: "This lady needs to be done in the OR." Wow! What had started out to be a simple incision and drainage (I&D) was going to turn out to be a case.

He was able to get us a room and we brought her to the OR. We still gave her an ample local anesthetic rather than a general because of her confusion and metabolic imbalance. He told me how and where to make the incision. As

I did so, it became apparent that the tenseness we had felt on our exam wasn't underlying muscle or inflammation; it was pus under tension. Her skin was paper-thin. The infection had eaten away the fatty layer of tissue and most of her thigh muscles. The suction was placed in the wound, whereupon a gallon jug was filled rapidly with yellow-green pus. Her blood pressure started to drop, and he ordered the nurse anesthetist to run in fluids. And then he said it: "This lady's going to die." One of my first "cases" was going to die.

We drained another pint of nothing but pus from this huge cavity that once had been her thigh. There should have been no space like this in her body, much less where muscle should have been. We could see her femur. There were no muscles or tendons attached to it. The bone had a moth-eaten appearance from the massive infection this poor lady had probably been dealing with for weeks. We irrigated the cavity with massive amounts of antibiotic solution (commonly called bug juice), packed and loosely closed the incision over a drain connected to suction and sent her to recovery. Despite more fluids, diabetic management, and more IV antibiotics, she did die that night.

One of my first cases had resulted in a death; death that probably could have been prevented if she had sought medical attention much sooner. I had learned a lot. Not only how to handle circumstances like that in the OR and some basic techniques, but things aren't always as they seem. Take time to examine the whole picture and don't jump to conclusions too soon. You're an intern.

Snogging

Another critical thing you learned at Charity when dealing with postoperative patients was dealing with atelectasis. During an operation there are portions of the lung that are not fully expanded. Normal bacteria that we all have would become concentrated in these areas of non-ventilated lung and were a source of fever. This in turn could lead to postoperative pneumonia if left untreated. The main treatment was not antibiotics; it was coughing. Expand the lung and cough out these mucous plugs that were blocking up the air passages, mainly located in the lower segments of the lung. Abdominal pain from an incision plus atelectasis is not a good combination.

One of our duties as interns was to see to it that our patients did not get atelectasis and subsequently pneumonia. There was a treatment for this in patients who were resistant to simple coaching and encouragement. It was called "snogging." The patient was placed with his or her head in a very erect position, sitting on the side of the bed if at all possible. A silastic nasogastric catheter was lubricated, and, while grasping the patient's extended tongue with a gauze sponge, the catheter was slipped into the nose, down the throat toward the trachea.

Even though barbaric in its performance, the results were very dramatic. The coughing that ensued often brought up "globs" of purulent greenish to brown material, the number-one cause of postoperative fever at Charity Hospital, second only to wound infections. The smokers had it the worst and the "knife-and-gun clubbers" topped the list in being resistant to treatment.

Charity did have a basic inhalation therapy team. Occasionally a consult to pulmonary PT would result in a pulmonary therapist with a Bird respirator visiting the patient and giving them breathing treatments. However, the effect of one resistant patient seeing another resistant patient getting snogged produced the best results. It wasn't uncommon, and was even humorous, to notice that when we merely walked onto the ward, some patients automatically started coughing.

When A.D. Smith, my third-year, was on his six-month cardiac rotation at the Ochsner Foundation Hospital, he encountered one of Dr. John Ochsner's post-op patients with fever. A.D. did what he knew best; he snogged one of Dr. John's "uptown" female very social patients, those select socialite patients who called him "Johnny." The repercussions were heard down on Tulane Avenue. That was never done again.

As a senior student, I had worked up a patient who chief residents Ed McGough and Maunsel Pearce had admitted with an acute gallbladder. During my physical exam, I discovered aneurysms in the artery behind both of her knees. Now this is a great find and a great case for the chief resident to do. Untreated, these aneurysms quite often clot off the blood supply to the legs and even with emergency surgery there is a fifty percent amputation rate. The chiefs were very impressed with my find, but the patient's acute cholecystitis placed her at greater risk than the incidentally found aneurysms.

After the gallbladder was removed she had a horrible case of atelectasis and was a very sick lady. Another treatment that was starting to gain favor rather than snogging was to inject a small amount (one or two cc's) of saline or Mucomist directly into the trachea. This treatment had been effective with this patient.

On Saturday rounds it was decided to leave a small silastic catheter in her trachea and sew it in place. The intern on call could come by once or twice during the evening and inject the saline, thus stimulating a productive cough.

The following Monday morning I went to check on my patient. The night nurse, not being able to start an IV because of the patient's poor veins, had connected her maintenance IV fluids to the tracheal catheter, thus effectively drowning her. Nothing could be left to chance.

It was not an uncommon occurrence for one patient to have more than one surgical condition or disease process as my popliteal aneurysm lady had demonstrated.

I was attending Bull Pen one Saturday when Dr. Creech asked the patient what kind of surgery he had. The patient told Creech that he'd been "whipped on." What he intended to say was that he had undergone a Whipple procedure for carcinoma of the head of the pancreas. Creech persisted and asked him what symptoms brought him to the hospital. "I had a "hernion," was the patient's reply. I'll never forget the expression on Creech's stoic face when he remarked how you could come to Charity with an inguinal hernia and have your pancreas taken out. We actually used the "whip it on them" term to refer to anyone we were going to operate on.

New Patients

The new experiences I had that first year have stayed with me forever. A few were cases that I did and others were experiences attached to cases of the more senior residents that I took care of.

One of these was Willie Falls. Mr. Falls was a patient on C400A in bed ten of a fourteen-bed ward. You couldn't miss him. He was on the ward when I came on that first day and he was on the ward later when I rotated off to another service. He had come in with a large gastric ulcer. He had bled several times and easily met the criteria for a gastrectomy. Because of the anatomy and other factors, he had undergone an operation removing most of his stomach, a Billroth II operation.

He had developed a leak where the intestine was sewed to the stomach. He had a draining fistula and a wound infection. Having been taken back to surgery more than once, naturally he was malnourished and protein depleted which led to poor healing. He was now mine to treat, take care of and learn on. And learn I did.

A.D. Smith saw to it that I was going to learn or he was going to see me get bounced from the program. Daily dressing changes were never done the way he wanted. I never had the lab results at the time he wanted them. If at six a.m., maybe I had not had time to draw Falls' blood work, which was even worse. It was A.D.'s duty to try to make me cry and he succeeded, more than once.

Was I really in the right place? Is this really what I wanted to do for a career? Had all these guys ahead of me really put up with this beratement, or was I just the only incompetent dumbass?

Steve Harkness was one of my interns when I was a senior resident. He had been assigned a patient on the medicine wards to go "work up," do a history and physical on when he was a medical student. This particular chronic renal failure patient was not responding to his questions at 5:30 in the morning. Also, being required to start an IV on her was proving just as unsuccessful.

He asked the medicine resident what he was doing wrong. "You stupid bastard, she's dead," he screamed. "Can't you even tell the difference between an alive and a dead patient?" This episode profoundly affected Steve. If he couldn't tell the difference between life and death how was he going to attempt to take care of living sick people? He dropped out of medical school with the belief that he wasn't cut out for it. Perhaps he had made a mistake in trying medicine as a career.

What he found out with his background in premed studies was that he couldn't find a job. He stayed out for a whole block of studies and eventually went back to Tulane and met with the dean. "Let's just call it a sabbatical," he was told. He successfully received his medical degree, finished the Tulane Surgery program and became a successful general surgeon in private practice.

When Mathis Becker was chief resident he had a knock on his on-call room door one night. It was one of the straight surgery interns. "Dr. Becker (we never called each other doctor), I've decided that surgery isn't for me."

From his prior performances Becker knew he was right; he just didn't have "it." He went to see Dr. Drapanas, relating the intern's request and was told to get a psych consult on him. Drapanas explained that the last time a similar request had been made the fellow had committed suicide. Although Becker thought that this was going a little too far, he complied. The intern went on to complete a successful residency in another field and to Becker's knowledge didn't commit suicide.

I believe many physicians, even later in their practice, experience second thoughts. These especially hit home after the death of a patient. During that internship year, I remember a couple of my cohorts expressing doubts to me about whether they should be there, just as I had. Charity was tough and could be a lonely place to train.

I survived Willie Falls. More importantly, Willie Falls survived me and all his complications. I learned how to take care of wounds inside and out, fluid management of chronically ill patients and most importantly, how to take orders.

I also survived A.D. Smith.

I may have learned how to take care of a wound infection, but I was yet to learn about colostomies. There are two acute devastating complications that a patient with diverticulosis can endure. One of them is perforation, when one of these inflamed out-pouchings of the colon blows out. When this happens, it not only requires an emergency operation, but because of the fecal contamination, the hole can't simply be closed, and a colostomy must be done.

One night on call we admitted and operated on a patient with this condition. Oscar Grablowsky, my chief resident, did the case. At operation, the belly was irrigated out with bug juice and a loop of colon was brought out on the abdomen and secured with stitches. This is the first stage of doing a colostomy. When the patient is over his infection in about eight weeks, he is brought back into the hospital, the affected segment of colon is removed and the ends are sewn back together, now under sterile conditions. The abdomen is then closed—no more colostomy.

What I didn't know about was a middle stage of the process. On about day three or so, after the patient begins taking a liquid diet, the colostomy has to be opened at the bedside and a bag is placed over the opened ends. Our patient was in the back left corner of C400B. He had been started on a liquid diet, but now his abdomen was starting to distend. I expressed my concerns to Gus. What they had forgotten to tell me, or I hadn't heard them tell me, was to open the colostomy.

The third-year retrieved a cautery set and at bedside made an incision in the loop of bowel, this way obviating any bleeding. The abdominal distention was caused by a great deal of liquid stool that was released under pressure from the patient's proximal colon. "Now clean it up" I was directed. Even though this had resulted in a huge mess in the bed and on the patient, he thanked me for relieving his abdominal pain.

"No Tubes"

A couple of weeks into my internship, A.D. took me aside one day. "I'm admitting a patient for you," he said. "You are going to work him up, I am going to help you operate on him, and you are going to take care of him postop. I don't want to see him!" I asked him when he was coming in and that's when he told me he was being admitted to the third floor closed psychiatry unit the next day. Robert Kilgore had one of those Charity Hospital-type histories. Years before in a very violent encounter, he had killed two Louisiana State Troopers with his bare hands. He was found criminally insane and was sent to East Louisiana State Hospital in Jackson, Louisiana. This facility was commonly referred to as just "Jackson."

The hospital began operations in 1848. Facilities were poor and inmates had no clothes or bare necessities. In 1874, Dr. John Welch Jones was appointed superintendent and he bought a brick-making machine. He had the inmates produce more than 3 million bricks, which were subsequently used to build at first one new building, which then led to building four more. The hospital is still in existence and functioning today.

While an inmate-patient, Robert developed peptic ulcer disease. It went untreated and eventually the ulcer perforated his stomach. This resulted in an emergency operation at Charity which also led to multiple complications, wound infections and draining fistulas. Amazingly, he healed all of this and was returned to Jackson. However, the end result was a very large hernia in the area of his abdominal incision. He had been admitted once before to Charity for surgical repair and at that time was simply placed on one of the fourth-floor surgical wards with minimal to no supervision. The night before his intended surgical repair he went into the little lab between the wards and attempted to drink a bottle of rubbing alcohol. Surgery was cancelled and he was sent back to Feliciana Parish and Jackson. Now, A.D. had done "*moi*" the great favor of resurrecting him again.

After being notified of "my" new patient I went up to the third floor. I had only been behind those locked doors to the east wing one time as a student. I found Robert in a corner eight-bed ward that over-looked Tulane Avenue and the front entrance to the hospital. After being with him a while and looking at the glazed expression over his face from his daily dose of 1000mg of Thorazine, I don't think he was concerned with the view or even where he was, and perhaps least of all, who I was.

I did a limited physical exam on him and drew some blood for basic tests. Because he was more than fifty years old, he was going to need an electrocardiogram before anesthesia would put him to sleep, and I was going to have to do it.

I left his ward, went out into the hall and found an EKG machine. If you have ever had an EKG or even seen a picture of a modern-day machine, forget about it. The EKG machines in Charity in that day looked like some kind of equipment that would be in the lab of "Morgus the Magnificent," a New Orleans Saturday late-night TV horror-movie host. Basically, it was a wooden oak box on wheels with a bunch of cables attached to little red suction cups dangling from it. The wrist leads were held in place with rubber straps and the red suction cups were attached across the bare chest as the precordial leads.

I informed Robert I needed to perform a heart study and asked him to take his hospital gown off and lay flat on the bed. As I was placing the rubber strapped leads to his wrist he said something and simultaneously, I noticed something. I was looking out the widow briefly and realized the only covering the open window had was a screen. There were no bars. Then he said it, "You're going to shock me, aren't you?" Oh my God, he thought I was going to give him electroshock therapy, probably like he experienced at Jackson on numerous occasions. "No, no, Robert, I'm not going to shock you; this is just a heart test. I promise you." "It's okay, Doctor, I've been shocked before," he slowly said in that inflectionless voice. "You can go ahead."

Now those old EKG machines made a lot of noise, when they worked at all. The needle went rapidly back and forth as they whirred and the paper would sometimes jam. This time, as impossible as it seems, I knew it was going to shock Robert. No matter what I had told him and what I knew, that machine was somehow going to shock him and I was going to be seen flying out of that third-story window. CHARITY HOSPITAL INTERN THROWN TO HIS DEATH FROM CHARITY HOSPITAL WINDOW, the *Times-Picayune* headlines would read.

My vision was not without some basis. As a student on the medicine block once a week we had an infectious disease lecture under the legendary Dr. William J. Mogabgab. The class was held on the fourth floor of the Contagion building, behind Charity and across Gravier Street from the Veterans Administration Hospital. The small corner lecture room had a couple of windows that looked right at the VA. Mogabgab had a monotonous, boring voice, no inflection whatsoever. He would drone on and on throughout the hour about the infectious diseases known in the day.

One day, he was lecturing on viruses, standing by the window with his back to the room so you could barely hear him. The inflection and tone of his voice never changed, as he said, "These Coxsackie B viruses someone just jumped out the window are the main cause of viral myocardopathies."

In the back of the room was whispered, "What'd he say?"

"Someone what?" another voice said. After the prescribed hour and the class was released, everyone made their way down the stairs to the ground level. The police had blocked off Gravier, and it was discovered that a psych patient at the VA had jumped to his death from a window.

Robert didn't get shocked, I got the EKG and I didn't make the front page of the morning paper. The phenothiazine drugs he was taking in large doses interacted with the anesthetics that were then used and could cause blood pressure problems during anesthesia. I knew that Robert would have to have none of the drug in his system for about a week. His being off his drugs only raised my anxiety level every time I went to see him. On the day of surgery as he was wheeled into the OR, I was at his side as he eased over to the operating room table. Just as the anesthesiologist started to put the black rubber mask over his face he whispered something. I leaned closer. "No tubes." "What did you say Robert?" "No tubes" and he went off to sleep.

I had him prepped and draped when A.D. came in the room. Robert had a very large ventral hernia that required a large piece of Marlex mesh. I sewed in this synthetic material that would later be incorporated into his tissues and add strength and reinforcement to the repair. As I was sewing the mesh into place, A.D. asked the circulator to get a Hemovac. This is a collection device with a spring in it that maintains a constant suction to remove fluid from the wound. It does so, however, with tubes. "A.D., he said no tubes, He didn't want any tubes," I said.

"He's not the surgeon," A.D. replied. "He's going to have a large dead space and if he gets a seroma (a fluid collection) with this mesh in, it will increase his chance of an infection." Robert's postoperative course was uneventful. He really didn't react to the tubes. They were taken out after a few days and he was sent back to Jackson.

The first couple of months had been intense. I got used to the pace and lack of sleep. I also learned to anticipate what might be the next step--any next step. The last day of August was a Friday and also Huey Long's birthday, a state holiday. Our team wasn't on call.

"Let's go fishing," someone volunteered. The other intern who said it had an aunt who owned a house in Bay St. Louis, Mississippi and a boat. It didn't take much persuading for everyone to agree to really take a break. We rode over there together and stopped in a small general store outside of Slidell to buy some "clear," also known as moonshine. It actually did come in Mason jars. One sip let you know where the term "firewater' came from.

It was a good day of camaraderie, something we hadn't experienced. We only caught one catfish. That, and the fact that once we got out in the Gulf and couldn't find our way back into the Bay at night didn't detract at all from the day.

"Topsies"

As early as the days of DaVinci and Michelangelo the dissection and study of the human body has been part of learning. DaVinci's Codices contain such detailed drawings and descriptions that a modern-day medical student could use them to study anatomy by. His early dissections were so detailed that he described a condition in blood vessels that we now call arteriosclerosis. These exams could not have been done without the careful dissection of human cadavers. Medieval artists and early physicians gained access to corpses by whatever means they could. Whether it was by paying morgues so that they would be allowed to come in at night and secretly do their dissections or stealing their way in undetected and examining bodies. One of the advantages of the early Medical College of Louisiana was its access to human dissection.

The term "autopsy" is used to refer to the examination of a body to determine the cause of death. Familiar synonyms often used are necropsy and post-mortem exam, but at Charity the most common term we heard was "topsy." Obtaining permission to do an autopsy was sometimes one of the more difficult chores I had to do as an intern.

Factors contributing to that difficulty had to do with not only access to the family after the patient's death, but the fear in the indigent population of the dead being examined. Glenn Pennington, a chief resident when I was a junior resident, had a patient die unexpectedly. He knew a topsy would be likely to give him the answer why. The family refused: "no topsy." The team persisted to no avail. Finally, in one last attempt, Glenn explained to the family that as part of their relative's treatment they had given him a solid gold ball to swallow and they needed to get it back. If the family still refused to grant the topsy, they were going to have to pay for the gold ball. Topsy granted.

The Appendix

If humans had a horse's anatomy, interns would never get to take out an appendix. In the horse it is a large functional organ. In humans the appendix is a small rudimentary finger-like tube we all have hanging off that part of the end of our large intestine called the cecum. It serves no useful purpose other than to occasionally get infected. Unrecognized, appendicitis can lead to perforation with subsequent peritonitis, the formation of abscesses and death. With modern-day antibiotics and CAT scans used today in its early diagnosis, the fatal complications of the disease have lessened dramatically. We relied on the patient's history, physical findings and possibly the finding of an elevated WBC (white blood cell count).

Pain and tenderness in the right lower quadrant of the abdomen with anorexia (decreased appetite) and the patient had appendicitis unless proven otherwise. Younger children were more difficult to diagnose. "Hey big guy, where's it hurt you?" and they'd point to their whole belly. Sometimes the best question I could ask would be, "Would you like a hamburger?" If they said, "No" and they had belly pain, more likely than not they were taken to the OR.

Beware of the surgeon who would tell you that he never operated on a negative appendix. That means he missed some. They don't all present with the classic symptoms. It usually only takes a small incision in the right lower quadrant, McBurney's point. The muscle is spread apart, the peritoneum is incised and hopefully the appendix won't be ruptured. If there is cloudy fluid present, culture it. You stick the gloved finger down toward the cecum, then slide off the cecum and down to loop your finger around the appendix. Bring it up in the surgical field and you can gently grab the cecum with a Babcock clamp to hold it there. Place three straight thermostats at the base of the appendix and with a scalpel cut between the second and third one. Then sew a purse-string suture of 3-0 silk around the base of the appendix on the cecum and tie a chromic suture on the stump below the first hemostat. While inverting the stump into the cecum, release the hemostats, then tighten and tie the purse-string suture and you're through. Irrigate and close. Even if it's the most normal appendix you've ever seen, you remove it.

Night Duty

Toes

With a couple of thousand patients, perhaps a thousand residents and interns, countless nurses, and lab and X-ray technicians, the population of Charity was larger than most Louisiana bayou or cotton-growing towns. It effectively was the "City of Charity." During the day there was a constant hustle of personnel shuttling patients back and forth for various tests or treatments. Student nurses and medical students were always tending to their patients. Nighttime was a completely different scenario. After midnight, the wards were fairly deserted and quiet. There was no beeping of IVAQ fluid administration sets because these didn't exist then. Phones didn't ring because there were no cell phones. If you wanted to find out how your patient was doing, you went to see them or paged an intern on his beeper and he would call you back. No one was paged over intercom systems. It was just quiet. There was usually a couple of LPN's or nurse's aides tending to most of the patients and "maybe" one RN (registered nurse or "real nurse") to cover several wards.

One night when I was on call I was instructed to bring a suspected intestinal obstruction patient to X-ray around 3 a.m. A Miller-Abbott tube had been inserted into his GI tract and progress of the tube had to be checked to help in the decision as to whether the patient would need surgery. This very long soft red rubber tube had a mercury-filled bag attached to its end. When in the GI tract, the normal intestinal motion would propel the tube as far as it could depending whether there was an obstruction or not.

I found a stretcher and proceeded to E402, one of the wards located on the cross bar of the "H" that was Huey's Charity. I loaded up my patient and proceeded to wheel him to the central elevators, the only ones staffed at night. Also, this late at night, the only X-ray unit open was the one on the first floor on the West side of the hospital.

I wheeled the patient through the dimly lit halls, past the darkened mail room and into the seemingly deserted X-ray unit. I called out, but only heard a slight rustling noise coming from a doorway. As I went around the corner peering into that seemingly empty space, on the floor I could make out bare feet, four bare feet, "ten toes up and ten toes down." I backed out, made some more noise and shortly a young man came running out adjusting his clothing. I entered the back room and encountered the female X-ray tech. She straightened her top, brushed back her hair with one hand and nonchalantly said, "Can I help you?"

"Just an X-ray of his abdomen will be fine, thank you."

Amputations

Whereas being on call on an LSU night was usually fairly slow, the Tulane nights weren't. When there wasn't any trauma coming through the ER, it seemed like there was always an amputation needing to be done. Those were usually intern cases. It is interesting that in 1881 dean of the medical school, Dr. Tobias Richardson complained to those in charge at Charity Hospital that his students were not getting to do enough amputations. It is quite possible those patients were dying at home or they were waiting for us. The cause of their dead legs was usually either diabetic gangrene or vascular insufficiency. Either one meant they weren't getting enough blood supply to their leg. The patients with diabetes had more diffuse blood vessel blockages. If they could be operated on that was always the first choice, but most of the time the amount of vascular disease was just too diffuse and there wasn't a normal vessel to hook the distal graft into. Many times the patients waited too long to seek medical attention. If the patient had wet gangrene, meaning they had an active infection, which most of them had, they had to be loaded up with IV antibiotics and then could be taken to the OR on an elective basis.

Very seldom would daylight operating room time be taken up with something like an amputation. The goal was to do it as quick as you could and ideally with as few swipes of the scalpel as possible. Most of the time we were doing either an AK (above knee) or BK (below knee) operation. If at all possible you wanted to preserve their knee joint. Although the vast majority of patients we saw wound up wheelchair bound and didn't walk again, they were more likely to be able to walk with an artificial leg if they had a BK.

While doing the amputation the thigh and leg were positioned on a pillow such that there was complete access around the lower thigh and lower leg. The diseased or infected foot and lower leg had been wrapped up and placed in a large clear plastic bag and secured with tape to a Mayo stand at the foot of the operating room table. The femoral artery, being the main blood supply to the leg is situated close to the bone, the femur. If the third-year was helping you do the case, it was his job to clamp the artery just before or just as you cut through it.

Standing on the same side of the table as the affected leg, you reached your hand with the scalpel underneath the thigh up around the inside of the thigh as far as you could such that the scalpel came back into view on the front of the thigh toward you. The patient had been given a light anesthetic with mask only and the third-year gave you the signal, "Cut, cut, cut." You would take the knife and try to cut as deeply into the thigh as you could at the same time taking the circular incision all around and under the thigh back to your side. The scalpel blade wasn't long enough to do it in one stroke, but two or three at the most was all that was needed. As you reached the artery, your assistant would clamp it so it could be suture ligated later. Once your scalpel blade had reached the bone you then took the Gigli saw and transected the femur. The Gigli saw was one of the most masterful Italian devices invented and about as simple as an instrument could be. It was basically a serrated wire with a handle at either end.

After wrapping the wire around the bone at a level a little higher than the muscle incision, a couple of quick back-and-forth pulls was all that was needed to finish the procedure. The nurse then took the amputated extremity from the field. You always flushed the clamped vessel to make sure there was adequate blood supply so the stump would heal and then it was sutured close. Never just ligate it; the pressure in the vessel could dislodge the tie and result in the patient hemorrhaging. If we were sure the infection in the lower leg was under control, the wound could be closed in layers transversely, otherwise the stump was left open and it was packed. If it sounds crude, that's because it was and why it was called a "guillotine" amputation.

Below knee amps required a little more dissection. Because there are two long bones in the lower leg, two bones had to be sawed through and two named arteries had to be ligated. It was not uncommon that during the course of a BK amp we would find that the blood supply was not going to be adequate enough to allow the stump to heal. In those cases we just moved the level higher. We erred on the side of taking too much leg rather than not enough and avoided having to bring the patient back to the OR because of a non-healing or dying stump.

As I said, there were only a small percentage of our patients who would learn to walk with prostheses. It was not easy to do and required a lot of motivation. I do not know if the new flexible titanium prostheses available today are easier to walk on. I do know that the motivation and resilience seen in today's combat veterans with single or multiple limb loss is amazing and is to be admired and saluted. It could not be easy to walk on a prosthesis and not be able to feel where your foot was.

The ability to maneuver on the old fiberglass prostheses brings to mind Dr. Ambrose Storck. Dr. Storck was a Tulane graduate and Charity Hospital-trained physician. He was a former chairman of the surgery department and was a Tulane attending until WW II. After serving in the US Army he returned back to New Orleans and the Tulane Surgery Department staff. When I was a senior student, he had already undergone his first AK amputation secondary

33

to the complications of diabetes. Unless you were looking for it as he walked the halls of Charity in his white linen or finely striped seersucker suits you would never know he was doing it on just one healthy leg.

He would position himself with about five or six of us students around him and we would present the patient for discussion. It seems like he would then lock that wooden leg and expound on all the causes of whatever condition was pertinent. It was amazing how much he could talk and discuss any surgical condition on end. Being a bachelor he had a valet who tended to his needs. One evening the valet drew his bath and unfortunately the bath water was too hot. Diabetes numbs the nerves in the foot so when he tested the water before getting in he didn't sense the intense heat. The result was more damage to his already diseased "good" leg. This led to a second AK amputation.

That didn't stop Dr. Storck, it just meant another prosthesis he had to learn to walk on, and he did. His rounds making on the wards slowed somewhat, but he was still a fixture at Grand Rounds in the Delgado amphitheater and never failed to miss the Friday afternoon D&C conference.

Meals

No night on call was complete without a visit to the late doctor's dining room. The main dining room was in the basement just as you got off of the center elevators. Three meals a day, room and board, what else do you need, right? Breakfast was definitely a busy time. You sat down at one of the long tables and just gave your order to one of the ladies. They had probably been there since the place was dedicated, and they were great. Name it, you got it, and it didn't take long because we didn't have a lot of time to waste eating; however, you didn't always get what you'd ordered. Notable among the servers was Mazie, who, when delivering a meal that was not exactly what had been requested, would say, "Eat it, it'll be good for you." You ate whenever it was available, because you might be in the operating room and unable to eat when the next meal was offered. My wife still doesn't understand how I can eat lunch at 10:30 or 11, or dinner at 5:00. Dinner was the same; if you were on call you ate down there, otherwise you got out and went home. There were no fast food joints like there are today, and Domino's didn't deliver because—you guessed it—there was no Domino's.

The closest thing resembling "take-out" was what happened when Ron Swartz was on call one night. On one of his wards, he was taking care of a family member from the noted Bon Ton Café. Located just a few blocks off Canal Street, the Bon Ton was famous for serving authentic Cajun food since the 1950s. The family brought to the ward enough food to feed everyone.

Every night about ten o'clock the late doctor's dining room opened. It was in a different room and further down in the subterranean bowels of Charity in the same hall that led to the morgue and the tunnel that led under LaSalle Street to the basement of Tulane. This dining room was probably used by the employees during the day. Most of the time this late meal consisted of leftovers from the regular dinner meal, but that didn't stop anyone from eating it. Sometimes when time permitted, we might just go in, have a cup of coffee and discuss the most trivial things you could think of. After the meal we could get a slice of pie or a cup. After that it was usually to the OR to do a case.

Having completed two months on the general surgery without many major screwups, I was ready to move on. I had thought that if you are going to be a surgeon you should know something about anesthesia. It was a definite change from the surgery rotation. I didn't know of any other surgery interns who did it.

Anesthesia Rotation -- "Passing Gas"

A month solely on the twelfth floor was a distinct break compared to surgery. There was no night call. It was similar to patient care in the ER. When you were taking care of a patient they were yours, but when the operation was through you never saw them again. There was no follow up. Ether, in gaseous form, was still in use as an anesthetic agent, but cyclopropane gas was used as an adjunct with it. I had a brief orientation and instruction by Kathryn Aldridge, the chief nurse anesthesia instructor. It wasn't long before I was put in a room and actually did a case.

Ether is very volatile; it evaporates quickly and doesn't stay in the body very long. Now if you're thinking of some old movie you've seen where a cloth mask was put over the patient's face and someone leaning over them poured a liquid onto the mask for the patient to breathe in, forget about it.

Although the anesthetic agents were primitive, the anesthesia machines, for the day, were fairly sophisticated. A delicate balance had to be kept by adjusting the flow of the gases to keep the patient asleep and relaxed, but still well oxygenated. Besides keeping the blood pressure stable you also had to stay awake yourself. It could get pretty boring. It gave me a new insight as to what happened "above the screen." If your attention even drifted for a short period of time, it wouldn't take long for the patient's abdomen to become tense and the surgeon to lose surgical exposure. "Hey, put him back to sleep, would you!"

There is no question that the changes in the administration of anesthetics and the types of anesthetic agents available then compared to now has markedly contributed to the lowering of morbidity and mortality rates for all surgical patients.

A few times a week I would join the anesthesiology residents and nurse anesthetists in the Miles amphitheater for one of Dr. John Adriani's drawn out lectures. Adriani was a true pioneer in the field of anesthesiology and his presence at Charity Hospital established New Orleans as a center in the training of not only anesthesiologists but nurse anesthetists as well. For thirty-three years he was the Director of Anesthesia at Charity.

In the 1940s, most anesthesiologists in this country felt that nurses did not belong in their specialty. Adriani not only did not adhere to this belief, he taught them, lectured to them and signed their certificates. A statement was adopted by the Society of Anesthesiologists (ASA) that it was unethical for any anesthesiologist to lecture to or participate in the training of nurse anesthetists. Paul Wood, the secretary of the American Board of Anesthesiology actually visited Adriani to tell him that if he persisted in signing nurses certificates of training, the board would revoke his certification. Adriani told Wood that if his certificate was revoked, he would contest the matter in Federal court. Nothing further came of the rule. The ASA then revoked the original rule and the action became known as the "Adriani Rule." While at Charity, he established the blood bank and a bone bank. He also assumed direction of the inhalation department.

Adriani was also a strong proponent of the practice of substituting generic drugs for more costly brand name drugs, a practice that placed him in strong disfavor of the pharmaceutical companies. This feeling against Adriani was so strong, that when he was nominated as director of the Food and Drug Administration's Bureau of Medicine his name had to be withdrawn. He retired in 1974 but continued to maintain a presence in the halls of Charity Hospital.

Adriani was succeeded in his position by Dr. Mohammed Naraghi, one of his students. Besides Naraghi, Adriani also trained Dr. Sam Welborn, head of anesthesiology at Ochsner Foundation Hospital, and Dr. John Parmley, director of anesthesia at Hotel Dieu Hospital. My month on anesthesia definitely gave me some cursory knowledge of anesthetic agents however, I think the main advantage of my doing the rotation was learning how to intubate patients, insert breathing tubes in the wind pipe. This is something every surgeon should know how to do.

Lallie Kemp

It was now time for my first of three non-consecutive months of an out-of-town surgery rotation. When I was informed that I would be going to Lallie Kemp Hospital, I felt like Brer' Rabbit having been told by Brer' Bear that he was going to be thrown in the briar patch. Independence, Louisiana was my second home. Not only had my mother been born and raised there, but my grandfather, Charles Anzalone, had been mayor of the town for a dozen years and had been a state representative longer than that. More significantly he had been responsible for Lallie Kemp Hospital being built in Independence.

Lallie Kemp had been the wife of a member of the Louisiana House of Representatives from Amite, a town up the road. Both had been friends of my grandfather. He died in office and she was appointed to take his place. After she died my grandfather petitioned for the hospital to be built in Independence rather than Baton Rouge as had been proposed.

Independence was a town split in two by railroad tracks. Its population of approximately 1900 was largely Italian. To be specific, they were Sicilian. The Sicilian countryside is very arid with rich soil similar to that of southeastern Louisiana. Opportunities for advancement were poor in Sicily then. Even today, your tour guide in Palermo may be a college professor working an extra job to make ends meet. Ships left Sicily for Ellis Island and the Port of New Orleans immigration station loaded with immigrants seeking work and fortune for their families along with a new life in America. My grandfather had landed at Ellis Island from the small town of Cefalà Diana.

I spent so much time in Independence, I felt like I had grown up there. My parents would put me on the Greyhound bus in New Orleans. The bus would travel down Airline highway, around Lake Pontchartrain, through LaPlace and Pass Manchac, eventually letting me off right in front of my grandmother's grocery store and gas station right on Railroad Avenue. In retrospect, her store was a forerunner of a 7 Eleven. My grandfather would be waiting for me. He'd give me a nickel and I'd run over to drop it in the slot of the soft drink dispenser. Not being very tall, I could barely lift up the door and slide a grape flavored "Spot" out of the racks.

I experienced "Uncle" Cleo's pharmacy and Biundo's drugstore. He didn't have a soda fountain and he wasn't really an uncle, but in Independence and New Orleans, with the Italian culture, any older person, no matter now distant the blood relationship, was called uncle or aunt. The same held for close friends of your parents and "cousins."

Aunt Celina, one of my grandmother's sisters had a musical horn on her car and an old actual hand operated water pump at her kitchen sink. She knew everyone's business in Tangipahoa Parish. My aunt Felicie, who taught piano at the school in Amite and played the organ at Mater Dolorosa Church on Sunday, used to say, "telephone, telegraph, tell Aunt Celina." Aunt Cecile made the best meatballs you've ever had and her husband, Pic, owned the bank.

In April, during strawberry season, I would go to "the country." My grandfather was a produce broker. The farmers would bring the strawberries to his warehouse, right behind the grocery store, and unload their pints and crates of berries; those old open kind made with the thin slats of balsa-like wood. The farmers would bring their crops in, usually on a pickup truck with the wooden boards for sides, but it was not uncommon at all to see a mule-drawn buckboard loaded up with strawberry crates. "I gots some berries, Mr. Charley," as they'd report in. My grandfather knew everyone in the parish, for sure. Mr. Mike, the inspector, would then grade the berries according to size and color. He might even taste them and you know damn well I tasted them. He also rolled his own cigarettes from a pouch of loose Picayune tobacco he carried in his front shirt pocket, that kind with the pouch with the string and tag that hung over the edge of the pocket. He also carried a silver-and-tortoise-shell container in his pants pocket that contained snuff.

My job was to label the crates. As they were stacked on my grandfather's large open truck and after each row was loaded, I would dip that large moplike sloppy brush into my bucket with the "flour paste" and paint the end of the crate. I'd then slap on the label "Anzalone and Son." It was a picture of a group of strawberries and my picture was on one of the berries.

Charles Anzalone & Son strawberry-crate label, circa 1950s.

Each produce broker had his own distinctive label. The different labels were actually an interesting art form.

After the truck was loaded it was driven a couple of blocks to the waiting refrigerated boxcars of the Great Northern Railroad. In its day, three to four boxcar loads of strawberries would leave out of Independence alone. Tangipahoa Parish was the "strawberry capital of the world," or so I was taught.

"Cousin Frances" Danna was the head nurse in surgery, and that takes us back to Lallie Kemp and the business at hand.

Miss Emily Alessci, nurse anesthetist, Lallie Kemp Hospital, 1968.

Miss Emily Alessci was our Adriani-trained nurse anesthetist. I would not dare call her "Aunt." I could just imagine her saying, "Boy, I ain't your aunt!" But she also knew more about my Independence family than I did. Miss Em was a real piece of work and a true iconic fixture around that country hospital. You never wanted to ask her what your hat looked like 'cause she sure in hell would tell you. She lived down the gravel road on the side of the hospital and occasionally she would have some of us for dinner.

Don Palmisano was chief resident at Lallie Kemp when I was a senior medical student. Don told a story of how he had been trying to get the hospital administrator to buy a defibrillator for the hospital. He was denied. Palmisano then went to New Orleans and discussed the need with Dr. Robert Sparks, dean of the medical school. Dean Sparks wrote the administrator a letter supporting Palmisano's position. He was again denied. One day while Don was making rounds with a visiting physician and graduate of the Tulane training program at Lallie Kemp, they encountered the administrator coming out of a patient room with a hospital gown on. Almost instantly he sustained a cardiac arrest. Palmisano started cardiac resuscitation and they called Miss Emily to intubate him. Just before doing so she leaned down in his face and screamed 'I bet you wish you had bought that defibrillator now." Despite everyone's attempts at resuscitation he died.

When I arrived at Lallie Kemp I encountered Al Guynes, the chief resident. Al had been in the Corps at Texas A&M and was a certified Aggie through and through. Al took the other intern and me on rounds. He laid out the rules and then it came. "Did you bring some tennis shoes? I've got that road alongside the hospital marked out every quarter of a mile," he started. "Every afternoon after rounds we're going to run. Anyone who does a five minute mile gets to do a gallbladder." Wow, a gallbladder! Brer' Rabbit had been thrown in the briar patch again I thought.

I had run track in high school and my senior year of college at Tulane. Tulane had a fellow named Roy Dubourg who was going to be their first "four-minute miler." I had been Roy's "rabbit." My instructions from Coach John Oelkers were to pace Roy. I'd run a fifty-seven-second first quarter with Roy, step for step, right behind me. I would then sit out while he ran the next two quarters. I'd then pick him up again for the last quarter and pace him to another fifty-seven second lap. Roy's running career was ended when he was hit by a car while crossing St. Charles Avenue one New Year's Eve.

There were several distinct differences one encountered when doing an out-of-town rotation. The atmosphere was more relaxed. The case load was lighter and although you were always looking for cases, it wasn't competitive. Although once a week an attending from New Orleans would drive up to "staff" a case, Al was the man in charge. Not only that, but the chief of surgery acted as the medical director of the whole thirty-bed hospital. There were also two major differences we saw in what came through the ER. The knife-and-gun club was not as active. You might see and accidental hunting wound, but not as much of the big knife-and-gun cub stuff we saw at Charity.

However, we did see more car accidents. When I was a senior student and Palmisano was chief, we experienced the famous "Black Cat" crossing wreck. The Black Cat Cafe was down the road a piece toward Tickfaw, right on the highway. The cafe was across the highway from one of the few road crossings over the railroad tracks. There was no crossing gate, the kind with the blinking light and bell that dinged when the train was coming.

One evening a car with five ladies in it was crossing the tracks and didn't see the train coming. The Hammond-bound train hit the car broadside. It completely disintegrated the car tossing the engine block about 100 yards down the track and instantly killing two of the occupants. Three survivors with massive injuries were brought to the Lallie Kemp ER. The student and intern quarters was, and is, a motel looking structure just off to the side of the hospital, but on the highway. The other students and I were in our rooms after dinner just hanging out. Someone burst through the door, "Everyone to the hospital there's been a bad accident." When we got to the OR, Palmisano and Phil Robichaux were already putting one lady on the table. A second lady had already died in the ER and the third lady was put in an ambulance and sent to Big Charity. We would be blood runners and gofers for whatever was needed. This poor lady made Humpty Dumpty look fixable, but they had to do whatever they could do; she'd made it this far.

I'll never forget the scene when Father Della Pinta, Independence's only priest, walked in the room. No gown, no mask, just a priest in his collar and black suit tending to one of his parishioners and the surgeons. "Father, you need a mask," someone screamed at him. Undeterred, with his Bible in his left hand he raised his right hand and made the sign of the cross, offered a blessing, turned and walked out. Father Della Pinta was a fixture in Independence and a Sunday regular at my grandparents table for the noon meal. He had blessed more meals than I could imagine. However, the odds were too strong against this lady and she expired.

The next day a few of us drove down to the scene of the wreck. There was hardly anything left of the car, and indeed the engine block had become airborne.

The second thing we saw in the ER was snake bites. Louisiana can call itself home to seven varieties of poisonous snakes. A couple of "rattlers" could be claimed, if anyone really wanted them, from neighboring Mississippi and Texas, but copperheads, coral snakes and water moccasins were definitely ours. The predominant bite we saw was from the moccasins and copperheads. Quite often a little kid in the country would go out to play in his back yard, turn over a sand pail or his wagon and get bit.

Now, I just don't like snakes, never have. I don't even look at pictures of snakes. On one of these snakebite occasions in the ER, the father of the child bitten by this Eden-ish creature, actually brought in the dead snake he'd killed. To paraphrase General Sheridan's famous biased remark, "The only good snake is a dead snake." There wasn't much in the way of snake anti-venoms available then and what was available was in New Orleans. Through my multiple stints at Lallie Kemp from when I had been a student, through my internship years and into my first-year residency, we had used a variety of treatments.

They usually got massive swelling so we would mark, with an ink pen, a line at the nearest edge of the swelling so we could determine its advance. Most of the time the swelling was self-limiting and in forty-eight to seventy-two hours the worst was over. There was the rare child who developed so much swelling that we had to make a long incision in the skin, a fasciotomy, to relieve the pressure. This stopped the circulation from being shut off to the extremity.

There was one other major difference between in-town and out-of-town rotations. When out of town you needed to cover the ER on a rotational basis and you got paid for it. The ER served as the primary emergency treatment for a large area. When you were on ER call you saw everything: trauma, appendicitis, diabetic problems, nose bleeds and birthing babies. There was one ENT treatment room with a dentist-like chair in it. On the little table was an atomizer with liquid cocaine. Cocaine is a powerful blood vessel constrictor. It was really a pretty innocent time with regard to drugs. When patients came in with nosebleeds, most often related to their high blood pressure, we would spray their nostrils with the cocaine atomizer and then pack their nose with a special rolled gauze sponge soaked in epinephrine and cocaine.

One late afternoon a slightly obese young woman came in complaining of a "discharge." She was about sixteen. I had the nurse put her in a treatment room and put her up in stirrups. The fluid she was draining was clear, which was unusual for a vaginal infection. I pulled her gown up to examine her protuberant belly and when I put my hands on her abdomen, something kicked my hand. Discharge hell, she's pregnant and her water's busted. I listened to her abdomen and heard fetal heart tones. I called her mother in from the waiting area, "Do you know your daughter's pregnant?" "Well I knew something was wrong with her, but I didn't know what it was." I called the OB resident and she delivered a healthy baby girl about an hour later.

When Don Palmisano was chief, he remembered a call he received one night from a junior resident manning the ER. A fellow, who had obviously been drinking, was in a severe car accident. He arrived in the ER covered in blood and minus one arm. Don happened to have a special perfusion kit used for donated cadaver kidney transplants. Anticipating that he could perfuse the severed arm and possibly sew it back on, he grabbed the kit and ran all the way across the Lallie Kemp grounds from the chief's house to the ER on the other side of the hospital. The sheriff had already gone back to the scene to try and retrieve the severed arm. It didn't take long after they started cleaning all he blood off of the victim to realize that his arm hadn't been severed in the accident. It had actually been surgically removed several years prior.

Every afternoon after rounds we would run down the road. Fred Sandifer, one of my medical school classmates, was also an intern there with me. Fred was from Greenwood, Mississippi and knew Bobby (Streeter) Gentry and the "Tallahatchie Bridge." He would later go into orthopedics elsewhere, but had to do a general surgery internship. Fred could run and he too was determined to get to do a gallbladder. Now even though I had these track credentials, I hadn't done any competitive running for five years.

After a couple of weeks our times had gotten down to within five to ten seconds of the magic five-minute mark. It seemed like every time Fred and I ran we were putting all out at the finish line. Each one of us wanted to win. And then it happened. I had tried too hard and got shin splints in both of my legs. I could hardly walk. I did not do a gallbladder on that first rotation at Lallie Kemp, Fred did. It just didn't seem right that a guy who wanted to be a bone surgeon should be doing a gallbladder, one of the neatest operations we could do.

In retrospect, there was another great advantage of being on an out-of-town rotation. The amount of structure that was Big Charity and that hospital's demands were much less in the country. There was time to sit with the older, more experienced residents and tell stories, learn the history of the "Program," and have them tell you the mistakes they had made with the hope that you wouldn't make them. These guys were "Creech trained." There was no full time chairman appointed then. It was Creech this, Creech that. Although I had casually know him, scrubbed on one case, and heard him lecture, he was gone. Who would replace him? You wanted to be able to say at some point, "I trained under doctor so and so." Who would it be?

Internal Medicine

I followed the ENT rotation with a two-month rotation on the medicine service. The first month was on general medicine, pretty much a blur. I saw patients in the medicine clinic a couple of times a week. Everyone had high blood pressure and was overweight. They all came in with their little brown paper bag full of pill bottles. There was not a huge variety in the medicines available for the treatment of high blood pressure or heart disease then. Digitalis and dig leaf aren't even used now, but then they were the basics for heart arrhythmias. The drugs used in the treatment of elevated cholesterol weren't even thought of then.

The disconcerting fact was that quite often most of the time when you looked in their bag of medicines there were many duplications. They would see one doctor and get one pill for their blood pressure and then see another one, not tell him what they were taking, and get a different prescription. If they asked you about diets I could refer them to a dietician, but trying to get a dietary history out of them was fruitless. "Oh no doctor I don't eat much at all." We saw a lot of the nurse's aides and LPN's in clinic. Down in the doctor's dining room you would see the same patients you had seen in clinic. Their plates were loaded with a half-dozen strips of bacon, eggs, and biscuits. Must be all that heavy air causing them to gain weight.

If one thinks of the practice of medicine like a war against disease, then the internists are the front line, the infantry. They see everything first and make the diagnoses. Surgeons are the special OPs and come in later, most of the time. The more specialized the surgeon, the bigger the effect, but the later he comes into play. I can understand the mental gymnastics of making diagnoses and ordering tests. I was just programmed to do more in a hands-on way.

The second month I did a specialty rotation on pulmonary medicine. I worked with two of the medicine residents who would later go into cardiology and although I didn't know it at the time, I would have some contact with them later.

The five-story Dibert Building on Claiborne Avenue, exclusively used for the treatment of tuberculosis (TBC), was still active then. It functioned as an independent self-sufficient unit. It had its own kitchen where patient's food was prepared and its own X-ray department. Although it only had a couple of floors being used when I saw patients there, they were some very sick people. One doesn't see cavity TBC now, but we saw it then. There was a significant mortality with those patients despite the triple drug therapy they were on.

Anyone who has seen any of the westerns with Doc Holliday, Wyatt Earp's dentist sidekick from Georgia, knows what "consumption" is. Dr. Oscar Creech during his time in Houston with Dr. Michael DeBakey had it and spent a year in a sanitarium. After Creech's death, Dr. Ed Lindsey wrote in the memorial note published in the Tulane medical publication, *Synapse*: "That year gave Creech time to delve into the literature on cancer treatment and vascular disease. One of the products of his convalescence was the classic technique for management of dissecting aneurysms."

The majority of patients we saw had emphysema and chronic bronchitis. The terms "pink puffers" referred to those with emphysema who could still maintain a good oxygen level and were not infected. "Blue bloaters" were those who also had chronic lung infections. I would never forget those terms. Alton Ochsner had stressed lung cancer being the main effect of cigarette smoking. Actually emphysema and chronic bronchitis affected and disabled more people than cancer.

Most of these patients were not surgical; in fact, if they did have surgically treatable conditions their pulmonary status often made them inoperable. The surgery for emphysema was limited to those isolated patients with what was called a giant bullous, the so-called "vanishing lung." Patients with this condition had one giant air sac. This air sac could occupy half the space of one lung and could compress their normal lung. It would flatten out the affected diaphragm and could even put pressure on the heart. I would later operate on some of these bullous emphysema patients as adults and infants.

A Shot Heard 'Round the World

The next couple of months, December and January, were spent in the medical admit room area and the ER, a duty required of all interns. The extra duty I had spent working in the Lallie Kemp emergency room had prepared me for both the month of medical admit and the ER. As an intern you worked both of these in twelve-hour shifts. After your night shift and breakfast you went to surgery clinic. There would be several other interns taking out stitches, cleaning wounds and putting on Unna boots, a treatment for stasis ulcers. It was at one of these morning surgery clinics that Bruce, from that first day in the elevator, further immortalized his legend in the hallowed halls of Charity Hospital.

That particular day was unique in that there were a higher than average number of pediatric patients having stitches removed. Our heads were bowed concentrating on the duty at hand, removing those small little stitches from little arms, legs or scalps. Bruce had a little kid who was more active than the rest. He was crying and really didn't want to be there. After a few "be still," "quiet," and "don't move" orders, there was a WHACK! It rang out like a gunshot. Everyone heard it. You couldn't miss it. Bruce had slapped a child. Just about simultaneously several of us looked at him and said, "Hey, we don't do that here." We had been cursed at in the ER by drunken night fighters, even spit at by them. I saw a resident once grab a gun-and-knife fighter's tongue with a towel clip to get him to lie still. I had never heard of anyone or seen anyone slap a kid. It just didn't happen. We didn't know it at the time, but Bruce had just punched his ticket out of town and out of an internship.

ENT

Mardi Gras Parade

I had spent January and New Years in the ER. I had never been big on going out and partying on New Year's Eve. It seemed to be making a lot out of nothing. Georgia's Bulldogs were playing the Razorbacks in the Sugar Bowl and that didn't hold a big interest for me. I had just as soon be in the ER sewing up knife wounds, which I did.

I was now scheduled to do a month on the ear, nose and throat service. The ENT surgeons were a busy lot. They did a lot of head-and-neck surgery for cancer. These were long tedious operations that I would assist on. It is really a one-man operation. It's very clean dissection. In medical school we spent very little time studying head and neck anatomy. In those days thyroid surgery was still in the domain of the general surgeons. Tonsils were not. The ENT clinics were full of children needing tonsillectomies. They could have filled up the hospital with them. I was in awe of the first one they helped me do. It was a bloody procedure, but when you were through it was essential that you left a dry field.

Mardi Gras happened to be in February that year. Having grown up with it I had gotten used to it. It was just another holiday. I got a phone call one day from one of my medical school classmates, Jack Covin. Jack was doing an internship at Barnes Hospital in St. Louis. We had gotten pretty close in school and unbeknownst to me an event had taken place involving the two of us that would not be revealed for another eighteen months. Jack said that there were two ICU nurses from Barnes coming down to New Orleans for Mardi Gras and he wanted Ron and I to meet them and take them out.

Now, I wasn't big on blind dates. I had been dating a couple of Charity nurses, a social worker and a blood bank technician, all on a very casual basis, with what few evenings I had available. I gave Jack our number at the apartment and told him to tell them to call us when they got to town. Now, Covin was somewhat of a prankster, so we had to figure out a scheme to check out these young ladies before we had to commit ourselves to being with them for even one day, much less two or three. On Friday night they called so we told them to meet us after the Krewe of Venus parade on Sunday, February 16, on the neutral ground at the corner of Rampart and Canal. Yep, right where Professor Longhair said that "If you saw the Zulu King, you would see the Zulu Queen." We waited across Canal, the parade passed and we found them. They were really cute. Thanks, Jack.

I continued dating one of the girls. She would make occasional trips to New Orleans and I even made one trip to the "Gateway of the West." Later that spring she and her friends took their week vacation to Puerto Rico. It so happened that during one of the weekends they were there I had a whole weekend that I wasn't on call. Continental Airlines had a nonstop flight to Miami from New Orleans and with a connecting flight to San Juan I could do the whole trip that weekend and be back at work for Monday morning, or so I thought. After a weekend in Puerto Rico I arrived back at the Miami airport on Sunday afternoon and checked in at the Continental desk. The flight had been cancelled. I was starting to get worried until I was able to get on a milk run Delta flight that went to Atlanta but stopped at almost every airport between the two cities. There was still a chance I could make it back to a Charity without being AWOL.

After spending the night in a waiting area chair in the Atlanta terminal, I awoke the next morning to see fog so thick you couldn't even see a plane through those large terminal windows. I called Dowling. "Jim, you gotta see my patients this morning and cover my service, I can't get back." I pleaded to him.

"Where in the hell are you?"

"Atlanta?"

"What the hell are you doing in Atlanta?"

"I'll tell you later," I said. "*Cherchez la femme.*"

Gallbladder Time

In March I was back at Lallie Kemp. I called Al to see if he was still running and see if that was going to be the requirement for getting to do a gallbladder. He said no, the afternoon sport was skeet shooting. He told me to bring my shotgun and before I came up to buy a case of clay pigeons. He assured me that I would get to do a gallbladder. I went by Security Sporting Goods. No longer there now, it was a huge sporting goods store on Carrollton Avenue not far from Tulane Avenue.

There was a huge field, probably five to ten acres, behind Lallie Kemp Hospital. Al had the hospital maintenance people trim the grass down to an acceptable level. He had purchased a foot-operated, spring-loaded, clay pigeon thrower, and just about every afternoon after rounds we would go out back and shoot skeet. There was nothing quiet about this sport, but I never heard anyone complain about it.

Al told me that if I found a patient who needed a gallbladder he'd help me do it. I worked extra hours in the ER and took a careful history from everyone who came in, especially if they had any abdominal symptoms. After a couple of weeks, I found a candidate. She was middle-aged, symptomatic and in otherwise good health. What's more I didn't have to, and wasn't going to talk her into it.

Another one of those stories from childhood told to me by my surgeon father involved a patient he had when he was first starting out. This particular man had gallstones and was symptomatic with gallbladder disease. Even then it was much safer to have the procedure electively than risk a complication and have the operation as an emergency. His patient really didn't want surgery. "Doc," he told my father, "I'm afraid that if I have that surgery, I'm going to die." "Nonsense," my father would tell him, "it's a low risk surgery and its far better for you to have it before it's an emergency; you'll be fine." This back and forth went on over a period of a few weeks and finally the man consented. The procedure was straightforward and uncomplicated, and sure enough, postoperatively, the patient died. My father never forgot it and neither did I.

My patient was ready to be scheduled. Al said that Dr. Bob (Buck) Rogers was coming up as a visiting staff and he would help me do the case. I had not met him formally but had seen him in action in either Saturday Grand Rounds discussing a case or rarely when he might come to Friday D&C conference. He was a big man, very confident and with Dr. Vernon Kroll they had a very successful practice at Baptist Hospital.

When Rogers arrived we had the patient ready to wheel into the OR. Miss Em would do the anesthesia; there wasn't anyone else. After she was prepped and draped and just before I was to make an incision, he said, "Now look, you do exactly what I tell you and don't stop. Don't worry about abdominal wall bleeders. I'll take care of that." "Yes, sir." One more thing you need to know, Buck Rogers had hands the size of catcher's mitts.

I made the incision through the skin and he kept saying "Cut, cut, cut," through the fascia, through the muscle, "cut, cut" and through the peritoneum. Now at this point, with both hands, he grabbed each side off the open wound with both hands and squeezed as hard as he could the cut skin and rectus muscle. He stood there squeezing for a few minutes and when he released the tissues, there was no bleeding. I started to place a Balfour retractor in the wound to gain exposure and "We don't need that" came from him.

He placed a Deaver retractor from above over a protective wet folded lap so it got the upper wound edge and edge of the liver. Miss Em then held onto the retractor through the drapes. He put a clamp on the top of the gallbladder and with his other hand held it and gave me more exposure. And then it came again, "Cut, cut, take it out." In twenty minutes the skin was closed. My first gallbladder and it was over already. It had taken me longer than that to drain that thigh full of pus I had done a few months ago, and this was a real case. "Let me know how she does," and he left. Wham, bam, thank you ma'am.

As a second-year resident, Butch Knoepp did a rotation at Baptist Hospital for a month. During that time he scrubbed with Kroll and Rogers. Butch had assisted Rogers with a gastrectomy on a very successful owner of a Mississippi River barge company. The patient had carcinoma of the stomach and had been turned down for surgery at "St. Elsewhere." As Butch was giving the patient his discharge instructions, he told Butch he would like to give him something. "What do you need, name it?" Butch really didn't need anything, and being a junior resident he wasn't going to infringe on this patient-doctor relationship especially when the patient wasn't really even his.

The patient persisted and finally Butch admitted that he had broken his stethoscope a few weeks earlier. Now surgeons really don't need stethoscopes. Dr. Creech had always said they only needed nasogastric tubes to decompress acute gastric dilatation, but Butch was going into cardiac surgery so he was thinking ahead. The next week in the mail, Butch received his new stethoscope.

He mentioned to Rogers about the gift of a stethoscope he'd received, whereupon Rogers told him, "Do you want to see the new Porsche he gave me?"

On coming back to Charity, I reflected what a good month it had been. I got to do my first gallbladder and I knew there would be more. I had two months left of general surgery rotation and one more month back at Lallie Kemp. Toward the end of the resident year, the first-year pretty much had his fill of inguinal hernia repairs. They were getting to do more gallbladders and bigger cases. Everything was passed down. It was like being out of town. They gave you more responsibility but also expected more out of you.

Before I finished my last month as an intern on general surgery at Charity, I had one more month at Lallie Kemp. That was my third out-of-town rotation. I got to do another gallbladder and some intestinal resections. The sporting venue had changed because Al had told me to bring my golf clubs. He had the hospital maintenance crew cut the grass behind the hospital, same place we had done the skeet shooting, such that it laid out nine golf holes. He found nine old tires and had made a par three course. Now the grass was cut, but you were still dealing with an old plowed-over field. You couldn't putt. Hit your ball in the tire or hit it in three shots and you made par. Just about every afternoon after rounds we would "hit the links." This was a lot more relaxed than running a mile and quieter than skeet shooting.

Al and his wife Kathy were great hosts, as on more than one occasion they would have a barbecue for the students and staff.

During my last month as an intern I was back at Charity. A patient (Sid B.) had been admitted with a large inguinal hernia. By the size of this thing the senior residents thought it was going to be a sliding hernia and not an intern case. At operation, they were right. Almost the whole right colon was in the inguinal sac and the scrotum. The posterior peritoneum (the lining around the organs in the abdomen) along with part of the colon was the "sliding" component of the hernia.

Postoperatively through no fault of his own, he developed a huge hematoma. It required drainage to remove the fluid and a drain was left in place. The whole scrotal sac then became infected. Twice a day I would change Sid's dressing. "When am I going home?" Sid would ask just about every day. He didn't fully understand what was going on. There was no way that he was going to be able to take care of this by himself. Over a period of a couple of weeks the wound was trying to heal, but was still open. There was still some necrotic material in the wound and I would clean and pick at it every day.

One morning when I came in to make rounds, I noticed a note in the progress notes from a house officer who had been on call the night before. Sid had gotten up to go to the bathroom and something had fallen out of the wound. The intern responded to the call. Sid was okay and he sent the material to the pathology lab. A few days later the path report came back. It described the shape and measurements of the object and down at the bottom of the report was the diagnosis—normal testicle. Sid was discharged.

I had survived my internship and I would move on to my first year of surgical residency. Looking back I probably could have only taken one month of Medicine and omitted ENT. I had made friends on those rotations that sometimes mean more than the cases you do. A.D. Smith would be chief at Charity and practice general surgery in Texarkana.

A.D. must have thought he taught me something, because much later when he was a practicing surgeon in Texarkana, Texas and I was a CV surgeon in Shreveport, he sent me a couple of patients with chest problems to operate on. That, my friends, is called passing the course.

Phil Robichaux also was chief at an out-of-town hospital and he would go back to his hometown of Raceland to practice surgery.

Tulane surgery faculty and staff, 1969.

Lagniappe – Dr. Theodore Drapanas

In the fall of 1968, at the age of thirty-eight, Dr. Theodore Drapanas became the new Henderson Professor and chairman of the Tulane Department of Surgery. He was to ably follow in the footsteps of Dr. Rudolph Matas (the father of modern vascular surgery) and Dr. Alton Ochsner, as well as Dr. Oscar Creech.

Dr. Theodore Drapanas.

Drapanas was born in Buffalo, New York, the second in a line of five children to very traditional Greek parents. He lost his father to an apparent heart attack when he was a teenager and according to Drapanas' son, Mark, his grandmother always wore black after her husband's death. Young Drapanas was not interested in sports like his older brother, but he excelled in school. Never making a grade below an "A," he finished high school at age fifteen and college at eighteen. He received all of his schooling from high school through medical school in Buffalo, but not by choice. Besides being ambidextrous, he had a photographic memory. He also is reported to have made a perfect score on his MEDCAT exam, something unheard of.

When it came time to go to medical school he applied to many of the noted teaching programs, but had to choose the University of New York branch in Buffalo, also not his first choice. This must have disappointed him, but he excelled none the less. Later in his career a chance meeting with the chairman of the Harvard Surgery Department would answer many questions. On meeting Drapanas, he asked him, "Why didn't you come to Harvard?" Drapanas' obvious reply was that he didn't get accepted. "But you did," was the reply.

As it turned out Drapanas had been accepted to Harvard and all the schools to which he had applied to. His mother did not want her genius son to go away and had torn up and discarded all the acceptance letters. That was the rest of the story.

When Drapanas was a freshman in medical school he made perfect scores on his first two anatomy exams, another rare-to-nonexistent phenomenon. He was called into an office before a couple of the anatomy professors. In an accusatory tone, he was confronted with the scores on his exams and asked to justify the results.

Sensing that he was, in fact, being accused of cheating, he noticed a copy of *Gray's Anatomy* on a desk. Now, even my 1948 edition of *Gray's Anatomy* has more than 1400 pages. He told the professor, "Open the book to any page." They complied and he asked what page it was. After telling him the page number, Drapanas then proceeded to recite word for word the contents of the page to them. "Open to another page," he then said. They told him the page and again he began reciting the page, word for word. They stopped him shortly and apologized.

He had been on the staff of the University of Pittsburg under the tutelage of Dr. Henry Bahnson, a very noted transplant surgeon and Drapanas' mentor. Dr. Drapanas and his wife, Arlene, could have graced the cover of any glamour magazine. They were a very handsome couple, well educated, and as confident as he was, she was personable and attractive. One of the more senior residents after meeting Drapanas described him as being "so smart and slick."

Shortly after Dr. Drapanas arrived at Tulane he called a meeting of all the residents. "This program has the reputation of having residents doing too much unsupervised work," he started, "and as of now that's going to change— OK!" About one month later, in the middle of the night, Mathis Becker had a patient on the operating table and per Dr. Drapanas' new ultimatum he called Dr. John McDonald at home, the attending on call. He presented the case to McDonald, whose response was "You can handle it"—click. The new policy lasted a month.

In 1968 at the yearly faculty-staff Christmas party held at the Tulane Alumni house on Willow Street, Drapanas made his debut. It was tradition that the residents drew the names of staff, part-time and full-time attending, and gave them presents. Dr. Drapanas received a small teddy bear dressed in a green scrub suit. The name tag on it read: THEODOPOLIS DRAPANOPOLIS, HE WHO TRANSPLANTS MONKEY ORGANS. After the cocktail party the residents took their new Greek boss to the French Quarter.

The first of many stops was Decatur Street's Acropolis. A round of ouzo was ordered for all. It seemed to me that he felt a little uncomfortable. It almost seemed like he thought they expected him to do a Zorba the Greek dance on a table.

By no means was he a "back slapper," but his facial expressions, and sometimes a boyish grin, let you know you were on the right track or you were incorrect in your assumptions or diagnosis. "Let me submit to you" and "suffice it to say" were two of his more commonly used phrases. He never dressed anyone down, that I heard, but could suggest his way to do something that let you know when you were wrong. His alternative to "hindsight is better than foresight" was "when looking through the well-polished retrospectoscope one can——." We always understood that to be a rigid proctoscope.

During his chief year, Mo Bethea and Dr. Drapanas were making rounds on the wards one day when Mo got a page to go to the ER. Drapanas went with him whereupon they found a chaotic scene of everyone attending to a severely injured gunshot victim. Blood was being pumped into the patient so frantically that the bag of blood exploded all over Drapanas' brown polyester suit. The entire team then turned their attention in to trying to clean the blood off of the Boss rather than tending to the patient.

During D&C conference one Friday afternoon in August, the discussion evolved as to how busy the ER had been. Drapanas then volunteered to take the chief resident's place on call the next night. To make sure the chief, Bethea, would stay away from Charity, Drapanas took a couple of extreme steps. First, he arranged for dinner reservations for Bethea and his wife at Antoine's, a well-known French Quarter restaurant. Then he took his beeper from him and answered all his emergency calls. Finally, to make sure he couldn't come in the hospital, he had Chet Noble, his third-year resident, tell the security guards not to let Bethea in.

Not only did Bethea enjoy a fine meal, but he got to see Bob Hope who happened to be in New Orleans for the Super Dome opening. After dropping his wife off at home he went up to Charity and sure enough the guards blocked his entrance. Knowing about the entrance via the tunnel from the basement of Tulane he made his way to the twelfth floor where the Drapanas team was operating. The rest of the evening was spent playing darts in the chief's room until all retired at about 2 a.m.

That night that Drapanas "took call" endeared him to the resident staff and also gave him a personal understanding of what his residents went through. It was almost like he had to prove himself to them and to himself that he could do it. He used every opportunity to teach, whether formally on rounds, at the weekly D&C conference or simply walking from his office to the hospital.

Every staff attending was assigned to a service and would make rounds with their residents and interns at least once a week or more if the need arose. Although he was available to the chiefs anytime to see a problem patient, he held regular walking Grand Rounds once a week to see selected patients picked out by the chief resident.

The chiefs would meet him at the central elevators on the first floor or walk him over from his office. They usually had a ward or patients in mind to present, but he, just as likely, could pick a ward. At the end of each side of Charity and on each patient floor were large screened-in "smoking" porches. It was not unheard of for the chief resident to "hide" a complication on the porch during Grand Rounds. In other words, if there was a patient he didn't want the Boss to see, the first-year resident and intern would wheel the patient, on his bed, totally out on the porch and sit with him until rounds were finished.

One particular day Drapanas got off of the elevator and told the residents he wanted to make rounds on the porch. There were no patients on it that day. "Tell me about this patient," he would say. It was not only a question-and-answer session but a teaching session. "Why did you operate on this patient at this time?", "Why didn't you operate on this patient?" Everything had to be justified in spades. The third-year residents did most of the presenting, but anyone was fair game.

The first of these walking rounds was held on E412, a female ward in the back corner of the hospital. The windows looked out at Tulane Medical

School. The first-year resident's duty was to have all X-rays pertinent to the patient available for review and inspection. The safest place for these films was under the patient's mattress at the foot of the bed. It may seem odd, but if you had a patient with any problem that had undergone a GI series, angiograms, or chest X-rays and you kept them in the seventh floor radiology department, you might never see them again. The chief resident kept X-rays pertaining to his cases in his sleeping quarters on the fourteenth floor.

That particular day the room was packed with residents adorned in clean, bright, white, starched full-length lab coats. Pants, white shirt, and tie were the dress for the afternoon and all the brown-coated medical students, doing their surgical rotation were required to be present.

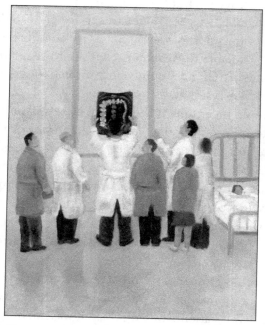

Dr. Drapanas examining X-ray on Thursday rounds.

The third-year resident started his presentation. "Dr. Drapanas this forty-eight-year-old female presented to the hospital with a history of abdominal distention and vomiting, etc., etc." After the presentation was over and it had been mentioned that abdominal X-rays had been performed, Dr. Drapanas asked to see them where upon the first-year took them from the foot of the bed and handed one or two of them to him. He took them and with a puzzled look didn't know what to do with them.

"Where's the view box?"

"We use the window, sir." was the reply.

"The window, what window?" he persisted.

Whereupon the chief resident took an X-ray and held it up to the light coming through the window.

A wry, slightly amused smile crept over Drapanas' face. He complied, examined the film and on handing it back remarked, "From now on there will be a bank of X-ray view boxes available any time I make rounds."

In actuality there was one view box available for each two wards. This single view box recessed into the wall with its dim light was located in each of the "treatment" rooms located between adjoining wards. Obviously, it wasn't suitable for examining a large number of films and because of the amount of light it afforded, it was customary just to use daylight from the windows.

On a later occasion of Drapanas' Thursday afternoon rounds, it was decided to present a patient who coincidentally had a thyroid goiter, a ventral abdominal hernia and acid reflux. These three conditions are not related and one does not cause the other. Coincidentally this patient just happened to have all three. In an attempt to trick Drapanas, they made up a name for her condition and called it "multiple middle anomaly "syndrome, or MMA.

After the patient was presented Drapanas asked Bill Browder, the third-year resident, what he thought she had. Bill responded, "Well, Dr. Drapanas we think this patient is an excellent example of MMA syndrome." Drapanas then proceeded to say, "Let me tell you about "Meandering Mesenteric Artery" syndrome. He then went on to discuss a condition, the residents had never heard anything about, and took control of the whole situation. As has been said, "Don't mess with the boss."

Drapanas developed an interest in patients with end stage liver disease. These patients developed congested blood vessels in their esophagus (varices) that when bled were life threatening. The standard operation performed at those times was fraught with complications. Drapanas proposed a Dacron graft interposition mesocaval shunt that he successfully performed many times. He published his results and was also invited to present his results and technique as a visiting professor to many outstanding medical centers.

Before coming to New Orleans he had never sailed. But the lure of living in a city surrounded by water and whose northern border was one of the largest recreational lakes in the South was too much to ignore. His first sailboat was the *Rampage,* a Morgan 33. He became a member of the well-known Southern Yacht Club and many of his friends were of the New Orleans' sailing circle. He quite frequently spent weekend days on Lake Pontchartrain, quite often sailing with Dr. Elmo Cerise, a local surgeon on the visiting staff. It was not a secret that his expertise in the OR did not follow him to the lake. While still in his learning phase he even was said to have rammed into Cerise's boat.

One Sunday afternoon a patient was admitted with bleeding esophageal varies, a potential candidate for his mesocaval shunt operation. Drapanas was notified of the patient and he came right from the Yacht Club to the Charity ER nattily dressed in his sailing attire: blue sport coat, white pants and tie. Right as he entered the hemorrhaging patient's room he was splattered with blood from almost head to toe. It was his second baptism by blood. He didn't say a word, but simply admitted his fate, turned and left.

Another time, Drapanas was making rounds when Jane Todd was an intern. A patient was presented to him who had ingested toilet bowl cleaner. Drapanas asked the third-year which brand of toilet bowl cleaner was the most caustic. Now, that's almost like asking which bird can fly higher. The third-year had no idea and he was told the answer was Snow Bowl. These products contain lye and cause marked esophageal scaring and narrowing. The resident then asked the patient if she had any problems eating. "Oh, I can eat anything," was the reply, "I just throw it all back up."

When I was a first-year we were making rounds with him on a patient in the first bed of C400B. The patient had claudication (ischemic leg cramping) when he walked and had been admitted for an intended femoral popliteal by-pass operation. While the case was being presented, Drapanas was standing at the foot of the bed with his hands on the patient's feet. When the senior resident was through, he asked the patient what he did for a living.

"Don't do much; mainly I just sit on the porch."

"Are you a mailman?" Drapanas persisted.

"Nossa," was the reply.

Addressing the senior resident he said, "Doctor, I think you should send him home; his livelihood doesn't depend on his legs and you're not going to improve on palpable pulses."

In 1974, Dr. Walter Ballinger, Bixby Professor and chairman at Washington University in St. Louis, was a visiting professor at Charity.

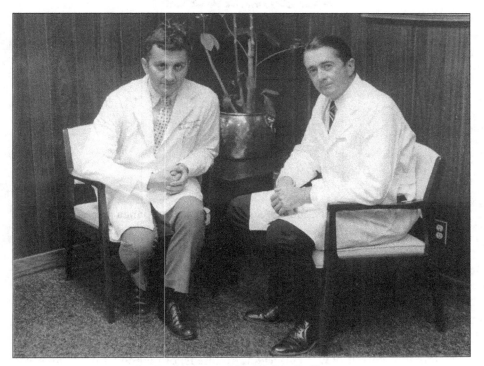

Dr. Drapanas and Dr. Walter Ballinger.

Not only were Drapanas and Ballinger coeditors of the journal *SURGERY*, but the two couples and their families would take ski vacations together. That day Grand Rounds was held on E406. The patient, a fortyish-year-old female, had presented with abdominal pain, a swollen abdomen, and a large abdominal mass. Her thick file of X-rays was reviewed on an appropriate view box, and lengthy discussions were held about the differential diagnoses ad infinitum. Nothing was omitted, or so we thought. Casually mentioned in her history was the fact that she had been in a car accident a few weeks earlier.

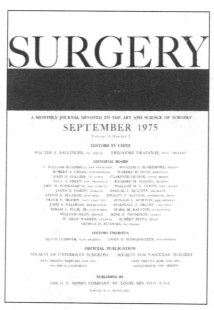

Last publication of the journal *Surgery* with Dr. Drapanas as coeditor.

Following the presentation, Dr. Martin (Marty) Litwin, our staff attending, insisted on doing the surgery the next day. At the time of operation, a very large spleen was discovered, and in fact what the patient had was a delayed rupture of the spleen and large sub-capsular hematoma of same. What was significant was the fact that Drapanas and Ballinger had earlier published an article on this condition in their prestigious journal.

Drapanas certainly wasn't perfect, no one is, but when he made an error it seemed more glaring than most. One chief resident presented him the case of a woman with abdominal pain. Drapanas' diagnosis was acute cholecystitis. The resident adamantly argued against this diagnosis. Drapanas asked for a long sterile needle and a syringe, whereupon he prepped the lady's right upper quadrant, inserted the needle in the direction of the gallbladder and withdrew cloudy fluid. "See." he said, "she has an infected gallbladder; operate on her, now." The chief resident had no choice and took her to the operating room. Her gallbladder was normal.

One Saturday morning before Grand Rounds, Drapanas was making rounds on E402. On his way past a patient who had undergone an inguinal hernia repair he noticed what looked like a portion of a urinary bladder drainage system partially hidden by the patient's sheets. The clear tubing contained bloody urine that the resident was trying to hide. "Tell me about this patient," Drapanas said. He didn't understand why a hernia patient should be bleeding, much less even have a catheter. As it turned out, the resident had inadvertently cut into the bladder while repairing the hernia. You just couldn't hide anything from him.

Tulane Surgery did not have a "pyramid" system like some other training programs. You weren't simply dismissed before your last year if you weren't going to be chief at Charity. Once you had been accepted into your first year of residency, you were fairly well assured you would make it through the program unless you really screwed up. Those few residents who didn't make the cut were usually "farmed out" to another surgery program at the University of Louisville run by Dr. Hiram Polk, a friend of Drapanas. Most senior residents who had not done a year in the lab, research, or cardiovascular surgery would become chief at either Lallie Kemp Hospital, Huey P. Long in Alexandria, or the VA Hospital in Pineville. Because there might be as many as five different hospitals involved in the Tulane training program at any one time, it was hard to keep up with who was on the same level of residency as you were or who was a level above or below you.

Some interns left the program to serve in the armed forces after their internship, others left after the first year of residency. After spending two years in the Air Force, I came back into the program at the same level with guys who had started out two years behind me or have guys two years ahead of me. A similar thing happened after I spent a whole calendar year at Ochsner. I came back to Charity and met fellows who had just come into the program. It was hard to keep up with. To this point, at one of the yearly Christmas parties, Drapanas was presented with a large wooden cutout of a hand with the middle finger extended. The various residents' names were listed on the fingers like leaves on a tree and at the top of the middle finger was the chief resident.

One of the most prestigious sailing races was the S.O.R.C. (Southern Ocean Racing Circuit) held in Nassau, Bahamas, in March 1973. The *Muñequita* (Spanish for Little Baby Doll) was owned by a local New Orleanian and based at the SYC. In heavy seas and a stiff wind, the Ranger 37 won the race by seven lengths, beating out a boat owned and captained by Ted Turner.

Drapanas had to have the boat. To this point he sold the *Rampage* and purchased it. To improve his sailing acumen, he enlisted the assistance of one of the first-year residents to become a better sailor.

His being a novice at the sport didn't deter him from taking his chief residents, Glenn Pennington and Russell Woo, out sailing one day. Woo remembers seeing a storm starting to form. Lake Pontchartrain's deepest waters are less than forty feet and as a result of the shallow waters, a slight wind would kick up a mean chop. As a high-school kid skiing and sailing on Lake Pontchartrain I had personally experienced this and had seen it capsize many sailboats. Unless he had been cautioned by a native, he had no way of knowing it. Nonetheless, in his confident and casual manner, he gracefully and unhurriedly guided the boat back to its berth. Nothing flustered him.

Eastern Airlines Flight 66

There are two accounts of what transpired prior to Dr. Drapanas boarding the plane for that fateful trip to New York on June 24, 1975. One account, as I was told that summer, had him at the New Orleans lakefront tending to the *Muñequita*. Knowing that he was running late for his flight his secretary, Carol Gaudet, drove to the Yacht Club marina to remind him. What we do know for sure is that back at the medical school Mo Bethea was on the eighth floor and encountered Drapanas carrying his briefcase out of his office. He was on his way to Boston for an American Board of Surgery meeting and possibly to give a Board examination.

Bethea had come up to Drapanas' office to give him a parting gift, as he would be changing programs and leaving at the end of June.

Butch Knoepp was on Drapanas' service waiting at Charity and was supposed to meet him for rounds that day. He didn't show up. It wasn't like him not to show up for rounds. If he was running late, and he was, and it wasn't the meeting with Knoepp that delayed him, then it is plausible that he was tinkering with the boat. Whatever the cause, he almost missed the flight. As he approached the gangway the doors were closing. The plane delayed its roll back and opened its door to admit one more soon-to-be-victim of what would be one of this nation's worst air disasters.

As the Boeing 727 started its descent into New York at about 500 feet above the ground, the tower radioed to the pilot of Flight 66 that the plane landing prior to it had experienced severe wind shear. It was recommended that he abort his landing and come into another runway. The last words to the tower from 66's pilot were, "I can make it."

He didn't.

As the wing of the plane carrying 124 souls severely dipped and struck the runway that stormy day, the crash and flames that followed were horrific. Drapanas, who always flew first class, was instantly killed, as were 109 other passengers and the pilots. Miraculously, two flight attendants riding in the rear of the plane survived, sustaining only burns and internal as well as back and ankle injuries. They walked out of the wreckage in a daze. They were taken to a hospital by a policeman responding to the disaster.

Amazingly, twelve others would also survive, mostly passengers in the rear of the plane. Again, Tulane had lost its leader. Not only Tulane, but the Drapanas family and the city, were in shock and disbelief.

At a memorial service held in the Tulane auditorium, his close friend, skiing partner and coeditor of the journal *Surgery*, Dr. Walter Ballinger, eulogized him, along with Dr. David Sabiston Jr., chairman of the Duke University Surgery Department and one of his chief residents. The lead article in the September 1975 issue of the Journal reprinted the remarks. Ballinger was able to reflect on the scientific and medical achievements Drapanas had accomplished. He spoke of the conversations he had with him about their families and children, of their growing up, and of their hopes, real conversations that could be picked up as if they had never stopped from their last meeting. He spoke of Drapanas the man, how proud he had been of his profession and what he hoped the future would bring for it.

With Drapanas' death, a young vibrant leader had been taken away much too early. Once again there were residents who had started out under one chairman's direction, but would now rely on another leader. Interns or junior residents would not know who their main mentor would be. I had experienced one chairman when I was a student and an interim chairman for half a year. Drapanas had been my chief for less than five years and now another interim chair would be at the helm.

Dr. Isidore Cohn Jr.

The sharp contrasts that were evident in the beginnings of the two medical schools that supported Charity Hospital continued between their two surgical leaders during the years of my training.

Theodore Drapanas was of Greek heritage and raised by a widowed mother in a very northern New York city. Isidore Cohn Jr. was a native New Orleanian. His father, Dr. Isidore Cohn, was very prominent in the Jewish community of New Orleans and a prominent surgeon. The senior Cohn had not only studied under Tulane's Dr. Rudolph Matas, but also had become his confidant and trusted friend. Cohn, with Matas' approval would actually write the definitive biography on Matas.

Isidore was raised in a family that valued education, classical music, proper use of the English language and the arts. His early schooling in New Orleans was followed by undergraduate and medical degrees from the University of Pennsylvania with his surgical residency at Penn.

On his return to New Orleans he joined his father in his surgical practice but at the same time was on the part-time faculty of LSU Medical School under Dr. James Rives. Ten years later, when Rives announced his retirement, Cohn would be named chairman of that department, a position he would hold until his retirement twenty-seven years later.

Cohn did not share in Drapanas' flamboyance. He projected calmness and also what some considered aloofness. Rather than a hands-on approach that we witnessed with his counterpart, Cohn was felt to be one more likely to delegate. Drapanas exhibited an unmatched prowess at the operating room table. Cohn's presence in the classroom or with his residents in a teaching situation was his strength.

He thought of himself, as others did, as a teacher and an educator. Whereas Drapanas enjoyed his time sailing on Lake Pontchartrain and on the ski slopes with his family; Cohn's interests seemed more inward. Isidore and his wife, Marianne, were both noted collectors and philanthropists. Their collection of Steuben glass and jade was not surpassed by many. Isidore Cohn Jr. died at age ninety-four, holding the titles emeritus chairman and emeritus professor of surgery at the LSU School of Medicine.

First-Year Resident, 1969–1970

Emergency Room

I went to the mail room to retrieve my new lab coat. I turned in the one with the generic "Intern" label. It now had stitched on the front over the pocket *Tulane Department of Surgery* and above it was stitched my name in script. A dream I had envisioned six years previously was now a reality. There was still a long way to go. I had moved up the ladder as a first-year resident. Jack Reeder and "Hot "Howard Nelson would be my chiefs.

I began a two-month rotation in the emergency room. As a first-year surgical resident you were responsible for every patient who walked or, more likely, was wheeled through that door. At the head of the middle hall was a small nursing station or office. When things weren't busy, this was one of the few areas where you could sit and get off of your feet. It was also an area where the occasional New Orleans cop would hang out trying to meet a nurse. There was a small desk in this room and above the desk on the wall was taped a piece of paper. Someone had written out the months of the year across the top of the horizontal piece of paper and underneath each month was a number, the number of patients seen each month. The numbers up until July ranged from 3000 to 5000 patients. That July we would see in excess of 6000 patients.

For those patients that couldn't be sewn up or treated otherwise and released, your job was to triage them, prepare them for surgery and notify the third-year resident. If they just had a fracture we would support the extremity and order appropriate X-rays. There was just about always an orthopedic resident in the ER.

Preparing them for general surgery included starting an IV, usually a cut down for venous access, inserting a nasogastric tube and urinary catheter and possibly a chest tube if there was a chest injury. If their vital signs were stable, they were then taken down the hall for appropriate X-rays. There was no operating room in the emergency room. With an available elevator, manned by a human at all times, the trip to the twelfth floor and a sterile operating room with any instrument you wanted took less than a minute. Eddie or one of his cohorts had control of that brass handle. Anyone pushing a button on any of the floors could not override the floor selected.

One of the nontraumatic conditions we saw over the course of my time in the ER was a recurring number of patients with stasis ulcers on their legs caused by venous insufficiency or end stage varicose veins. The treatment was an Unna boot. Basically it was a zinc oxide and calamine lotion-impregnated gauze wrap that was wrapped around the lower leg and left in place for a week. The patient would then be scheduled to be seen in the second-floor surgery clinic and have a new "boot" put on.

There was no surgical treatment for these patients. One day one of these recurring Unna boot patients came into the ER. His dressing was ragged and filthy to the point it wasn't pink any longer. There is no telling how many return appointments he had missed. I put him up on an exam table and started to unwrap and cut off the bandage. When I got down to the flesh of his leg I noticed something crawling in his ulcers. It was maggots. He had the cleanest ulcers I had ever seen but his leg was infested with maggots. Maggots only eat dead tissue. They do not eat living tissue. To be honest, I didn't handle that very well. Blood and guts didn't bother me but, maggots crawling around on your body was something else. I washed them off of his leg with a bottle of ether, put on a new dressing and sent him out.

Because of the volume of patients coming through the ER over the course of a month's duty I would usually come in contact with most of the other surgery residents stationed at Charity. During my first year I had come in contact with most of the other surgery interns. I was either on call with them or would see them on Grand Rounds. Because of out-of-town rotations or nonsurgical rotations, it was possible to not have actually met most of them until the end of the year. It was like those lottery balls you see with the different numbers on them bouncing around in the large basket, no two going on the same direction.

It was very hard to understand the actual total number of people in the program and who they were. You never saw everyone all together. There were several things that contributed to this. With residents coming in and out of military service and residents coming back from two to three-month out-of-town rotations, it was like people going through a series of turnstiles. You almost didn't know who wore the same uniform. "Who's that guy? Where's he been?" The one common denominator that labeled us all was the red stitching over the pocket of our lab coats that said TULANE SURGERY DEPARTMENT. Being the "gatekeeper," if you will, in the emergency room gave you exposure to just about everyone who was "stationed" at Big Charity.

For a two-week period I worked twelve hours, 7 a.m. to 7 p.m. The next two-week period I worked the twelve-hour night shift. When I worked days I had no other responsibility other than what came through the ER doors. If I wanted a follow-up on a patient I had treated, I could ask the resident or intern the next time they happened to be on call. Unless the case was very dramatic, like a stab wound to the heart, the cases just ran into each other and I forgot about them.

When I was on the night shift, it was different. I got off at 7 a.m., went downstairs, had some breakfast, and then went to general surgery clinic. Here I filled in and saw new patients for whatever service was in clinic that day. After a couple of hours I'd go home and crash. I found myself only needing five, maybe six hours of sleep.

If it was a really slow night, I would find an empty stretcher, hopefully a clean one, in one of the trauma rooms away from the entrance where it was quieter. Tell the head nurse and your interns where you would be, turn out the light and grab some sleep hoping of course that someone wouldn't come in while you were sleeping and start an IV on you, ram a nasogastric tube down your nose or worse.

When Steve Harkness was an intern, sometimes he would go up to the twelfth floor and find an empty operating room, the advantage being that the twelfth floor was air conditioned similar to the ER. After turning out the lights he would climb up on an operating room table, fold some sheets to make a pillow, put a restraining strap across his waist so he wouldn't fall off and catch whatever sleep he could until the day crew came in turning lights on or his ever-present beeper went off.

After my night shift, in the afternoon, depending when I woke up at home, dictated what I did next. We didn't do a lot of grocery shopping, but there was some laundry that might need to be done. I wore a scrub suit constantly, except when I was out of the hospital. During those summer July and August months I might even have time just to sit out by the apartment pool and catch some rays.

One afternoon when I was walking by the pool, two young mothers were busy talking as one of their toddlers walked right over and fell in. It was strictly fortuitous that I was right there when it happened. I was able to reach down and grab his outstretched flailing arm and pull him out. Mom hadn't seen him fall and wasn't completely sure what transpired; it all happened so fast. It was like you've always got your uniform on and you're never away from it.

Moonlighting

As a first-year resident, I had the opportunity to make extra money moonlighting. On an out-of-town rotation, it was necessary for the house officers to man the ERs. Hospital's emergency rooms were not staffed by trauma specialists. The closest thing to a trauma specialist was a Charity Hospital surgery resident. If there was a physician on duty at a private hospital, it was usually an internist or a general practitioner who had retired from private practice. There were no "intensivists" or "hospitalists" that are so prevalent in medicine today. Hospitals would hire residents to be on call in their hospital at night to do histories and physicals on preop patients going to surgery the next day. They would also see the occasional trauma patient. These duties mainly amounted to suturing lacerations. You might be asked to "pronounce" a patient who had expired or assist a surgeon with an emergency operation.

One night when I was moonlighting at Hotel Dieu Hospital I got an emergency call to rush to the obstetrical area. A young lady in labor was on the delivery table. The baby was delivering but was in fetal distress. As it turned out the umbilical cord was wrapped around its neck. Her obstetrician had his hand in the birth canal trying to retard the progress of the baby's delivery.

"Hurry up and prep her belly. Hurry, hurry, make an incision," he frantically yelled. "Hurry, hurry." The scrub nurse was frantically trying to set up her table with some needed instruments. I threw some sterilizing solution on her belly, swabbed it around and the nurse hurriedly draped her. I made an incision down her belly trying to be careful not to carry it through her thinned out abdominal wall and into the uterus.

As soon as I started on the uterus, her obstetrician had re-gowned and gloved, and finished the incision. He grabbed the baby, retrieving it into the abdominal wound, clamped the cord, and passed the baby off to the pediatric nurse. The baby was fine. The whole thing had taken just a few minutes, but a few minutes that could have made the difference in not only a live baby, but one with oxygen deprivation and possible brain damage. Most nights were not that eventful.

There was even a group of residents that used to moonlight at Angola State Penitentiary. Located on the banks of the Mississippi River just outside of Baton Rouge and nicknamed the "Alcatraz of the South," this facility housed as many as 6000 prisoners. Angola was, and is, a legendary facility where death is usually the only way an inmate leaves.

Around 1970, Baxter Laboratories was sponsoring a program at Angola where they were paying inmates five dollars for a unit of donated blood. The blood was being separated into its components, plasma, red cells and cryoprecipitate.

Mathis Becker, the thoracic resident when I was a third-year, was in charge of scheduling residents to work there just on a daily basis. In order for blood to be drawn, a physician, the moonlighting resident, was required to be present during the procedure and take a history from the prisoner "donors" to assure that they had never had hepatitis. Because there was no blood test for hepatitis in those days, the main questioning centered around whether the prisoner had ever been jaundiced, or as our patients called it "yellow jaundice." There were some interesting vignettes from Becker's "term" in prison.

On one occasion when answering a knock at his office door, Becker said he was staring at a prisoner so big he felt like he was looking at his belt buckle. The man was upset because Becker had vetoed one of the prisoners. This probably meant that the big guy didn't get his kickback from the other prisoner.

On another occasion while a prisoner was on the table with the needle and tubing connected to his arm and blood draining out, the guards burst into the room, ripped the needle out and dragged him away. As it turned out a prisoner had escaped from the prison and the prisoner on the table was in charge of the blood hounds used to search for the escapee.

Becker had a prolonged conversation with another one of the prisoners who, like all of them, swore to his innocence. He swore to Becker that his wife had actually done the murder he had been convicted of, but to save her from going to prison he admitted to it.

Although there had never been an incident involving the residents at Angola, after the famous Attica riots in 1971 resulting in forty-three deaths of correctional officers and other personnel, most residents were afraid to go up there anymore and the moonlighting at Angola stopped.

General Surgery, Charity

Burn Patients

After my stint in the ER and back up on the wards, one of the memorable cases I took over care of was that of a burn patient. This young woman had a fight with her boyfriend and was very depressed. She had gone home to her second-floor apartment in the uptown area determined to end her life. The apartment had a pair of French doors that opened to a small balcony over-looking the front yard.

She placed wet towels at the bottom of those doors and did the same thing with the front door. She then proceeded to turn on all the gas burners on the stove, the gas space heater in her bathroom and the gas logs in the small fireplace. She then sat down in the living room area awaiting her fate.

As the apartment filled with gas she kept thinking about what she was doing. Was the guy she had just broken up with worth her taking her life? She changed her mind.

Appropriately, she went around the apartment turning off all the gas jets. Inappropriately, she sat down and lit a cigarette before opening the windows and doors. The resulting explosion blew her through the French doors onto the front yard below.

When I assumed her care she was in a roller Stryker bed. Because she had burns over about 60 percent of her body, back and front, she couldn't stay on one side for a very long time. The advantage of this bed is that the patient can be strapped in and rotated from back to front at periodic intervals.

Every day she required dressing changes and periodically she would be taken to the OR for skin grafts. The management of burns in those days was difficult. There was no specialized area to keep the patients in.

I learned how to take split thickness skin grafts with a mechanical device called a dermatome. I also learned to take these skin grafts with a special dermatome knife. That knife was the sharpest thing I had ever encountered. With time I was able to guide the blade over the skin of the thigh just removing the upper layer. It would leave an area resembling a second-degree burn. I rotated off that service after two months and found out later that she had thrown a large blood clot to her lung and expired.

One of the most common burns we saw involved children's night gowns catching on fire. New Orleans was famous for its use of wall-mounted space heaters. Natural gas is very cheap in the South and natural gas was the main source of heat for most homes. Either mounted in the wall, most commonly in the bathroom, or in the living area as a floor-mounted unit with concrete "logs," they all provided excellent and cheap heat. However, they all had an open flame. In the days before flame-retardant material for children's night clothes it didn't take much for a child to get too near the flame and their pajamas, more commonly their nightgown to go up in flames. Fatal burns resulting from children playing with cans of gas and kitchen matches, unfortunately, were also seen.

Angiograms

One of the duties of the first-year resident when on call at night was to do arteriograms for the chief resident on his patients who had vascular disease. In the sixties and early seventies these were all performed by direct needle puncture of the blood vessel that needed to be studied. The Seldinger technique, although brought into use earlier, required special needles and catheters that weren't available to us at that time.

Tony LaHood was in charge of the X-ray unit on the seventh floor at night. Tony was a hard worker. He walked with a limp that was a residual from an earlier bout with polio. It didn't slow down Tony one bit. I never saw him idle and he always tried to be accommodating as his schedule permitted. Tony used to say," Doc, if you want something done, ask the guy who's busy, not the one just standing around." If there were studies that needed to be done, anything at night that involved an X-ray, you had to deal with Tony.

First you had to tell him ahead of time what kind of study and how many you needed to do. He would either tell you a time to come back or beep you when he was ready. Tony would set up a Mayo stand with syringes and needles for giving a local anesthetic to the area. The anesthetic, 1 percent Xylocaine, was in a small bottle. There were also glass beakers containing plain saline, used to flush the syringe so the needle didn't clot and most importantly, the radiopaque dye. This solution was also a clear fluid.

Tony would have it all laid out on a sterile drape along with the syringes and needles of varying lengths and gauges. Most patients with arteriosclerotic blockages in their legs manifested their disease as calf pain (claudication) or thigh and buttock pain while walking.

In order to do the study, we laid the patient face down on the X-ray table. The back was prepped along the vertebral spine and an area deadened just to the left of their spinal column below the rib cage. With an eight-inch-long spinal needle and a 10cc syringe filled with saline, you could advance the needle aiming for the vertebrae. Sliding off of the vertebrae would put you in the aorta. Blood would come back under pressure in the syringe.

After flushing the syringe with the saline you would then connect a 20cc syringe filled with radiopaque dye to the needle with a metal stopcock in between. A test flush, with an X-ray, was needed to be done to assure exactly where your needle was located. Ideally, you wanted the needle below the origin of the renal arteries. Now it was just a matter of where you wanted the dye and timing.

These were not cines; they were still shots. Tony would take the X-ray when you told him to "shoot." The dye in the syringe was thicker than saline so it took a fair amount of pressure to force the dye in the aorta as quickly as possible using the glass syringes available to us. The idea was to have the whole aorta filled with a bolus of dye at any one time to get the best pictures.

If the patient was suspected of having blockages in the arteries in the pelvis, your first picture would be taken right when you got to the end of the syringe. "Shoot!" Tony would take the picture, you would flush out the needle with some saline, and wait. He would then have to develop each film individually.

It was time consuming and took some practice to get it right on the first shot. If the patient had blockages in the lower legs you had a much longer delay before you told Tony to shoot, one second, two seconds, three seconds, four seconds, shoot ! Wait for the film.

The worst were the carotid artery studies. The patient was now flat on his back, prepped and draped. I never felt comfortable about sticking the carotid. Two fingers of one hand were used to press down at the base of the neck to try and immobilize the vessel and you literally stabbed the patient with the needle trying to hit it.

The carotid artery is smaller than the diameter of your finger. When, and if, you got the needle in the vessel, you injected the dye almost immediately when the dye was entering the vessel.

Direct needle puncture of the carotids yielded itself to several disasters. Most commonly, the patient could develop a large hematoma at the injection site. One resident even managed to clot off the whole carotid requiring the patient to be taken to emergency surgery. And the worst was the case of the hydrogen peroxide.

Unbeknownst to the resident performing the case, a beaker of hydrogen peroxide wound up on the sterile Mayo stand. It is also a clear fluid. The dye had been injected and unknowingly a 10cc syringe of hydrogen peroxide was drawn up and injected as a flush directly into the carotid and hence into the brain. The patient seized and died. It was a terrible complication, but one that every resident thereafter knew about. Most of the time, it became a practice for the person doing the study to be the one drawing up any solutions in the syringes to be used.

"Things"

The annual Christmas Party in 1969 was kicked up a notch from the entertainment standpoint. This time besides the usual name drawing and gift giving, Larry Cohen, then a third-year resident, dressed as Santa Claus.

Dr. Larry Cohen as Santa, surgery Christmas party, 1969.

It just wasn't enough to give the staff attending a gag gift; a poem usually accompanied it. This was Dr. Drapanas' second exposure to this event. He received a life-sized poster of himself.

Drapanas with Christmas-present poster, surgery Christmas party, 1969.

The real highlight of the evening was the presentation to Dr. Ed Lindsey. A Korean War veteran, he also had training in transplantation following a thoracic residency. Lindsey was a very thoughtful individual, sometimes too thoughtful. His nickname was things, "things to do." He would always have a different more esoteric way to do something and was always trying to reinvent the wheel.

I scrubbed with him on a vascular access case for dialysis at Hotel Dieu one day. The procedure involves joining the radial vein to the radial artery to make a fistula that, when it matures, can be a used to put renal failure patients on dialysis. As we were starting the case, Lindsey produced a little metal device, that he said was to facilitate the procedure. It was a Russian-made gizmo that was supposed to couple the two ends of the vessels together and then unite them with these minuscule staples.

This thing was actually a prototype of larger vascular and intestinal stapling devices that would come into popular use a few of years down the line. I don't know where he got it, but he should have left it there. In the time it took to set up the device and try to fit the blood vessels in it, we could have done two fistulas. It didn't work and he wound up doing the fistula in the conventional way.

In his office was a shelf with multiple sealed jars of various fluids. For some reason he was trying to grow gallstones.

The evening of the party, "Santa" Larry had been handed the list of the attending's names and the poems to go with each gift. When he got down to Lindsey's poem he knew that it was not going to be a sober night. He wasn't going to be able to read it out loud to all present without alcoholic reinforcement—and he hadn't even seen the present yet.

When it came time for Lindsey's gift, Larry started, "Things to do, things to do, Ed Lindsey, things to do (it went on and then ended)—hooray for Lindsey, hooray at last, hooray for Lindsey he's the horse's ass." Where upon when Lindsey unwrapped his gift he was looking at a large poster-sized picture of the south end of a northbound horse.

Dr. Ed Lindsey with Christmas-present poster, surgery Christmas party, 1969.

He took it in stride as the gentleman he was.

At a later Christmas party when Jim Dowling was an attending his continued love of the Big Ten football conference was used against him in the poem read to him.

"We've listened to his tales of the Irish and Big Ten and how all the Yankees are really big men, but Parseghian came down with the rest of his bunch and the Tigers (LSU) proceeded to eat their lunch."

Fluids

The use of "fluids" is essential and mandatory in any postoperative patient who is unable to take an oral diet. Also, antibiotics are most efficient when given intravenously. In patients with severe alimentary tract problems, caloric loss, burns, massive intestinal resections and others, "IV hyperalimentation" has been proven to be lifesaving.

The nurses on the wards were responsible for the maintenance of the IV's. If a nurse was unable to start an IV on a patient the responsibility moved up the ladder to the intern or first-year resident. To say there was a nursing shortage at Charity would be a severe understatement. One Charity Hospital RN or even a senior nursing student might have as many as thirty patients under her care at any one time. At night a LPN (licensed practical nurse) might be in charge. IV drips were controlled manually, that is, you timed the drops with your watch as to how many drops per minute you wanted to administer: that's how you knew how many cc's the patient got per minute or hour.

It was not uncommon for the nurse to charge the patient's family with the duty of letting her know if the fluid in the bottle was running low or if the line was kinked. If the IV got kinked and clotted off, became dislodged or the fluid ran out, a new IV would have to be started.

On one particular occasion the family of a post-op patient with difficult veins was told, "Don't let it run out, let me know when he fluid gets low," the nurse cautioned the family. Despite the warnings, much later a family member sought out the nurse to tell her the IV wasn't dripping. When the nurse arrived on the scene she found a yellow fluid in the more-than-half-empty bottle. It was routinely written into most orders to add an ampoule of vitamins, which had a yellow tint, to many of the IV bottles. The nurse realized this was different.

On closer inspection she found a seed blocking the flow of the orange fluid in the IV tubing—an orange seed. The family had realized the IV was running out. They couldn't find the nurse and trying to do their best to "not let the IV run out," had taken down the bottle, unplugged the rubber stopper and filled up the bottle with orange juice. Orange juice is a "fluid," but in the vascular system it is not compatible with life. Death by orange juice poisoning was the result.

Blood is the ultimate and most necessary of all the body fluids. It was a difficult commodity to come by. The knife-and-gun club members used up more than their share and seldom replaced it. Patients needing elective surgery were required to have two to four units of blood donated in their name before they were admitted for surgery. Even a preop hernia repair was required to bring in two units of blood.

Because blood usually was not administered in most of these elective operations, those donated units of blood helped build up the blood bank supply. Pads of printed "blood donor slips" were available on all the wards and interns and all residents carried a pad in their lab coats. Tulane offered the reward of a free book from the bookstore to the intern or resident who brought in the most blood donors each month.

Quite often, trauma patients were told they couldn't be discharged until some blood was donated in their name to replace what had been used.

Initially, the blood bank was located on the twelfth floor near the surgery suites under the direction of the anesthesiology department. "Uncle Earl" Robinson was in charge of releasing the blood. If we needed to give blood to a patient on the wards an order was written in the chart, then a blood request slip was filled out by the nurse or intern. A medical student certainly couldn't order blood and even an intern had to have the slip signed by a more senior resident. It was a very frustrating scenario. You would hand the slip to Earl; he'd tweak his mustache and ask you what you needed it for. If you told him the patient was anemic, he'd want to know what the blood count was. Hopefully, he would then countersign the slip and the technician in the blood bank could release the whole blood to you. Not until the mid-1970s did things in the blood bank change.

Dr. David DeJongh, a hematologist and blood bank specialist on the LSU Medical School staff, took over as head of the blood bank. The changes he brought about were striking. We still had to get donors, but the begging stopped. More importantly, DeJongh started fractionating each bag of whole blood into packed cells, plasma, and cryoprecipitate, which aided clotting. This concept, although the beginning of a new dawn in blood administration, was very hard for us as surgeons to accept. We felt that nothing was as good as giving a patient a unit of whole blood when they were bleeding whole blood.

We soon learned that when a patient developed a clotting abnormality, giving them fresh frozen plasma or bags of platelet concentrate solved the problem in most cases.

As revolutionary were the contributions made by DeJongh in blood administration and development of the blood bank, the development and use of IV hyperalimentation was even more significant. In 1973, Dr. Donald Palmisano, then in private practice, operated on a thirty-six-year-old pregnant woman who had suffered acute venous thrombosis of her intestinal tract. Palmisano had to resect her entire gangrenous small intestine, a situation not comparable with life. He could not keep her alive by normal means.

He had the hyperalimentation solution made up by the hospital's pharmacy. Because of the caustic nature of the fluid, he devised a technique to thread a catheter subcutaneously along her chest and into the major vein bringing blood back to her heart.

He would frequently report the patient's progress to those assembled at Tulane Saturday Grand Rounds, and on one occasion, after the patient's discharge from Baptist Hospital, the very patient came in herself. She managed at home for over two years before succumbing to a massive fungal infection.

Palmisano's ability to take charge of a situation didn't come by accident. His father had a long and outstanding career with the New Orleans Police Department. He had received notoriety when he single-handedly and without his weapon confronted a man attempting to kill a hostage. He was able, in turn, to disarm the offender by telling him, "I think you have a fever and I know some people at Charity Hospital to take care of you."

Naturally, we started using IV hyperalimentation in our critical ill patients. The calories we were able to administer with this solution were massive compared to a standard IV or even a feeding stomach tube.

One of the oddest, but unfortunately tragic examples of unusual fluid administration involved a postoperative patient on C400A, "under the clock." The patient had undergone a total removal of his esophagus. His colon had been used to make a new conduit to his stomach. The patient also had a chest tube, standard after any trans-thoracic procedure, and a feeding tube in his stomach. The patient was several weeks post-op and had developed a leak and was not able to take food by mouth yet. His very attentive family brought him some homemade gumbo one weekend.

Now gumbo, a staple of any native Louisianan's diet, when cooked right, is fairly thick. It contains rice, vegetables, sausage, chicken and/or seafood as the protein. They had difficulty getting the solution down his stomach tube, so they did what they thought was the next best thing—they put it in the much larger-diameter chest tube and clamped it off for a little while. On the following Monday he had taken a severe turn for the worse even though the condition was discovered. He succumbed to "gumbo thorax."

Sonny Trammell remembers one of his patients who overdid his access to fluids with disastrous results. A severely alcoholic patient had been admitted who also had a stomach feeding tube. After a couple of days he was found "dead in bed" one morning on rounds. Nearby were found a couple of empty vodka bottles. Acute alcohol poisoning didn't take long when one doesn't have to swallow and come up for air.

When patients needed large volumes of fluids, as in a trauma patient in the ER, the standard modality at Charity had been to perform a cut down on either the vein at the ankle or the cephalic vein just inside the shoulder below the clavicle. The rapidity with which this was could be done was very impressive when performed in the hands of a trained resident or even intern. A sterile eight or ten French infant feeding tube was threaded into the vein and massive amounts of fluid or blood could be administered in a short time.

Around 1970, a new technique was brought from Baylor Hospital by a first-year resident (DL) who had done his internship there. DL had been an undergrad student at Tulane and a Tulane medical student. He had always bounced along a little differently than other students.

As a T1, he carried all his medical textbooks in a medium sized suitcase to class each and every day. Now these books are large and heavy. Most of us might have our anatomy book with us, but more importantly you carried spiralbound note books to take your volumes of notes in. Lugging his suitcase with him, DL would get his daily exercise by jogging around the whole square block that Tulane occupied each morning before classes started.

The new IV technique involved a special catheter that had been developed which could be inserted through a large-bore needle stuck directly into the large subclavian vein below the clavicle. The needle was then withdrawn and the catheter sutured in place. A cut down was not necessary; it was quick and could be done with minimal instruments. The main complication was the potential of giving the patient a collapsed lung (pneumothorax). With proper technique that complication could be avoided.

The first-year resident had demonstrated the procedure to some of the more senior residents with success. An attending heard about this procedure and told the new resident not to do any subclavian sticks on his patients on LM 4, the cancer unit. He felt that the risk of causing a pneumothorax in a critically ill patient was too much. Why add another domino to what could be a cascade of problems these compromised patients already had?

One night the first year was asked to see one of Dr. Krementz's patients who needed a new IV for administration of his chemotherapeutic agents. The patient had poor veins and had been stuck many times for venous access.

Despite what he had been cautioned not to do, DL proceeded anyway, and you guessed it, a pneumothorax on one of Krementz's patients. DL finished his general surgery training at another training program and subsequently became a cardiovascular surgeon.

When I was a senior student at Lallie Kemp my first experience with a long intracath did not go well. Phil Robichaux had a patient in the ER going for an appendectomy. "Go put an intracath in her," he told me. Just because I'd never seen the procedure didn't stop me. These were large-bore needles. It was standard practice to tape the needle to a wooden tongue depressor before taping it to the arm.

Before taking her to the OR Phil came back one more time to check and see what I had done. Something didn't register and suddenly he grabbed her arm above the IV site with a grip so strong you would think he was stopping her from falling off a cliff. "Call X-ray, call X-ray! What'd you do?" Now to say I was getting a little panicked would be putting it lightly, but I wasn't nearly as panicked as Phil. And then it hit him, "Where's the wrapper?" Still on the floor, I picked up the cellophane wrapper the intracath had come in. In it was the long tubing I was supposed to have inserted through the metal needle and threaded into her vein. I had not sheared off the catheter and he could release his grip.

Visiting Professors

There were several very prominent visiting professors who came to Tulane that 1969-1970 academic year. These were usually heads of departments at some of the more prestigious medical schools in the country. A notable exception to this was Dr. Christiaan Barnard of Capetown, South Africa.

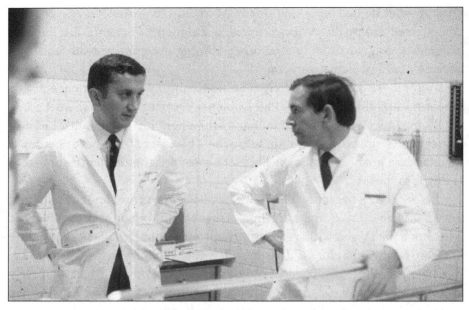

Drs. Drapanas and Christiaan Barnard, 1969.

In December 1967 Barnard performed the first human-to-human heart transplant. Although Louis Washkansky only lived eighteen days and died of pneumonia, this operation shook the world and put South Africa on the "medical map." A few weeks later Barnard performed his second successful transplant at Groote Shuur Hospital on Dr. Philip Blaiberg, a retired dentist.

From South Africa, Barnard had training in the United States and had been influenced by notable pioneers such as Owen Wangensteen, C. Walton Lillehei, and Norman Shumway. In 1969 Barnard went on a world tour. Dr. Dennis Rosenberg, a local thoracic surgeon in New Orleans, originally from South Africa, encouraged Barnard to make New Orleans and Tulane one of his stops. And so it happened. Before his transplantation days, Barnard had developed a keen interest in congenital heart disease. A child with an atrial septal defect (ASD) had been prepped as a case for Barnard to perform during his visit to Charity. Barnard deferred, stating that he only operated with his team from Groote Shuur.

The day was spent making rounds on patients on the pediatric wards with congenital heart disease. Phil Brewer was the CV resident and it fell on him to do most of the presenting to Barnard. We then sat around with Barnard on one of the end porches while more cases were presented.

Dr. Phil Brewer presenting cases to Dr. Christiaan Barnard, 1969. Seated, L–R: Drs. Dennis Rosenberg, Drapanas, and Barnard.

Later that afternoon he gave a talk in the Tulane auditorium.

Dr. Christiaan Barnard, Tulane Medical School Auditorium, 1969.

One particular visiting professor's stay didn't go as smoothly. This particular surgeon had an interest in doing inguinal hernia repairs under local anesthesia to the point he was known as the "Father of Hernia Repair." Mathis Becker vividly remembers a patient with a hernia on his service who had been waiting for an extended period of time to get on the schedule. The case was a natural fit for the visiting professor to demonstrate his technique and at the same time get the patient's hernia fixed.

Things didn't go well in the OR. The local anesthetic wasn't very effective. The patient was screaming because of the pain and the surgeon was screaming at the anesthesiologist. Finally the visiting surgeon lost his cool and walked out, leaving Becker to finish the case. To add to the craziness, the patient later developed a wound infection.

Becker took care of the patient until the wound was healed and discharged him. Upon discharge the patient told Becker, "Dr. Becker if you ever get to Galatoire's, I work there and I'm gonna buy you a drink." Now Galatoire's, one of New Orleans' oldest and finest restaurants, is not on the list of hangouts for a Charity Hospital resident.

It so happened that Becker's in-laws came to town and they dined at where else, Galatoire's. Upon entering the dining room, Becker's patient was true to his word and treated them to adult beverages.

Grand Rounds were held one Thursday afternoon with a different visiting professor. A postoperative gastrectomy patient was presented who had been having a varied lists of problems after his surgery. The double row X-ray view boxes were situated at the "clock" end of C400A in front of bed six and the room was packed with residents in their bright white starched coats, shirts and ties. Students occupied the back row.

The discussion between Drapanas and the visitor went on and on with reference to a myriad of complications seen after stomach resections. I was on the second row at the far end of the room as the third-year resident who had done the case also discussed it. I noticed Howard Nelson slowly lift his left hand to his face. Shielding his mouth, he whispered something to Jack Reeder. Not out of the ordinary, since it was a didactic discussion and I thought he was just commenting on something that had been said.

When the entourage left the room, the patient was hurriedly placed on a stretcher and wheeled to the OR. What Nelson had whispered was what they had finally noticed on the X-rays, the cause of the patient's postoperative problems—a retained lap. Laps and sponges (which are actually folded absorbent gauze squares) are used at surgery to absorb blood and keep the field dry. Before closing a case they are counted multiple times and they are never intentionally left in the surgical field. The lap was removed, the patient did well. The second operation did not make it to the Bugle that week.

J. Lynwood Herrington was Professor of Surgery at Vanderbilt University Medical School and another noted visitor. He was not only a colorful character but he had a distinct interest in surgery of the stomach and had written endlessly about those disorders. Therefore it was only natural, during his visit, to present him a case of a gastric resection.

As I remember the entourage was massed on W405. The surgery and the discussion of acute peptic ulcer disease was nothing compared to the backstory that accompanied the patient being presented.

Several weeks before his stomach problems arose the fortyish-year-old male had been stabbed in the chest by his wife. He got in his pickup truck and drove to Tulane Avenue and Broad Street to the central lockup and courthouse. Parking his truck in front of the large, columned building he started the ascent up the granite steps.

"Hey, you can't park there," a New Orleans cop yelled.

"My ole lady got me," was his reply, showing his bloodstained shirt.

"Well, get on down to Charity," the cop came back.

The injured man went back down the stairs, got in his truck, and drove about a mile down Tulane Avenue to Charity Hospital. Again he parked his truck in front in another No Parking zone. He started to walk past the visitor's check-in booth to the front doors where upon, "Hey, where you goin'? You can't park there!" a guard screamed at him.

"I've been stabbed," he replied.

"Then get back around the block to the ER." He got back in his truck, drove around La Salle Street, pulled up on the ER ramp and passed out. He was hurriedly brought inside where a stab wound to the heart was diagnosed. A needle was inserted into his chest and blood was removed from around his heart—a procedure called a pericardiocentesis. He was then whisked off to the operating room. After this lengthy story, Herrington's reply was, "Only at Charity."

Michael DeBakey also came back to Tulane as a visiting professor that year.

Drs. Michael DeBakey and Drapanas, Tulane Medical School Auditorium, 1969.

After giving a lecture in the morning he attended the D&C conference that afternoon. One of the cases brought up for discussion was that of a bezoar. These are a mass of food particles, similar to hair balls in cats, that can stay in the stomach and cause obstruction.

After Dr. DeBakey had made a few comments about the case, Dr. Drapanas asked Dr. Storck what he had to say about bezoars. Now, I don't know if Drapanas could see Storck or not, but his head was canted to the side, his eyes were closed and he was asleep. "Ambrose, do you have anything to say about bezoars?" Drapanas prompted him.

Now if you own a dog you know what it's like when your dog is asleep and you ask it if he wants to go for a walk. It jumps up and is ready to go. There is no hesitation whatsoever. It was like turning on Storck's light switch—he didn't miss a beat. "Bezoars, bezoars, hmph, snort, there are two main types of bezoars: phytobezoars and trichobezoars. In Africa the most common kinds of bezoars are the phytobezoars the natives get from eating the whole locust and its indigestible shell." Whereupon he went back to sleep. He was a beautiful man.

Raspberry Plan

During the year I did two more nonconsecutive months of out-of-town rotation at Lallie Kemp. Gerry Baugh was the chief. He was also a runner but didn't make us run in order to be able to operate. My surgical experience was growing, but I knew that pretty soon the inevitable was going to catch up with me.

Back at Charity in the spring I received a letter in the first-floor mail room. Opening it, I found out that it was my notice as to when and where I would be going into the military. I had not received a full Berry Plan deferment and was assigned to the 368th Medical Group, Anderson Air Force Base, Guam as a GMO (general medical officer).

Where in the hell was Guam? I was up on the twelfth floor when I was reading the letter and Earl Robinson asked me about it. I'll never forget his comments, "Sonny Boy Jim is going to Guam with the Gooney birds," and he tweaked his mustache.

Earl didn't know that the Gooney birds weren't on Guam; they were on Midway. Nonetheless, we dug up a map from somewhere and found Guam out in the middle of the Pacific Ocean.

Guam was and still is a major military hub. Anderson was a very strategic base for the Strategic Air Command (SAC) and at that time was the headquarters for the Eighth Air Force that was doing most of the bombing missions in Viet Nam. The base did not have a hospital, but just a Class B dispensary, no beds. Anything requiring hospital admission had to be sent down island to the Naval Hospital.

I wasn't scheduled to report for duty until September 10. I met with Dr. Drapanas and informed him of my plans. Because of the war, people were coming and going all the time. It was something the department had to deal with. "I can't put you in the general surgery rotation for two months; it would mess up the whole schedule. You're going to be assigned to Urology, running the male outpatient clinic and assisting with night call," he told me.

Well, that was going to be interesting, I thought. At least I'd have something to do.

During those last couple of spring months while I was still on a general surgery rotation another life changing thing happened. One Friday night I was in my apartment and the phone rang. Answering it I found out that it was one of my country cousins who was a social worker in New Orleans.

Off and on for the past couple of years Beverly had been trying to fix me up with this gal who had gotten her master's in psychology the same year that Beverly had gotten her masters in sociology and when I had graduated medical school. They had both worked at a children's home on the West Bank and had become friends. She had then moved to Atlanta where she worked in a psychiatric hospital.

I had managed to put Beverly off using my work schedule, other dates and cloudy days as excuses, anything not to have a blind date. She had caught me. My date for that evening had been broken and when she asked me what I was doing. I told her the truth, "nothing."

"Why don't you come on over, Pete and I are grilling some steaks?" Her friend was now working in Atlanta and was just in town for the weekend, but she neglected to tell me that part of it.

Hook, line and sinker! I had never been in a serious relationship before. To say I had "played the field" was putting it mildly. I was twenty-seven and Len (which was an abbreviated form of Helen) was a year younger. I'm not sure whether it was her long blond hair, the little bit of a Georgia drawl she had or the fact that she was probably smarter than me. We saw each other the next two days before she flew back to Atlanta. For eight or ten weekends until I had to report for Basic Training at Sheppard Air Force Base in Wichita Falls, Texas, she made repeated visits to New Orleans.

In August I flew to Atlanta. In discussing marriage we realized we had not only known each other less than five months, but in actuality had only seen each other a little over a dozen times. We got engaged with plans to get married after I had been on Guam for six months. It would be a true test of time. We corresponded by cassette tapes we sent back and forth and sometimes by a ham radio operator. I met her parents three days before the wedding and that was forty-nine years ago.

Lagniappe – Tales of the ER

Hospitals have two main centers of constant activity, the operating rooms and the ERs. As much as the operating suites at Charity were in constant use, the volume of cases definitely slowed down at night. Other than a major catastrophe usually not more than one or two operating rooms would be in use at night. There just wasn't that much staff available to cover non-emergency cases in more than a couple of rooms.

The emergency room was a different matter. It was a twenty-four-hour show. Even at night when it got slow we joked about going out and spreading nails on the Interstate. If we had to be there we wanted to be doing something exciting. Many new doctors and nurses seek a position in the ER as their first job. They want to be where the action is. As a first-year resident I did a month rotation in the ER doing twelve-hour shifts. When you were on call as a more senior resident, the chances were that at night you would live down there evaluating cases or be in the OR doing those cases.

There was always a steady dribble of minor stuff such as dog or even human bites. You learned quickly that the human bites were the worst. Seasonally, we would see an influx of Mardi Gras beads stuffed in any orifice, mainly children's ears and noses. "Doctor, she has a runny nose ever since we went to that parade. What's wrong with her?" Look in the kid's nose and you'd see something shiny, red, green or any color. "Doctor, she keeps pulling at her ear." Same finding. During Mardi Gras, the number of stab wounds always markedly increased. What seemed like an endless string of lacerations quite often were handled by medical students, eager to learn how to sew and tie knots.

Unfortunately, there was the rare case of the mama that brought her little boy in complaining that he was always wetting the bed and now his penis was black. On exam he was found to have a gangrenous penis with a rubber band fastened around it. He certainly didn't wet the bed anymore.

Luckily, there was only one mother whose ten-year-old son fell through the non-tempered-glass shower door, cutting his brachial artery. She kept checking it at home to see if it was still bleeding and he bled to death on the way to the hospital.

Then there were the patients who came back complaining that the suppository they had been given didn't work. On exam, most often you found that the foil wrapper had never been removed.

The New Orleans cops could be a rough bunch. If they were being harassed by a handcuffed prisoner behind the metal screen in the backseat of their cruiser, they would step on the gas and speed up, then by jamming on the brakes the prisoner's face would get tattooed by the screen.

Just about every night you would be approached by one of the nurses, "Doctor, there's one on the ramp."

Emergency room ramp, Charity Hospital.

The first time this happened to me I said, "One what?" "A patient you have to pronounce, out on the ramp." When citizens died at home from natural causes, rather than call out an individual from the coroner's office to pronounce someone dead, a Charity Hospital ambulance was called. The patient was then hauled to the back ramp of Charity. An intern would go out and assure the individual was indeed dead and write down the time on the death certificate. The coroner filled out the rest of the form, but you had to "pronounce" them.

One July night when I was the first-year resident in charge the ambulance crew was pushing a lady through the doorway full speed ahead. She was a large lady who filled up the stretcher. Her head was covered in blood and although she was a black lady her swollen face with its black and purple discoloration was evident even from my vantage point. Her clothing was wet and blood stains were also all over the rest of her body.

"She's been shot seven times in the head, Doc," they screamed. (I never did like "Doc.") "Slow down," I said, "If that's true you're going to hurt someone and it won't make much difference to her." They guided her into trauma room one. Everyone jumped on her doing something. Her hair was caked in dried blood. Her clothes were all wet. She was in such bad shape I was thinking about calling the kidney transplant team. As I pried opened her lids I was looking at two reactive and equal pupils. "BP is 120 over 90," a nurse's voice called out. Someone else called out that she was moving her extremities. "Shave her head and get her clothes off," I barked.

There was a bullet hole through and through the middle of her left wrist. There was another bullet hole through and through the side of her large right shoulder and as it turned out neither one hit bone or a significant blood vessel. There was another bullet hole through and through her left flank area. I said she was big and I meant it. She had a lot of extra girth, not just on her torso, but on all her extremities. There were one or two more bullet holes on her lower extremities, all through soft tissue only. The coup de grace, however, was the bullet hole right in the middle of her forehead, one of those Roy Rogers shots. The bullet had penetrated the skin and subcutaneous tissue, coursed upward under her scalp outside of her skull until it got to the back of her head and then exited the flesh directly in the back leaving a large stellate blowout of her scalp.

The story was better than the physical findings as was told to me by her two daughters who arrived a little later. A few days earlier she had gotten in a big argument with her "ole man" and she had thrown him out of the house. He came back this night begging for her to let him in to get his clothes. She did and he then pistol whipped her severely, hence the black-and-blue face and swollen eyes. There's more. He put her in his car and told her he was going to take her to the hospital. Instead, he took her to an accessible area of the Mississippi River and threw her in. While she was clinging to some kind of drainage pipe sticking out of the bank, he started shooting, trying to finish her off. Lucky for her he was a bad shot. She hung on and started screaming, and screaming. Someone heard her and took her to where else, Big Charity.

We X-rayed everything and gave her IV antibiotics. The X-rays revealed no boney injuries at all and remarkably no skull fracture. We treated her wounds, sewed up the large fractured area on the back of her scalp, and sent her home.

I saw her in clinic about ten days later. Her two attentive daughters came with her then also. Her swelling and bruising had markedly diminished and I took her stitches out. She was discharged.

On a particularly slow night, I had to start an IV on a patient in room one and was looking for some IV tubing and normal saline. Trauma room four was a double room. It had a double set of those heavy wooden swinging oak doors opening up to the main hall leading to X-ray and the elevators and another set of back doors opening to the hall where the cast room was.

As I opened the door into room four, I was greeted with a picture of a New Orleans police officer standing next to a stretcher.

On the stretcher was an inmate from Parish Prison who had recently been sewn up. The prisoner's left wrist was handcuffed to the bright metal tubular railing of the stretcher. With his right hand, the prisoner had reached over his chest and had his hand around the grip of the cop's holstered .38 caliber service revolver. The cop's right hand was holding on to the prisoner's right hand and his gun, and with his freed left fist he was pounding the prisoner in the head trying to get him to release his hold on his gun. I stood there with my mouth open. All I could think of was .38 caliber bullets exploding and ricocheting off all the tile walls and terrazzo floors. Bam! Bam! He pounded the prisoner's head. Nonchalantly the policeman looked at me and said, "Hey, some of my buddies are probably down the hall in that little"—Bam! Bam!—"office. Would you mind getting one or two of them?" Bam! Bam! It kept up. Sure enough, they were sitting in there talking with the nurses. "One of your buddies needs some help in room four. You better get in there and give him a hand."

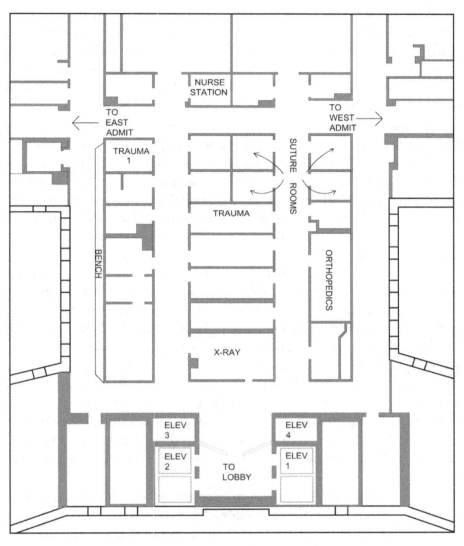

Emergency room layout, Charity Hospital, 1968.

It was not unheard of for prisoners to do anything to themselves to get out of prison and be admitted to the hospital. A favorite trick of theirs was to ingest light bulbs. Interns would get all excited and obtain X-rays showing multiple opaque fragments of the glass in their stomach. "You gonna admit 'em? You gonna operate on 'em?" was the excited question. "Nope, send them back, they'll pass them out, send them back."

The other trick frequently seen involved a wire coat hanger. To do this trick most of the time they had had previous surgery and knew they didn't have a spleen. They would take a section of coat hanger and sharpen it. Slowly inserting it into their left upper quadrant where their spleen had been, with about four inches of wire sticking out of their belly, usually got them a trip to the ER. We had learned from other residents just to pull it out. "What, you're not going to admit me? Doc, I've been stabbed. You can't just send me back, it could be serious."

I remember one guy in particular who managed to get hold of a sharp enough blade that he used to make a right upper-quadrant incision through his skin, through fascia, and through the rectus muscle, just stopping at the posterior fascial sheath. It was an amazingly perfect gallbladder incision. Of course he didn't have any hemostats or a cautery and he was bleeding like stink. I spent a considerable amount of time drying him up and doing a very nice multilayered closure. I applied a dressing and went out to chart what I had done and tell his handlers he could go back to Parish Prison. When I came back he had ripped off the dressing and ripped out all the carefully placed stitches I had put in. I was pissed. I irrigated the wound with some antibiotic solution, and this time I Steri-Stripped everything closed and sent him out.

Another trick prisoners did was to inject the webbing between their toes with spit, or sometimes even something from the bathroom. They'd get a roaring infection that would require IV antibiotics and sometimes incision and drainage.

There was a third parallel hall that ran behind trauma rooms one, two, and three. It ran down to the elevators also and eventually through two large doors and out to the front lobby. There was a bench that ran the length of the wall. This was our main waiting area. The only non-trauma cases we saw in the ER were asthma.

During some summer months before New Orleans East was fully developed they would set that area on fire and burn the marsh. As a kid I would go out there to shoot my .22 rifle and hunt nutria. The marsh was eventually drained and that area of town, east of Downman Road became a huge residential area. During the times when it was burned, huge clouds of acrid smoke would drift into the low-income areas of that part of the city. The smoke triggered epidemics of asthma cases. Patients would be lined up on the bench with their aminophylline drips running after getting an epinephrine shot. The aminophylline had to be given slowly.

The story was told about the new intern treating an asthma patient who was having a pretty rough time breathing. The wife of the patient didn't think the intern was doing enough or doing it fast enough. She kept screaming at him to speed up the aminophylline drip. In his nervousness, he opened the IV wide open. The patient experienced cardiac arrest and died.

When Mo Bethea was chief resident, one night in January 1975 he was in his room on the thirteenth floor when he got a call. Chet Noble, his third-year, had a patient in the ER with abdominal pain. He thought the patient had appendicitis, but he wasn't sure. MO, "Well Chet, if you think he's got it, operate on him; if you don't, don't operate on him." Chet called back a little later with the same query. Mo reemphasized his point, "Chet, it's up to you; you're going to be chief in a few months and you have to be able to make these decisions." By the time Noble called back a third time Bethea knew what he had to do. Grabbing his white coat he took the center elevators down to the ER.

What Noble had failed to tell Bethea, besides the fact that the next day was Super Bowl Sunday in New Orleans, was that the patient had an entourage of several very large men with him. Mo was then greeted by none other than Mr. Art Rooney, owner of the Pittsburg Steelers. Riding shotgun for Rooney was a fellow who went by the moniker of "Mean Joe Green." Yes, the same one of the Coke commercial. On the stretcher in the role of patient was Dwight "Mad Dog" White. "Mad Dog" was a card carrying member of the Steel Curtain and would go on to be a two-time Pro-Bowler and retire with four Super Bowl rings.

Bethea put some experienced hands on White's belly and examined him. Everyone reached a compromise: Rather than whipping it on him (our term for operating) and taking his appendix out, they would admit the ex-Aggie defensive end to the doctor's infirmary for overnight observation. The decision was the right one. White went on to tackle quarterback Fran Tarkington in the end zone for the only points scored in the first half of Super Bowl IX leading to a Steelers victory over the Minnesota Vikings. For his experienced decision, Bethea and his team got four 50-yard-line tickets from Rooney himself.

One afternoon a man was seen running for his life up the back ramp behind Charity, through the glass metal framed sliding doors and into the waiting area. Another man was chasing him with a gun. One shot had already rung out. Just as the first man got through the automatic back entrance doors, they closed. Another shot rang out aimed right at the man. The timing was perfect because as the doors met in the middle the bullet struck the vertical metal frame stopping the bullet.

On one particular night when the ER was slammed, which happened very often, the waiting area was full and it was standing room only. The intern went out to the waiting area and called the next person's name. As the patient stood to walk back and be seen, the intern dropped his clipboard, fell to the ground, and had what appeared to be a grand mal seizure. After a period of violent thrashing around on the floor, he lay still for a short time and didn't move. The patients in the waiting area were paralyzed. Shortly, he "woke up," got his clipboard, stood back up, and called out the next name from the list of expectant patients. The room cleared.

As serious as life in the ER was, pranks were often pulled to relieve tension. When Sonny Trammell was doing his tour as a first-year resident running the ER, two of his chiefs, their names rhyming with Woolverton and Gage, found a patient that had expired and was waiting on a stretcher to be taken to the morgue. They couldn't pass up the opportunity. Folding back the sheet covering the expired patient's face, they raced down the hall pushing the stretcher with the "victim" into one of the trauma rooms. "He's coded, he's coded." Trammell and his team jumped on the patient, one doing a cut down, someone taking vitals and Sonny trying to intubate the patient. Things weren't going like he thought they should have and as he looked up, he could see the two chiefs laughing their butts off. He then realized what had happened.

The back ramp of Charity was a busy place. Ambulances from not only New Orleans, but the surrounding parishes were continually bringing in patients. Not infrequently, patient's relatives or friends provided needed emergency transportation. In Larry Hollier's case one Saturday night, he was the eyewitness to the accident, resuscitated the patient, rode in the ambulance and provided eventual emergency treatment in the ER.

Larry and his wife had a Saturday night off call and were on their way to a movie. As Hollier was going over the Claiborne Avenue overpass, not far from Charity, a car sped by him and hit the concrete junction of an off ramp. There were none of those large water filled plastic barrels to absorb the force of a head-on collision in those days. The intensity of the crash was dramatic to the point that Hollier stopped to offer assistance.

The passenger in the front seat was dead. The driver was slumped over with the broken steering wheel puncturing his neck. That, plus a broken jaw, resulted in very difficult gurgled breathing. Hollier found he could relieve this by manipulating the driver's jaw. When the ambulance arrived, he rode with his "new patient" to Charity all the while maintaining the fellow's airway. Arriving in the ER, he proceeded to perform a tracheotomy.

If that wasn't enough excitement for one night, while this was happening a police officer approached Hollier, "Sir, there's been an accident." As it turned out when Hollier's wife was leaving the scene to pick up her husband from the ER, a teenager driving another car sideswiped the car she was driving. No one was injured; the teenager's mother paid for the damages and the Hollier's missed the movie. Just because you're not in the hospital and don't have your uniform on doesn't mean you're not on call.

Jane Todd was the second woman accepted to the Tulane Surgery Program. When she was on ER call one day, she and Elizabeth (Liz) Hilliker, Tulane's first female surgery intern and resident, had a patient come in with a Coke bottle in his rectum. Unable to retrieve it, Jane thought the patient needed to go to the OR. Liz's hands were smaller and she was able to manually retrieve the unusual foreign body.

Liz wound up being the recipient of ER care herself after an episode with some of New Orleans' "finest." A fellow soliciting in Audubon Park had been brought in by the undercover police. When they were through assaulting him, he definitely needed medical attention. Liz was not one to hold her tongue when it came time to voice her opinion, and she verbally let the cops have it. During a heated exchange, a piece of paper was shoved at one of the four police officers confronting her and they accused her of assault. With the help of Dr. Charles Mary, the Charity Hospital administrator, the assault charge was dropped, but from the cops' standpoint that wasn't the end of it.

One night about a week later, after she had been on all night ER call, Liz was asleep in her Dauphine Street apartment when her doorbell rang. The man at the door told her he was looking for her next-door neighbor and asked if he could he come in. Still half asleep, she obliged, whereupon he proceeded to beat her about the face. Bruised and swollen, she called a friend who took her to Charity. She was treated, and for her own safety was admitted to the doctor's infirmary for a period of observation.

The story became well known in the halls of Charity, but since this thing we call life is contained in only a small world the story followed her. Later, when Liz assumed a position on the staff of an ER at a Midwestern university someone asked her where she trained.

"Charity Hospital," she proudly said.

"Oh, that's where the female intern was beaten up."

Jane also became a patient herself when she noticed a painful necrotic lump on her side. It turned out it was a brown-recluse spider bite that needed to be operated on. At the time, she happened to be dating one of the other surgical residents. Jokingly, some accused him of biting her.

Larry Cohen was in the ER one night when a knife-and-gun club member was wheeled through the doors in shock. As he and two other house officers were working feverishly to do cut downs, insert a chest tube and intubate the patient, their language would have made the paint peel off the walls. Nothing was left unsaid. A nun walking by the room paused briefly and said, "Doctors, I'm praying for you."

A slightly more serious case involved an ophthalmology resident who was shot while he was getting into his car in the French Quarter. Luckily, a chest tube was all he needed to resolve his problem.

There are a million stories that could come out of that ER. Everyone had them. It was amazing how many rolled through those doors and how many walked out. Like Dr. Creech had said, "Bring me to Charity Hospital."

Second-Year Resident/General Medical Officer, 1970–1973

My two months spent on Urology went quickly. Although I was in the same hospital with other residents I'd spent the last couple of years with, it was like I was in a different city; our paths seldom crossed. The urology residents were pretty low key and they were generous with their knowledge.

I manned the male outpatient clinic four days a week where I did out patient cystograms (dye studies), kidney studies and dilated a million prostates. That number was only surpassed by the two million urine samples I looked at. I didn't get to do many cases but scrubbed with the urology residents on some of their elective cases and the occasional emergency trauma cases.

One night a lady was admitted with pyelonephritis, a severe infection of the kidney. I don't know why she was admitted to a surgical specialty, but it was just one of those crazy Charity rules. She was running a high fever and was a little confused. We started IV antibiotics on her, scheduled some tests and went about our other duties.

The next day, she was feeling a lot better when I made rounds on her. Then she asked, "Doctor, you ever work on the tenth floor?" I told her no, that I was a surgeon and I only worked on four. My demeanor was probably not the best, still conscious of my pre-military banishment from surgery for these two months. She even unnecessarily apologized.

The next day and the following day, she asked the same question, "Doctor, you sho you never worked on the tenth floor?" Finally, coming down to earth and remembering that I was a medical student once, I answered her, "Yes, when I was a medical student, I worked on ten." Then with a smile on her face, "I know doctor, you delivered my baby."

Now before I release the punch line to this "only at Charity Hospital" story, we must go back three years, to September 1967 during my senior year when two things happened. The first was that I did a month out-of-town OB rotation in Alexandria with a broken finger. The second more important thing was the inaugural opening regular season game of the New Orleans Saints when John Gilliam ran the opening kickoff back ninety-four yards for a touchdown. Unfortunately, that would be the biggest highlight the Saints would have for many years to come.

Up on the OB unit, then, a young woman was admitted in labor. She had three or four other kids and after a short while I ruptured her membranes and delivered her baby. She was the happiest person I had ever seen. It was amazing. You would have thought she had won the lottery except for the fact that there was no lottery in Louisiana then. When she calmed down, she told me she wanted to name her baby after me and asked me what my name was. I told her my name was Jim. She was very pleased, "I'm gonna name him Jim." She was definitely not my first delivery, but I was still kind of proud that she would want to do that.

One must remember that there were many unconventional names that had come out of the Charity system: "Nosmo King" (from the No Smoking sign on the back of the doors of the delivery unit), "Paj Ama," or "Orang Ello" and many others. I finished charting the delivery and went down to the dining room for some lunch. Later, on my return to the unit, her whole mood had changed. In fact she was downright sad. I asked her what was wrong and she replied, "Doctor, I just remembered something, I already have one named Jim."

As time passed, I thought I'd gotten over it. As we skip ahead about six months, I was still a senior student and back on OB, but this time doing a one month rotation at Charity for the intown portion of that block. A young woman came in and delivered. It was her first baby, and like most of the young mothers, she had no prenatal care. The baby was fine, and she was elated, extremely happy. Then she started that "I'm gonna name him after you" business. "What's your name doctor?" "Nope," I said, "we're not going there." I guess I was still feeling let down from my previous "un-naming" incident.

It was time for me to go to class and my classmate, Jack Covin, came in to relieve me and finished up the delivery and the paper work. Now this is the same Jack Covin who fixed Ron Swartz and me up with the nurses from St. Louis.

Now we're back to summer 1970, we're at Charity, and I'm doing the urology rotation. Miss Green has told me she had named her baby after me. So naturally I said, "You did? You named him Jim?" "No doctor, I named him Ciaravella, Ciaravella Green."

Guam "Where America's Day Begins"

I reported for duty on 10 September 1970 at Sheppard Air Force Base for two weeks of basic training. One of the ortho residents who had a full Berry Plan deferment and I drove up to Wichita Falls together.

We spent the night in Shreveport and the next day just south of our destination, I had a blowout. I was clipping along about seventy-five and there was a truck beside me when it happened; we had a few tense moments as my car wanted to turn into him. The other driver realized what I had done to avoid an accident and he saluted me. I didn't even have a uniform on yet.

We checked into our quarters and the next morning filed into a huge room with no less than three or four hundred other newbies, doctors, nurses and medical technicians who were all coming into the military. We filled out forms constantly for the first week and learned our Social Security number backwards and forwards as you wrote it multiple times on every form.

We were taught how and when to wear the uniform and they even tried to teach us how to march. To the career military guys that must have seemed like herding cats. We were all out of step and because we did not see any future need for it, we weren't really trying that hard.

The one highlight of the two weeks was a simulated airplane crash. They took us out to an area at night where the remnants of a plane fuselage had been scattered with fires burning in oil drums. Airmen simulating crash victims made up with moulage (makeup and masks to simulate injuries) were scattered around on the ground and walking around dazed and bleeding. We had to triage them into groups as to whether they were potentially salvageable or didn't have a chance of surviving. Although this is a standard process when dealing with a mass casualty, when you have limited resources, it's not something you practice in medical school or residency training.

This is not an easy thing to do. It's almost like saying, "You're gonna die." At Charity with the amount of trauma we saw, we often had to prioritize who was going to the OR first. I never remember triaging someone to die. You have to put yourself in the mindset that if no one else is around, if I only have one tourniquet or one unit of blood who am I going to give it to so that it will make that much difference in their living or dying. If it's just me and I can only help one or two people, who's it going to be? It would be like a battlefield scenario from the War Between the States or WWI.

There's a great book by the noted author William Manchester, *Goodbye Darkness*. The book is a detailed memoir of Manchester's experiences in the Pacific in World War II. What is incredible is that Manchester's father fought in the Great War and had his leg blown apart. The battlefield surgeons did not feel he was salvageable and "triaged" him to the tent with the dead and dying. When he was still alive two days later they decided to amputate his leg, thus saving his life and allowing William Manchester to later be born, fight in the next war, write books, etc.

The Mount Everest saga *Into Thin Air* by Jon Krakauer speaks of the Dallas anesthesiologist Beck Weathers when he and the rest of his group of climbers are making their last leg of the ascent to the peak. As the whole scenario unfolded, it would have probably resulted in his death if he had finished the climb. His eyes have just about frozen, and he is told by the head guide to wait on the side of the iced trail until he comes back for him. On their way down the mountain numerous people passed up Weathers' almost frozen lifeless body, "triaging" him to die. Amazingly, just about blind, he makes it alone further down the mountain to a base camp. Again, the next day he is "triaged" by his group's survivors and his fellow climbers as they get ready to leave him. The tale of survival that follows is incredible, but needless to say, he survives.

Dr. Charles Dunlap taught us pathology our second year of medical school. A great teacher who spoke to us, not lectured, as if he was your grandfather telling you a life lesson. On one occasion he spoke to us about dying. No one from that class of 140 students will ever forget him saying, as he looked over his rimless glasses, "Never tell a patient when they are going to die, because they will live to piss on your grave."

The Island

I had two weeks back home before I was due to fly from New Orleans to Travis Air Force Base and then Guam. It was during this period at home that Len and I got engaged. I would not see her again for six months.

The dispensary was a one-story building. I checked in and met the other GMO's (General Medical Officers). There were six of us. Each one of us had some training in the particular specialty we were eventually going to practice. I was the only one with surgical training. Two had a year of internal medicine, one was psychiatry, and one was radiology. The most important was Hal Kantor. Hal was the pediatrician. I could fix their hernias and take out their appendix, but since there was no operating room, none of that was going to happen. There were lots of dependent kids with colds, sores (Guam sores) and all those myriad of diseases that kids get and none of us wanted to treat. So, naturally, during sick call, we herded all the pediatric problems down to Hal.

We saw military walk-in, sick call for ninety minutes in the morning followed by dependent walk-in sick call for an hour after that. For the time remaining before a lunch break, we had fifteen-minute appointments per patient. The same routine carried over after lunch with fifteen-minute appointments until our day was over at 5 p.m. However, sometimes Mike Meagher and I would make up names for the last three fifteen-minute appointments in the afternoon. This gave us time to head down to Tarague Beach and go scuba diving with the sharks. Mike and Carolyn and Len and I became lifelong friends after leaving Guam.

Any married officer stationed there would be serving a two-year overseas "accompanied" tour. The military would send his whole family and all his house whole goods with him wherever he went unless it was a war zone. This practice applied to high ranking sergeants also. Airmen or airmen basics did unaccompanied tours and could only have their wives with them if they paid for their travel, and few did.

Because I was single and an officer on an unaccompanied tour I was quartered in the BOQ (bachelor officer quarters). In the morning I would walk or drive down to the Officers Club for breakfast. It was one of my first mornings.

I had just finished breakfast and walked out to a beautiful Pacific morning. I was shielded from the sun under the curved awning over the front doors.

As I was adjusting my hat a couple of staff cars drove up. There were flags on the front of the fenders with stars. Everyone snapped to attention and threw up a salute. I was flustered and not at all used to saluting so I did it in a way I was used to as a kid, the Boy Scout salute. I didn't even know I was doing it until I was looking directly in a three-star general's eyes. I knew he saw it, and I would get court martialed my first day. I corrected it quickly and hurried to work.

After I got married I would have to bring Len over on my own and find "off base housing." Housing in the villages was at a premium. Although the Island was only thirty miles long you were not allowed to live more than a certain distance from the base. Those who had accompanied tours might wait as long as six months to a year for a house on base.

Besides a dozen dentists stationed at the dispensary, as well as us GMO's, there were two flight surgeons. Their job was to see just the people on flying status. They received more pay than we did and they also flew with the B-52 crews on bombing missions to Vietnam. They had a pretty relaxed time of it until the spring of 1972 when the North Vietnamese started firing missiles back at the B-52s and actually shot down one of the "BUF's" from Anderson.

Bill Kinstrey was a dentist waiting for on-base housing. He was renting a house in Dededo, a village a few miles south of the base. If the timing worked out, I could take over his house after I came back from getting married and he had been assigned his quarters. As it turned out the timing was as good as I could hope for.

Len and I had to stay in the BOQ for about a month until his house was available. The house was concrete block with three bedrooms, one bathroom, kitchen, eating area, and a living room. We had no furniture but were allowed to check out anything we needed from the base housing supply. Now, three bedrooms sounds very spacious, but to put it in perspective, the only thing in the bedroom was a queen-size bed. With the bed in the room there was access to a closet and twelve inches of space on either side of the bed, barely enough room to walk around it. In a second bedroom we placed a couple of dressers for our clothes and the third bedroom was used for storage where we kept our scuba gear, rubber raft and our three-and-a-half horse power Sears outboard motor.

Dededo was a village and we may have been the only non-natives there. The house across the street from us was actually a Quonset hut with a blanket for a front door.

Cockfighting was a big business and a major recreational pastime on Guam. Most of the villagers had at least one fighting rooster caged in their yard. They were very prized possessions to the point that every afternoon they would brush and preen them.

One afternoon we decided to go back up to base Officers Club and have dinner. I was driving out of the second of two dirt roads that serviced Dededo when two roosters ran into the road, the first one running into my right front tire, killing it instantly. Now I was really worried. I can't emphasize how much the locals thought of these fighting roosters, not to mention how much they might be worth.

I pulled over and as I got out of my car couldn't help but notice a young boy on the steps of the house we were in front of. He got up and went inside through another one of those blankets hanging from the frame serving as a front door. Once up a few steps I knocked on the door frame. Instantly, a Guamanian came raising his suspenders up as he came out the door. I had barely opened my mouth to apologize when he said it: "God damned rooster."

"Hey, man, I'm real sorry. He just ran right in front of me, Can I pay you?" Then he said it again: "Goddamned rooster."

Have you ever been confused? No, I mean really confused. I had just wiped out one of this guy's roosters and he was cursing—the rooster?

And then he came out with it, "Sorry, it's not your fault. That's the third rooster that other rooster has killed by chasing them into the street." He wouldn't accept any payment for the dead bird and as I got back in the car I could see him picking up his axe to finish off another rooster. We had a very anticlimactic dinner.

Any of us who served two years in the military could tell service related stories. I was not getting shot at and most of the people I knew who served weren't either. Some were, and the GI's on the ground sure as hell were. So, I will only tell a couple of stories from that eighteen-month tour of duty on Guam.

During our lunch period, one of the GMO's always had to stay in the building and be available. One day the dispensary phone rang and Bob Hanchey was on the line. Bob had been an LSU graduate, but was a Charity intern on the Tulane Service with me and was going into neurosurgery after his time in the service. He was returning from an R&R trip to Hawaii and was on his way back to Laos. The plane had stopped in Guam to refuel and with some free time he managed to find me. I hopped in a cracker box (the military ambulance) and drove down to the terminal and out on the flight line. It was good to see a face from home.

He was at a hospital in Laos with one other Laotian physician. Most of their patients came to the hospital on elephants or water buffalos. Hanchey was doing all types of surgery as well as delivering babies and neurosurgery, anything that came through the door. I later found out while reading his obituary that Bob received the Bronze Star for his service.

Anyone who has been in the service knows that if you want to get something done, you don't go to a guy with an eagle on his collar or even stars. You find a guy with more stripes than a zebra. The chief master sergeants really run the whole show. As it turned out, the chief master sergeant for the 8th Air Force was Oris Kemp. Sergeant Kemp's niece was the fiancée of my classmate and roommate, Abe Andes. Serendipitously, we met up in my office one day for his yearly physical. I explained to him that I needed to get back to the states to get married.

It didn't take long for him to fix me up with the chief master who ran the air terminal. He arranged for me to get a hop on a KC-135 that after a few stops in the frozen North would deposit me at Barksdale Air Force Base, a short commercial flight distance from New Orleans. The 135's are tankers used to refuel the B-52s on bombing missions, but they are also used to move cargo and military personnel from base to base around the world.

Sitting in the cargo area dressed in my borrowed flight suit I started talking with an airman on his way back from Nam. He was a photographer for *Stars and Stripes*, the military newspaper. Seeing my medical insignia he asked, "Hey doc, you want to see a hero?" Now, if you get right down to it, and to be honest, the word "hero" was not really used that much prior to "9/11." Sure a fireman running out of a burning building cradling a baby in his arms or a policeman charging into a bank holdup or hostage situation certainly qualified to be called heroes. I personally think the term has been overused. He reached in his canvas rucksack and pulled out a bunch of black-and-white, eight-by-ten glossies. "See that guy, doc, that's a hero," he kept repeating.

It was a shot taken from a helicopter of another helicopter hovering above the thick jungle. There was a slight clearing below the chopper and there was this guy in midair, carrying a backpack. He had jumped from the chopper. "There's the hero, doc, that's him," he kept repeating. I just didn't get it. "C'mon look, look in the leaves, in the bushes and trees. You see all those little white dots, you see 'em? That's machine gun fire. All those hundreds of firefly looking dots are guns going off. That guy's a medic jumping into a fire fight to help the wounded and that's the Cong shooting at him."

He was right. He was a hero. I had a hard time complaining about my assignment after that.

After the wedding in Georgia we made our way back to New Orleans. A side trip to Keesler Air Force Base got Len a dependent's ID card.

In December 1971, after I was married, my parents came to Guam for a visit. I thought it would be nice to have a party down on the beautiful Tarague Beach one evening, a luau. I was told that as per protocol, it was proper to invite the base commander, Colonel Dunlap, or the wing commander, Colonel Kelly.

Now, to put things in perspective, all doctors went in the service with their time of service starting when you started medical school. So, any of us who went in after a couple of years of training were given the rank of captain and if you finished your training, you entered the service as a major.

Most of the career military officers didn't approve of us and really didn't want to have anything to do with us, unless of course they'd been TDY (temporary duty) to Thailand and needed a prescription for penicillin. They felt that we obtained our rank too easily. Whereas, they were career military and had waited six to eight years in between promotions, medical officers came in with instant rank.

I had no contact with either of the commanders and opted for inviting Dunlap, thinking that neither one of them would probably come. As it turned out, Dunlap did. He was personable, but very military. The "brass" all walked around with walkie-talkies, constantly. I introduced him to my father and left the two of them to talk as I went to mingle with other guests. A little while later I looked back and the two of them were still talking.

They finished their conversation and Dunlap approached me. "Doctor, I didn't know you went to Tulane and trained at Charity Hospital." Bam! I couldn't believe it. Not only did he know both institutions, but he called me "doctor" and not captain. Out here in the middle of the Pacific Ocean on an island thirty miles long and ten miles wide, this full bull colonel knew about Charity Hospital. We talked a minute or so and he left. I still never had much contact with him, but every time after that when our paths would cross on base, he acknowledged me.

As it turned out, one of my three chief residents from my internship days, George Barnes was also on Guam stationed at the U.S. Naval Hospital. George was board eligible and fully trained from his years at Charity.

The Vietnam war was a helicopter war. George Armstrong Custer's 7th Cavalry now flew into battle on choppers. It expedited their mission considerably. More importantly from the medical standpoint, these same helicopters were used to evacuate the injured much more rapidly. Within a matter of minutes, injured GIs were treated initially by corpsmen and lifted to a staging area. If they required immediate surgery at that stage they got it. If they could be patched up a little and lifted again to the next station they would be, and so on.

Quite often George and the medical personnel from "Big Navy" would go out to the flight line to triage shot up soldiers fresh from the jungle, not as to whether they would die, but whether to take them off and operate or send them on.

There were many instances where the injured soldier with fresh wounds might have been seen by only one station and if he was stable, he would be sent to Clark Air Force Base in the Philippines or Guam. George and his team could take them off and operate on them there or send them on to Hawaii and then to the states. The system was very efficient and was a major breakthrough in saving soldier's lives.

During major North Vietnamese offenses in 1971, the doctors at Big Navy often operated around the clock. Barnes' vascular training at Charity paid off. He related to me that other surgeons in his group had trained at Yale and other major centers, but they hadn't seen the vascular trauma that George had and they didn't feel comfortable in doing it.

By the spring of 1972, I was close to serving my eighteen-month unaccompanied tour on Guam. I was scheduled to rotate back to the states and had been assigned to an air force base in Alexandria, Louisiana as a surgeon. I really didn't know what would be in store for me, but I did know that we would be close to home and I should be able to do some surgery.

Two things were happening about this time. First, Len and I had been married about a year, still living in Dededo. She was not feeling well. Some foods were not agreeing with her and I thought she had classic symptoms of cholecystitis. I ordered a gallbladder visualization test at the dispensary and it showed—a normal gallbladder. Her symptoms persisted, then "Dr. Len" informed me, "I think I'm pregnant." I sent her to see one of the docs at Navy we had seen socially, and he called me confirming Len's diagnosis. "Congratulations, you're going to have a baby." The timing was good because it meant we would be having the baby stateside.

About this time a fellow started coming in my office. He wasn't a patient; he just wanted to talk. He didn't have on a uniform, just one of those flowered shirts you see in movies that the islanders wear not tucked into his pants. He wasn't a native and as it turned out he was some kind of investigator for the military. We talked about scuba diving, the island and all sorts of just plain bullshit. I think he was just trying to make me feel relaxed, maybe even just setting me up.

Now, over the preceding sixteen to seventeen months or so, I hadn't exactly been a conformist and certainly not a perfect soldier. None of us had. I didn't paint peace signs on the dispensary doors before the SAC inspector general's visit like Rick Friday did. I really had only gotten one letter of reprimand and one threat of a court martial. I should have kept a copy of the letter. The weekly threats by the dispensary commander, Colonel Jones, to send us to Vietnam if we didn't cut our hair were not even taken as a serious threat.

After a few of these visits by my "flower-shirted" friend he came out with it, "Why don't you stay here for the remaining six months of your tour and not go back to the states? We'll change your tour to an accompanied one and take care of everything when your time is up." That basically meant the military would cover my wife's transportation rather than my having to arrange for it. I told him I'd think about it.

The two main negatives were, first, our baby would have to be delivered on Guam; and, second, I would miss getting to do some surgery in Alexandria. More importantly, I would not be getting out of the military until a few days after the day I was supposed to be reentering the surgery program for my second year of residency.

I wasn't too concerned about that being a major point, but it might be a point of leverage. On one of his subsequent visits, I mentioned the timing concern and his response was that they would give me an "early out", meaning that I wouldn't be serving my full twenty-four months tour of duty. I had known of physicians who had been released from serving in WW II with an "early out" and had been called up again to serve when the Korean conflict broke out.

After several more visits and discussions, I turned down his offer. His reaction wasn't what I had expected; in fact, he was angry. It was then that I was told I would not be going to Alexandria as a surgeon; I would be going to another dispensary. This time it was Lackland Air Force Base, again as a GMO. I verbally let him have it. He hadn't been honest with me from the start and the military had a hard time wondering why they couldn't hold onto physicians. I didn't know it at the time, but the fates were looking out for us.

After Len and I rotated off the island we found out that the Air Force was part of a new major offensive in Vietnam. They went on twenty-four-hour duty with bombing runs being made around the clock. Five thousand additional TDY (temporary duty) troops were brought in for support along with 100 B-52s. To support this, the dispensary, also went on twenty-four hour service. All leaves were cancelled. If you wanted to go to the movie at midnight you could do it or get a stereo at the BX at 4 a.m. you could do it. And it also meant if you wanted to have an appointment with a doctor for your knee or backache at 2 a.m., everyone would be available.

The Guamanians have a saying, "Guam is good." It was, but mainly from the standpoint of our extracurricular activities. We had experienced in detail Hong Kong and Japan. We had explored the Banzai Cliffs of Saipan, the vine covered airfields of Tinian and dived the ship graveyard of the Truk Lagoon. I had also survived running out of air at eighty feet while diving on a sunken

WWI German gunboat. Most importantly we had made friends we would know and see the rest of our lives.

Big Willy

In April 1972 we left Guam for Lackland Air Force Base, San Antonio, Texas. While on leave in New Orleans, I went to the Medical School and visited with Dr. Drapanas. It turned out that he knew the chief of cardiac surgery at Wilford Hall, a Colonel Bill Stanford. "I'll make a call and maybe he can do something about you getting your hands wet again," he told me.

In San Antonio I was able to make rounds with Colonel Stanford once a week. If he was doing surgery I was allowed to watch, and when he was in his research lab I was able assist in his research. He was investigating two new membrane oxygenators for cardiac surgery that would later replace the bubble oxygenators that I was destined to have a very bad experience with in a few years. It wasn't exactly what I had hoped for, but it beat being in the dispensary all day examining the healthiest young men in the country.

Very early one morning in late August Len woke me up, "I think I may be bleeding." Having already proven that I knew nothing about diagnosing pregnancy, I was now proving that I didn't know anything about the complications of pregnancy. She wasn't due for another six weeks, but when the bleeding persisted we called the OB resident on call and got in the car and headed down the I-410 loop to Big Willy. I dropped her off at the ER door while I went to park the car.

On entering the ER entrance and approaching the admission desk, I saw a fresh pool of bright red blood on the floor. The corpsman sitting behind the desk was ashen faced and still had a shocked look on his face as if he'd never seen a woman almost bleed out before. He wouldn't have made it at Charity. "She, she's over there," he pointed. Len had an abruptio placenta. The placenta had prematurely separated from the uterine wall and she was bleeding, but hadn't gone into labor yet.

Her physician was the head of the OB department. He was very capable and, in our other, non-emergent, visits with him, he had impressed me. Not only that, but he had raised my esteem of career military physicians compared to the experience we had with my dispensary commander on Guam. The chief of the pediatric department was Dr. (Colonel) Robert Delemos. Both Delemos and the head of the OB department met with Len and me. They were going to wait a short period of time to see if she would go into labor if not they would do an emergency C section. The baby would weigh about four pounds and the risk of hyaline membrane disease, the same condition that killed President John F. Kennedy's premature baby just ten years earlier, was significant and almost expected.

As it turned out Delemos was the first and only fully trained Air Force neonatologist at a time when neonatal medicine was in its infancy. If that wasn't enough, Delemos had invented the prototype machine of what had become known as the "Baby Bird" ventilator. Thank you unnamed, flower-shirted Air Force agent for punishing us to Wilford Hall. There was no place else on God's green earth better equipped for this child to be born than right there.

Weighing in at four pounds five ounces Jay would be in the neonatal ICU and on the Baby Bird for about a week. During this period, he received superior care, and it gave time for his body to manufacture its own surfactant, the substance that prevents hyaline membrane disease.

Over the next few weeks I was promoted to major, strictly because of the length of time I had served, starting with medical school. Our premature son came home to sleep in a plastic tub on our dresser and I was separated from my two years of duty in the United States Air Force.

Charity Hospital Cancer Service

Back in New Orleans, we rented an apartment in Metairie which turned out to only be a couple of blocks from my earlier bachelor apartment. As a second-year resident I was assigned to the LM-4 cancer service for two months, Dr. Krementz's service. I would take general surgery night call, mainly on LSU nights. It seemed like I was learning all over again.

I had done some minor surgery while on Guam, but I hadn't seen a sick patient or scrubbed on a real operation in two years. At one point I had even run a vasectomy clinic. When you are at a dispensary with no inpatient beds and you're seeing aches and pains all day, you do anything that "specializes" you. I got to go down to Big Navy, scrub with the urologist and watch him do a few. There really wasn't anything to it and the best part was that I could schedule thirty-minute consultations with those hopeful to have the procedure and also take a whole afternoon every Wednesday to do the cases.

The same thing had happened when I had an orthopedic fracture clinic. One day a week I would just see patients who had casts applied from the preceding week. I then got to take the films down to Big Navy and check them with Dr. Don Sprafke, the Navy orthopedic surgeon. It wouldn't take him long to go over the films and give me a game plan for each patient. Then with the remainder of the afternoon he and I had the opportunity to go scuba diving. This worked well until Gene Farris, a new GMO, who had actually had a year of orthopedic residency, came on board. The key to survival was to try and develop a niche so you wouldn't have to just see the general non-threatening, problems the service men all had or thought they had.

A lot of the faces had changed in the program. Jim Dowling who I had served with as an intern was now chief resident at Big Charity. Gary Dotson was a chief at an out-of-town hospital. Guys who had been in medical school when I was a resident were now the same year that I was and other guys had moved on to different pastures. The Charity turnstile was still turning.

Steve Golladay had finished Tulane undergrad a year ahead of me and had served his two years of duty in the Navy following his first year of residency, similar to my scenario. Because of a delay in his being discharged, he was three days late in returning to start his residency and a rotation on the pediatric surgery service. A pediatric resident, seven years his junior and a graduate of a Caribbean medical school with only six months experience chewed him out for arriving late. And then, when responding to a question put to him by Steve, because of his military experience, responded with "Yes, sir." You never knew when someone who had been your junior would be your boss.

Drs. Krementz and Lindsey were the staff surgeons doing the bulk of the cancer surgery. During my two months on LM4 I scrubbed on about thirty cases and I was the surgeon on only three of them. Two of them were lymph node biopsies and one was a simple mastectomy for cancer. I assisted on all the other cases such as regional perfusions of the upper and lower extremities for melanoma, axillary perfusions, gastrectomies, and biopsies. Most of these cases were done at Hotel Dieu Hospital.

Then one night it happened. I was on call on a non-Tulane admit night, Dowling was taking call at home and an intern and I were in the hospital.

A young girl who had been a patient of one of the visiting staff at a private hospital had been transferred to Charity. She had been admitted to him with some kind of abdominal infection. He had operated on her and supposedly "drained something." Whatever it was she had not received definitive treatment. The insinuation had been made that her family had run out of money and that was the reason for the transfer.

I received a call from Dowling that she was hemorrhaging out of her wound. He was on his way to the hospital, but he wanted me to get her in an operating room. It was a virtual nightmare. She was in shock and was bleeding profusely from this small opening in her belly. The scar tissue was so intense and concrete-like you couldn't even cut into it. All this while anesthesia was trying to get an IV started to give her blood. She died right there on the table and I wasn't able to do anything to change that. If I thought I had some experience before going in the service, I don't know where it went.

Dowling was very upset at the whole situation. The surgeon who had transferred her had the best shot to treat and take care of whatever she had. It was thought she had some horrible infection and had eroded into a major blood vessel.

For the two months that I had been back, I had done nothing but assist others operating on cancer patients and this one girl dies of the complications of an unknown condition. I was scheduled to rotate up to Alexandria and Pineville for three months, one at the Veterans Administration Hospital and two at Huey P. Long Hospital. I was ready to get out of Dodge.

Luckily, the apartment we had rented in Metairie had been furnished. The only furniture we owned were a few pieces we were allowed to be shipped from Guam. One was a womb chair, also called a papa-san chair. We also had brought back a fan chair—lots of bamboo. We had a crib, a Johnny-Jump Up, and a few incidentals, no other furniture.

Oh, and I must not forget Nikko, the Australian Yellow Creek Beagle that Len had bought at a pet store in Agana, Guam one afternoon. "A beagle, you bought a beagle, no one in Louisiana buys beagles unless you want to hunt rabbits." "She licked me," was Len's response.

Pineville

For three months we lived in a large fourplex on the grounds of the Veterans Administration Hospital in Pineville. We had a spacious apartment on the bottom floor of this building that had probably been built during or right after the war, and I don't mean Vietnam. It was furnished from the same era, but that didn't bother us. We even got used to the banging noise from the radiators that kept us warm. The overall grounds were spacious with several three- to four-story buildings scattered throughout.

One building just housed surgery patients, one medicine, administration, and so on. It was a large facility for the care of veterans. Amazingly, the patients were all older. I don't recall any young Vietnam vets; it was almost like one large nursing home although patients did come and go.

Whereas, Tulane surgery residents took care of the surgical patients, the medicine patients were tended to by full-time permanent staff. When we were asked to see consultations in the medical buildings, it did not seem like those patients were being seen on a regular basis which meant that the surgical conditions were usually of an urgent nature. Tom (Tomoo) Tajima and Art Benson were the chief residents.

Tom was a fully trained surgeon from Japan who in order to be accepted as a Fellow of the American College of Surgeons(FACS) had to complete a residency in the US. Everyone who ever operated with Tom knew that he had the best hands anyone had ever seem. Besides that, he was as nice as he was efficient and proficient. During those two months I did a lot of diagnostic bronchoscopies and esopahgoscopies. There was a smattering of hernias, biopsies and the occasional gallbladder. Dr. Louis Knoepp was the chief of surgery who mainly helped the chief residents with their cases.

Dr. Louis Knoepp

There could not have been a more fitting physician to be chief surgeon at a Veterans hospital than the ultimate veteran surgeon, Dr. Louis Knoepp. He had completed a general surgery residency at the Mayo Clinic and was contemporaries with the Mayo brothers. He had seen action in the European Theater serving in, none other than General George Patton's 6th armored infantry during the Battle of the Bulge. Like Oscar Creech, he had also been awarded a Purple Heart. When Creech started the rotation of Tulane Surgery residents to the VA Hospital in Pineville, he called on Knoepp to head the program. He was an icon at the Pineville VA and was trusted and highly thought of by all those who had the privilege of his teachings.

During that month of December a patient was readmitted to the VA who had previously undergone an abdominal aortic aneurysm (AAA) resection and now presented with an aortic graft infection.

The worst late complication one can incur following an abdominal aortic aneurysm repair is a graft infection. The patient needs massive amounts of IV antibiotics. The graft has to come out, but the lower half of the body cannot survive without its blood supply.

After a course of antibiotics, he was brought to operation where the only procedure that would take care of his problem was carried out, removal of the aortic graft, over sewing of his aortic stump and an axillofemoral bypass graft. A Dacron graft was sewn into his subclavian artery high up in the axilla. It was then tunneled under the skin and subcutaneous tissue along his rib cage, down along side of his abdomen and then sewn into his femoral artery. These surgical access sites were then closed thus accomplishing the first part of the operation. The abdomen was then opened, the graft removed and the aorta below the renal arteries was over sewn and sealed.

Herein lays the potential for another late problem. Knowing that it is extremely difficult, but not impossible, to sterilize an area with a foreign body (the graft) present, you have no other option. You have to hope and pray that the antibiotics would do their job in sterilizing the area. If they didn't, the patient would become reinfected and the surgeon would be back where he started, at best.

It was a big procedure and a long surgery, but it went as well as expected.

Skipping ahead about eighteen months, we proceed to a Friday afternoon when everyone is present at the weekly Tulane Surgery D&C conference. Ernie Kinchen was the program's first African-American resident and was one of my third-year residents when I was a first-year. Following his senior year at one of the satellite hospitals Ernie had gone into private practice in one of the larger south Louisiana cities. It was not uncommon for those finishing the program to occasionally return to the D&C conference whether they lived in

New Orleans or elsewhere. Most found that a weekend visit and some good food couldn't be passed up.

A case of an infected vascular graft was on the Bugle and the various treatments of that complication were being discussed. Ernie spoke up, "I had an interesting patient come into the ER a few weeks ago." He went on to discuss a patient who while living in the Alexandria area, had undergone an aneurysm resection and subsequent reoperation for an infected graft. The patient had then presented to his ER with a blown-out aortic stump and died. It was our patient, the same man that I had held a retractor on back in Pineville for a four-hour-long operation. Like I said, it's a devastating complication that can take a long time to manifest itself.

The two months at the VA Hospital were fairly relaxed and because there was no emergency room like Big Charity or even Lallie Kemp, it was even more laid back. There was no trauma. Art Benson was going into plastic surgery in his home state of Utah. He was an avid skier and, as my wife said, "was a very good looking guy."

He had a dinner party one night where he showed us movies of him backcountry skiing. It was only fitting that the other highlight of that December was that it snowed. Yep, snow in central Louisiana. It really brightened up that old hospital. There is nothing like green trees with snow clinging onto the branches, the original frocked tree.

Dr. James Ciaravella and son, Jay, Pineville VA Hospital, 1972.

Following his Tulane residency and plastic surgery training Art continued his love of snow skiing. On one of these excursions with a group of friends he was let out on a mountaintop by a helicopter. This was the ultimate back-country and powder experience for any experienced skier. Benson never made it down the mountain and was never found.

In the beginning of January things started to pick up when I did my first gastrectomy for duodenal ulcer disease. This is a big hill to climb for any resident, especially a second-year. But that's the way it usually was on an out-of-town rotation. It was almost like you were a level higher in your training. Tom helped me do the case. I had assisted him do gastrectomies during the preceding month and it had been a magical experience. There was absolutely no wasted motion. I sometimes felt that even if his eyes had been closed I wouldn't have been able to tell the difference in the way he operated. I knew I couldn't do the gastrectomy like he did so I soaked up every correction or bit of advice he would yield.

For the most part he was very quiet and there was no extraneous talking. At one point in the operation when I was doing a long anastomosis (suturing intestines together) I brought up the fact that I had been to his country on several occasions. It broke the ice. He loosened up and we briefly talked about the cities I had visited and the culture.

He enjoyed the story of how we named our Australian beagle "Nikko" after the famed northern Japanese city. There was a saying that "You haven't seen beautiful until you've seen Nikko," and it wasn't referring to the dog. There were always diagnostic procedures to be done using the rigid esophagoscope or rigid bronchoscope. Gastric feeding tubes, cecostomy tubes for advanced colon cancer, chest tubes and other drainage tubes. Tubes, tubes, and more tubes- we inserted them almost everywhere. I did two more gastrectomies that month and my first colon resection.

Toward the end of the first week of January, the Howard Johnson's shooting unfolded on live TV. We watched and re-watched the coverage of it shown over and over. I called Dowling knowing that he was right in the middle of it. At first I was only talking with Ann. Jim hadn't made it home in a couple of days. When I did get him, "Hey man, you okay? What's going on?" (The account of the Howard Johnson's (HoJo) shooting will be covered later in more detail than has ever been written.)

Although we kept our living quarters on the VA Hospital grounds, in February I rotated over to the Huey P. Long Hospital across the Red River in Alexandria. In the two months at VA I had done almost sixty cases. In one month at Huey Long I would do almost the same number. Huey Long had an active ER and with it again came the gunshot wounds (GSWs). Because it was winter we also saw more burn patients of all ages. The acute appendectomies were more frequent and I took out more gallbladders.

I thought back to how busy and what a good experience I had at Big Charity especially at Lallie Kemp, before I went in the service. On my initial return to the residency program things had felt very awkward. There was no doubt that I had been unsure of my ability. Now things were rolling again from a surgical standpoint, with regard to not only the quantity but the quality of cases I was doing.

Was it all planned like that? Did the powers on the eighth floor have that much insight into what a resident could or couldn't do after he'd been out of the program for a couple of years? In reflecting again, it is most interesting that just about every major player on the Tulane surgical staff had WW II or Korean War military experience. Creech and Knoepp had been wounded and received a Purple Heart in WWII. Even Drapanas had been in the Army Reserves. Bob Hewitt, being the youngest, was fresh from the fighting of Vietnam. Now, here we were, this whole group of new residents and we all had either just gotten out of military service or were destined to go in after our training was finished.

Sir Walter

Baptist Hospital

Because of some scheduling problems, we were kept at Huey Long for several days into March. My next rotation was for a month at Baptist Hospital. Although assigned to Dr. Walter Becker's service, when he was not in the OR I could assist any of the other surgeons who needed help. Becker (Sir Walter) was an imposing figure. He was a big man with a big voice. A very positive voice. I don't think he'd ever heard of or ever used the word "maybe." He was the most definite individual I'd ever met.

Dowling had told me a story about when he was at Baptist on Becker's service. Becker had come out with this stuff that he was the captain of the ship. As it happened, Dr. Drapanas was at Baptist to do a case one day. Although Drapanas had not asked Dowling to scrub with him, it was expected. Dowling told Becker about his intentions and he reminded Jim who the captain was. Jim's quick witted reply was, "Yes sir, but the admiral just came on board."

On one of his surgery days he would always have at least a half dozen cases posted. He wasted no time doing the cases and in between even helped mop out the operating room. He didn't stop. He took out a gallbladder in the time it took most people just to make the incision. He would sew, and I would tie and tie. One time I got a little carried away and tried to see how fast I could throw in a bunch of knots. I exceeded the normal three or four knots. I was on a roll and just kept going, but of course I finally slipped up. He had been watching patiently and just said, "I was wondering when that was going to come to an end."

During the whole month I only got to do one case, a ruptured appendix on a little boy. He developed a cul-de-sac abscess, so I got two cases out of him.

Becker had done a stomach on a middle-aged fellow who as it turned out had been a pretty heavy boozer. Post-op, he developed DT's (delirium tremens) and one night he went wild. During his ranting and raving the patient threw the metal IV pole and his glass liter bottle of IV fluids not only out of the third-floor window, but through it, glass panes and all. This guy wasn't just some bum off the street, but a successful businessman.

I found out about the escapade on early rounds before Becker came around. The patient's wife and the patient were very embarrassed. They asked that if at all possible, could I refrain from telling Becker. I knew that if I didn't tell him someone else would, that is if he had not found out already. Upon entering the room the first thing Becker did was to walk right up to his bed and ask him, "Been throwing anything else out the window lately?"

Dr. Becker used to go home every day for lunch and then take a nap on the sofa in his study. One day several years later, he didn't wake up from his nap.

I had scrubbed in and assisted on several lung resections during that month at Baptist. The anatomy in every case seemed different and it was hard for me to grasp. I knew it was something I had to have a better feel for, even though at that time I had not yet decided to become a thoracic surgeon.

In April I was put on the transplant service. Dr. John McDonald (The Big Mac) had been brought to Tulane by Drapanas as his transplant surgeon. If the ER resident had a candidate that he thought would be a good donor, I would be paged to go talk with the family. With all the trauma that was seen, the only candidates were those with severe head trauma and the only organ that was being transplanted was kidneys. It was a slow month. I did assist Dr. Mac with a transplant at Hotel Dieu, but also assisted the LSU transplant surgeon, Dr. Marx, with a couple of kidneys.

Probably the most noted "transplant" surgery, or attempt at a transplant, was engineered by Dr. Mac. A young woman had been admitted with severe liver failure secondary to hepatitis and was dying. McDonald proposed bringing the woman to the OR and removing her spleen. In its place he planned to put the liver from one of the primates kept on the ninth floor. This wouldn't be done as a replacement, but as an auxiliary organ until her liver might recover.

Mo Bethea was a junior resident and on the "donor" team that would help take the primate liver out. The donor animal, a baboon, was put to sleep in the ninth-floor lab at the school, transported down the back elevators to the tunnel that went under LaSalle Street and through the basement of Charity. It would then be taken up to an OR and have its liver removed. Unfortunately, during the transport the baboon woke up and pulled out its breathing tube. Maintenance was called and managed to shoot the animal with a tranquilizer dart. Not only was the procedure not successful, but the team had to get painful gamma globulin shots because of their hepatitis exposure.

In May and June, I was back at Charity assigned to thoracic surgery. For the next two months I did all the diagnostic scopes, lung biopsies, and empyemas. I was operating, I was back in my element, the atmosphere was relaxed. Most importantly I scrubbed in on my first open heart surgeries, pump cases. I had to prepare myself mentally for what would be the biggest jump in training I was to make yet: becoming a third-year resident.

Lagniappe – Watering Holes

New Orleans has always been known as the "city that care forgot," a center for twenty-four-hour on end entertainment and nightlife. If you're on a block and you don't see a bar, you may have wandered into a cemetery or a very exclusive neighborhood near the lakefront.

As a teenager in the fifties if you could reach the bar and put a "quail" (a quarter) on it, you got a beer, no questions asked. In high school we knew and frequented many of the establishments in the French Quarter. We didn't "live" down there, but we had made the rounds and had "done that." As an undergraduate student at Tulane, it was not uncommon to show up for a Wednesday chemistry class and find a classmate sitting next to me hung over and ready for bed.

"What happened to you?" I'd ask.

"Man, we found the greatest little bar down in the Quarter." was the usual reply. The students from elsewhere, outside of New Orleans were spending weekday nights at places we had long gotten over. They usually weren't back second semester. It never ceased to amaze me. Most of this kind of partying was curtailed by a natural selection process before one got to medical school. The medical school, internship and residency years demand almost undivided attention.

Medical fraternities offer parties for their members and actually were open for anyone to attend. The Phi Chi and Nu Sigma Nu medical fraternities were both housed in old post-Civil War mansions located on historic and oak tree-lined St. Charles Avenue. Their spring South Sea Island parties were a highlight of the year. Five gallons of grain alcohol donated by a revered embryology professor every year, Dr. Robert Vaupel, mixed with whatever rum, fruit juice or other accessory, provided enough fuel to enliven any party.

Any dress that fit with the theme was accepted. Riding the St. Charles streetcar between the houses and having Sweet Emma, the "Bell Gal." or Deacon John and the Ivories music added to the festivities.

Some of the most notable establishments were the bars in the city closest to Charity. Nick's Original Big Train bar was located a few blocks down Tulane Avenue across from the Dixie Brewery. Nick Castrogiovanni was a world class mixologist, noted for being able to mix a Pousse-Cafe. In his hands this multilayered drink of various cordials was thirty-four layers tall. In 1918, "Mr. Nick" opened a grocery store at the site on Tulane Avenue. It evolved into a bar and delicatessen. In 1965, Hurricane Betsy damaged the building such that the upper story had to be removed and it "just" became a bar. It always seemed to me that it still had a little lean to it every time I entered. On entering the bar from its Tonti Street entrance, three things were most notable, besides Mr. Nick. On the wall to the left was painted a mural of a fast-moving train. To the right was a long wooden bar with any liquor or cordial known to man on the bar back. Scattered in the back of the room were cases and cases of beer stacked one on another.

Reportedly, the "Big Train" moniker came from his buying beer by the trainload back in the day. Oh, you could buy a beer or simple highball, but what Mr. Nick was noted for on an everyday basis was his mixed drinks. "Skip and Go Naked," "Banana Banshee," "Pregnant Canary," and "Between the Sheets" were the names of just a few. The desirable seats were at the bar, not only because you were right where the action was, but there were not many tables to sit at. If your date didn't know what she wanted, Mr. Nick would ask, "What's your favorite color?" He would then make a drink in that color sometimes giving it a new name.

One evening I went in early to get a refreshment. Initially, I couldn't find Mr. Nick. After a short search, the place wasn't that big, I found him in the back behind a stack of cases of beer. He was opening a can of Campbell's pork and beans with one of those old can openers that looked like it could double as a weapon.

"What are you doing Mr. Nick?" I asked.

"I'm getting some dinner," was his reply, dipping his spoon into the cold beans.

"Mr. Nick, why don't you call up the Royal Orleans (now the Omni Orleans) and have them bring you one of their prime rib dinners?" "Cost too much," was his reply. It was said that Mr. Nick owned the whole block of shotgun houses that the Big Train was on and maybe most of the houses on the next block. The legendary Mr. Nick died in 1979 before Hurricane Katrina would flood his watering hole and close it down.

Within a two-block walking distance of Charity were Larry & Katz and Joe's Bar. Larry & Katz was a "bare bones" bar in the true sense of the word.

This wooden building was located on Cleveland Street. The facade in front had two openings. On the right was a doorway one entered after climbing a couple of steps. On the left was a walk-up window where one could be served any alcoholic refreshment just for the asking without going inside. This window had originally been designed to serve the black patrons of New Orleans who were then not allowed inside.

Larry & Katz bar, 1960s.

New Orleans had no open-container law, so it was not a problem to grab and go. Upon entering the door you entered a long narrow room. The bar ran the entire length of the left wall. On the shelf behind the bar, besides the usual supply of spirits, were .38 special revolvers spaced about six feet apart. A lone pool table in the back of the room was always covered. It provided the only seating. Stacked in back were cases of beer. It wasn't the austere, bare-bones appearance of L&K that was the attraction, and it certainly wasn't the pool table, as I never saw it in use other than for female patrons to sit on.

Larry & Katz had the cheapest prices for alcohol anywhere in the city and perhaps south Louisiana. If you were a dyed-in-the-wool New Orleanian and were going to have a party, this is where you bought your cases of liquor. Cases of bourbon and scotch rolled out by the dolly load.

Joe Raviotta owned Joe's Bar. Located on LaSalle, between Tulane Avenue and Canal Street, Joe's was *the* hotspot for the Charity Hospital drinking crowd. Although mainly a Friday night center of activity, it wasn't unusual for an occasional house officer to wander over to Joe's on a non-admit night for a quick beer.

In November 1973 following Tulane's first football victory over LSU in twenty-four years, a wild night of celebration ensued. Dr. Drapanas (Tulane Surgery) and Dr. Carter Nance (LSU Surgery) had waged a bet on the outcome of the game. The loser would pay for all drinks at Joe's the first Friday night after the game. Even if you didn't drink, it was an event worth attending.

As I walked down LaSalle toward the door, the noise from inside filled the sidewalk and street. I opened the door and was met with a wall of humanity. I inched my way in but, there was no access to the bar. It seemed like every Tulane and LSU resident was in that room along with many of the professors. I left early and learned that later in the evening Dr. Nance stood on the bar and waving his arms shouted that the "open" bar was closed. He had fulfilled his end of the bargain in spades.

Lagniappe – **"Breaking News"**

During the nine-year period from July 1968 to July 1977 several major events occurred in New Orleans that directly or indirectly impacted Charity Hospital. Although, twenty-four-hour news channels did not exist, the local channels did their best to cover these events, live, as they happened.

Shootout at the "Dirty D"

In 1970, the Black Panthers chapter in New Orleans had become one of their largest in the country. They had set up headquarters in a house located in the Desire housing project located in the Ninth Ward, historically one of the poorest and most crime-ridden sections of New Orleans. It was referred to by locals as the "Dirty D." Governor John McKeithen had vowed that the Black Panthers would not be allowed to establish a foothold in Louisiana. On September 15, 1970, a combined task force of 100 policemen, Louisiana State Police troopers, and Orleans Parish Sheriff's Department deputies converged on the Panther stronghold. Arriving in patrol cars and busses they were met by local citizens standing outside voicing their support for the Panthers. Within fifteen minutes of their arrival, shots rang out. A barrage of tear gas and more than 30,000 rounds of ammunition were fired.

The Panthers had lined the inside walls of the house with sandbags almost to the six-foot level. Amazingly, no one was killed or injured—on this first encounter. By the next month, the Panthers had moved their headquarters to a different apartment.

Tensions between the Panthers and the law continued to escalate and on November 17, police again headed back to the new Panther headquarters. Local residents, again, stood with the Panthers. However this time when shots rang out five people were shot and injured.

John Gage was on duty at Charity in the ER. A woman was brought in with three gunshot wounds to her right chest. Gage went over to attend to her and was greeted with "Get your white pig motherf---ing hands off of me." This definitely was not the way the average patient greeted a physician trying to save their life. Gage rolled her stretcher over to a corner of the trauma room. "When you're ready to be taken care of, I'll take care of you." It didn't take long for her to change her mind and accept care from his "white pig" hands.

The Rault Center

The Rault Center was a seventeen-story building on the corner of Gravier Street and South Rampart, about three blocks from Charity Hospital. On the top story was a beauty parlor, the Lamplighter Salon and one floor beneath it was the exclusive Lamplighter Club, a dining club and lounge for members only. A fire broke out on the fifteenth-floor during the afternoon of November 29, 1972. Although never fully determined, it was thought that arson was the cause of the fire.

Five women were trapped in the salon with a raging fire. The pressure of the firemen's hoses was not strong enough to reach the top floor of the building and ladders, even from a neighboring roof, still failed to reach the needed height. As the windows of the salon exploded out from the flames, the women could be seen in the opened portals. Knowing that help could not reach them they had to select one of two bad options, stay and be burned to death or try to jump to a nearby roof.

From my vantage point on the twelfth-floor of the east side of Charity I watched the scenario unfold. I had been in that club. My wife and I had actually eaten dinner there. I could not imagine what it would be like to be trapped up on top of a burning building. Several of us watched as one silhouette jumped or fell from the inferno, and then another.

In all, four women jumped or fell to their deaths. A forty-two-year-old woman, the fifth, although sustaining multiple fractures and injuries, survived to tell her story and reached the age of eighty-one. Two other men were trapped on a stair well and perished. Eight other men made it to the roof.

With the flames heating up the roof below their feet, a passing helicopter saw their dilemma. It took two groups of three men each to safety until a second helicopter rescued the remaining men from the roof. As fate would have it, it would only take a few months before another helicopter played a significant role in a roof top scenario.

HoJo's

On New Year's Eve of 1972, in the area of Tulane and Broad streets near Parish Prison and the Central Lockup, Mark Essex stalked, shot and killed a New Orleans police officer and police cadet Alfred Harrell. After fleeing the scene, he then broke into a warehouse on South Gayoso Street, purposely setting off a police alarm. Officer Edwin Hosli Sr., responding to the call with his German Shepherd police dog, was then shot by Essex immediately upon getting out of his patrol car.

He was taken to Charity Hospital. Hosli underwent surgery by the LSU resident on call and was later taken care of by Larry Hollier. He had sustained multiple abdominal and chest injuries. Postoperatively, Hosli would go on to develop tetanus, from which he would recover. Unfortunately, despite reparative surgery and care by the LSU residents when it came time for his endotracheal tube to be removed, he had developed a tracheal-innominate artery fistula. Hosli expired in March 1973.

Essex escaped capture that first day. These shootings signaled the beginning of a murderous rampage carried out by one man that modern day New Orleans had never seen before and to this day still hasn't been seen since.

On January 7, a cold misty Sunday morning, Essex shot a local grocer in the midtown area of New Orleans. After hijacking a car, he drove to the eight-story tall Downtown Howard Johnson's Motor Lodge on Loyola Avenue. The decision to use the Howard Johnson as his platform for murder was probably not by chance. The view from the roof offered visual access to City Hall across the street, an area known to have a large police presence.

Essex had sent a warning letter to a New Orleans TV station saying he was going to attack and kill downtown New Orleans police officers. The letter would not be opened until January 6. He was armed with a .44 caliber, five-shot, semi-automatic Ruger carbine, the same caliber bullet made famous by Clint Eastwood's "*Dirty Harry.*" Rather than give you statistics on the muzzle velocity, size of the bullet, range, etc., it has been shown that a .44 magnum bullet will knock down or go through an American bison or a bull elk. Essex initially made his way through the hotel lobby. It is not clear whether it was here that he shot the hotel manager and another employee, or later, but they were shot.

Making his way to the roof, via the stairwell, he would stop on different floors taking more victims: a young couple on their honeymoon and another hotel guest. As a diversion and to attract more attention, he also set multiple fires in different parts of the hotel. There was no doubt that his goal was to bring more law enforcement and uniformed targets to the scene.

Once up on the roof, armed with his rifle, he proceeded to assassinate police officers down at street level.

Essex had a troubled past. Although he had joined the US Navy as a dental technician, he was subsequently given a general discharge for "unsuitability." According to a *Times-Picayune* article, he then became involved with "black radicals" in San Francisco and later joined the New York Black Panthers.

New Orleans Fire Department Lieutenant Tim Ursin was just four blocks from the scene when he responded to the first fire alarm. Upon arrival at the Howard Johnson he saw parked in front hook and ladder truck 8, a truck he used to work on before his promotion. He and his supervisor entered the lobby and were met by police officers with drawn weapons in front of the elevator. They were told that someone with a gun had people trapped in the elevator. They then attempted to ascend the stairwell but were confronted with too many hotel patrons trying to flee the burning building.

Ursin was told to go outside and see what he could do. Outside there were no firefighters on truck eight. Looking up he heard and saw hotel patrons screaming from the eighth-floor windows. The jacks had already been lowered on the truck to stabilize it in preparation for lifting the ladder, a procedure he had done many times before.

Since he was the only one available, he acted. There were people on that top floor who needed his help. Surprisingly at that time he didn't recall hearing any gunfire. He raised the extendable long ladder up to the eighth-floor level knowing that standard procedure dictated that he should not let the tip of the ladder touch the building. From experience, he knew that when he started climbing up and those in the hotel started to climb down, the weight would force the ladder against the building.

He grabbed a one-and-half-inch hose with its attached nozzle. He slung the hose, called a "doughnut roll," over his right shoulder and started his ascent. Despite the fact that the dangling nozzle kept hitting his right leg, he continued. All the while, people above kept screaming at him to hurry up. Before he reached the top, the hotel guests actually started to climb on the ladder and climb over him at about the seven-and-half-story level.

Then things happened almost simultaneously. Fortuitously, he reached down to grab the nozzle that had been banging his leg. As he brought it up in front of his head, he heard what sounded like a cherry bomb explode.

It was then he realized that he had been shot. The bullet tore through his left forearm and blood poured out of the sleeve of his fireman's turnout coat. Amazingly the force of the impact didn't knock him off of the ladder, especially considering that his right hand was not holding onto the ladder. It was grasping the heavy fire hose nozzle. The discharged .44 magnum bullet was lodged in the nozzle, saving his life.

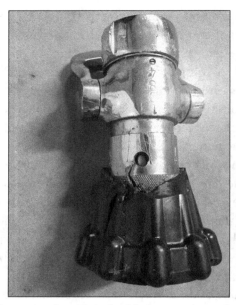

Firehose nozzle with imbedded .44 magnum bullet.

His hand had brought the nozzle up at just the right time, and as fate would have it, it served as an unintended shield in front of his neck and head.

Realizing that he was bleeding profusely he backstepped down the long ladder. Essex, however, wasn't through with the wounded and bleeding firefighter. As Ursin looked up, Essex had appeared again, took aim, and shot at him. The semiautomatic carbine jammed and Ursin's life was spared a second time. Police officers at ground level witnessing this started to fire their service revolvers at Essex, driving him back from the edge of the roof.

Ursin could feel his pressure dropping and his life leaving him. Was he even going to be able to make it down to the ground to safety and medical help? Close to the ground, police and other firemen yelled at him to jump. He did and when they took his coat off they described him as having "three pounds of ground meat for an arm." Still bleeding profusely, he felt himself getting weaker and weaker and urged them to take his belt off and use it as a tourniquet. They did so.

As it turned out, Ursin's best friend was on the emergency truck that came to get him and take him to Charity Hospital. To add to the chaos and confusion, a NOFD "Flying Squad" vehicle on its way to the scene over-turned while taking a sharp curve a short distance from the chaos.

Once in the ER, the last thing that Ursin remembers was the fire depart-ment chaplain giving him the last rites of the Catholic Church. Ursin then passed out.

Bob Hewitt, head of the section of cardiovascular surgery, had made rounds with general surgery residents the previous Saturday. He had seen a female patient with the residents who had ascending cholangitis, a severe gallbladder infection. She needed a common bile duct exploration and her gallbladder removed. They had loaded her up with antibiotics and placed her on the schedule for the next day.

Sunday morning Hewitt was driving down Loyola Avenue in his MG convertible from his uptown residence and witnessed the Howard Johnson on fire. "There were cops and firemen all over the place and I actually had to drive over the fire hoses lying in the street. I could see the police shooting up at the building, but wasn't able to fully grasp what was going on," Hewitt later recalled to me. At this point all he saw was the building on fire and didn't realize what they were shooting at.

After being stopped by the police, he told them who he was and that he had to get to Charity. The police filled him in on the events of the morning. After parking in the Tulane garage he proceeded to the ER where his years of experience as a trauma surgeon in Vietnam kicked in.

He knew that casualties would be coming through the doors so he had the residents cancel the gallbladder patient until the next day. He was on hand as the first of many victims rolled through the doors and also proceeded to assist the residents in surgery.

That Sunday happened to be a Tulane admit day. Bill Browder was the Tulane first-year surgery resident in charge of the emergency room that morning and the subsequent twenty-four hour period. Larry Hollier, then an LSU third-year surgical resident, had been on call the sixth, and found he was unable to leave the hospital as it had been placed on "lockdown."

Both of these surgeons, and many others from Tulane and LSU, would play significant roles in caring for injured police officers, firemen and civilians, including firefighter Tim Ursin. Critically injured police officers and those with injuries from shrapnel soon began filling up the ER. Not only were gun shots being heard at Charity, but spent bullets were landing on the back ramp of the hospital, the emergency room entrance.

The local ABC TV station went to a live feed on the air. The station's anchor erroneously broadcast that Charity Hospital was being attacked and that "any and all available individuals with a firearm should go to Charity to protect their hospital from being overrun."

The chaos in the ER was worsened further by this announcement as non-medical civilians started walking around the ER and first floor of the hospital armed with loaded weapons. To make matters worse, a Charity security guard dropped his loaded pistol; it hit the hard terrazzo floors and discharged. Amazingly, no one was injured and more amazingly it didn't start a chain reaction of gunfire within the hospital.

Shooting at the HoJo continued into the night. Earlier in the day, chief resident Jim Dowling had brought the manager of the Howard Johnson's to the operating room with a gunshot wound to the abdomen. At the same time he called Russell Woo, thoracic surgery resident, at home telling him to "get his ass to the hospital." Woo raced to Charity from his home across the Mississippi and scrubbed in.

Upon removing the packs Dowling had placed, he put his hand in the abdominal cavity. His hand touched the operating room table. The .44 magnum bullet had torn away the manager's back. Amazingly, after multiple blood transfusions and hours of reparative surgery, they were able to get him out of the OR to ICU. However, the next day because of continued bleeding a second surgical team brought him back to the OR. About thirty units of blood later he was returned to ICU. Ultimately, the manager succumbed to a diffuse pseudomonas infection.

Most of the wounded and noncritical postoperative police officers were kept in the doctor's infirmary on the sixth floor. Mathis Becker, then a senior resident, distinctly remembers standing on the back ramp of Charity and being an eyewitness to the chaos happening down the street at HoJo's. Becker, like other Charity Hospital residents, had served a lot of time taking care of the knife-and-gun club members. He had never seen injuries like those inflicted by Essex and his .44 magnum carbine.

Jan McClanahan, Dowling's third-year resident, and his team attempted to reconstruct the arterial supply to Ursin's lower arm. There just wasn't enough tissue. Attempts were made over several months and multiple operations to save the arm, but eventually it was amputated and he was fitted with a prosthesis—a hook. Ursin recalled to me three other firefighters who were shot and survived. One was shot in the right shoulder, one was shot across his back and the third, Charlie, was shot in the face. Charlie lost half his jaw. Ursin still sees Charlie for an occasional two-man beer reunion of Howard Johnson survivors.

The one-armed ex-firefighter hero who risked his own life climbing up an eight-story fire ladder and lost an arm to save civilians later became a charter boat fishing captain in south Louisiana. He's proud to use the moniker "Captain Hook" for his web site.

Between cases, McClanahan walked out of the OR to the changing area. There was no formal doctor's lounge at Charity in those days. Sitting in a chair was Louisiana Lieutenant Governor Jimmy Fitzmorris holding a loaded pistol. "What are you doing up here, sir," Jan queried. Fitzmorris replied that he just thought that he needed to be there.

McClanahan got word from the ER that there was an elderly lady with an abdominal problem, not related to the shootings who needed to be seen. Unable to get away he sent his intern down to evaluate the situation. The report came back that she had an intestinal obstruction. The intern had ordered some abdominal X-rays and had her admitted. It would be forty-eight hours later before they would be able to make rounds and evaluate her. McClanahan reviewed her abdominal films which showed air in her biliary tract and made the diagnosis of a gallstone ileus. Despite the fact that they had been operating almost continuously, Nessie Flower would also need emergency surgery.

At operation she was found to have indeed, a large gallstone lodged at the junction of the small intestine and the large intestine .McClanahan was able to digitally move the stone past the point of obstruction relieving the problem. As he was closing, one of the attending staff (ML) came in the room telling him that he couldn't treat it that way, that the stone needed to be removed. On the verge of exhaustion, McClanahan objected, "If you think it needs to come out, then you take it out." The staff then took over the case.

Moving the stone down the colon so it could be extracted was easier said than done. The further down it was moved and the more the stone was manipulated, the more thinned out the colon became. The ensuing result was a colon perforation which required the patient having a colostomy. She later died. If it ain't broke, don't fix it.

At the end of the year the attending was awarded the coveted Golden Albatross award for the worst case result of the year.

At one point during the day, bullets ricocheted off the twelfth-floor outer walls of Charity forcing surgeons and operating room personal to move anesthetized and patients being operated on to a side of the hospital out of the line of fire.

While McClanahan was operating on another one of the thirteen patients operated during that twenty-four-hour period, an assistant hospital administrator came in his OR. Seeing the nurse anesthetist on the floor shaking and trying to hide from the bedlam down the street while administering an anesthetic, he told McClanahan to move to another OR. Jan, a country boy from a small Mississippi town told him, "If he can get a shot through that window then let him try."

During the night, while Hollier and his team were operating on one victim a bullet did smash through their operating room window. The operating room circulating nurse realized that their room was the only one with lights on. Fearing that perhaps the shooter saw that, she then proceeded to turn on all the other operating room lights on the darkened twelfth floor.

Susan Balser Berry, a graduate Charity Hospital nurse, came to work and remembers having to change into her scrub clothes in the dark because of the black out. Another fairly obese patient had been shot in his abdomen. Luckily, the bullet had not entered the abdominal cavity, but had coursed across the fatty portion of his abdominal wall. On exploring him it was found that the underlying intestines, not even hit by the massive high-velocity bullet, had been bruised and damaged by blast injury, requiring attention.

A day after the carnage stopped, Dr. Drapanas who had been out of town during the shooting, made rounds with the Tulane surgical residents and their teams. He wanted to see each patient they had operated on. Fearing what the necrosis and increased tissue damage caused by the high velocity bullets would do, he had them take each patient back to the OR for exploration and further debridement. This decision was not met with agreement by all. Was it really necessary? They had passed the point of exhaustion and now had to reoperate on many of these patients a second time. In fact two of the reoperated patients did have significant tissue necrosis.

The force of the bullet was devastating. Hollier was assisting ER personnel move one patient from an ambulance stretcher to a hospital bed. As nurses and others grabbed the extremities and body of the patient to move him, Hollier placed his hands on either side of the victims head to stabilize it. As he did so, his hands met in the middle. The bullet had completely pulverized the man's skull.

Search lights placed on taller buildings were aimed at the roof and physicians and other hospital personnel were able to be eye witnesses to the chaos happening just three blocks away.

At that time Lieutenant Colonel Charles "Chuck" Pitman was the commander of the Marine Air Reserve Training unit in Louisiana. After watching the slaughter at the HOJO unfold on television, acting without permission, he grabbed another pilot and two crew members and commandeered a CH-46 Sea Knight helicopter, a "flying banana." Once downtown, Pitman landed the CH-46 at a vacant parking lot allowing several New Orleans police sharpshooters to get on board.

Colonel Chuck Pittman, Howard Johnson's, 1973.

As a veteran of combat in Vietnam, these were all logical actions for Pitman to do. Once airborne every time Pitman approached the roof, Essex would fire on the advancing helicopter. Pitman finally outsmarted Essex with a series of aerial maneuvers. Although CH-46 helicopters had been outfitted with Browning .50 caliber machineguns in Vietnam, it is more likely that the NOPD personnel on board actually did the firing. Doctors back at Charity watched as literally hundreds of tracer bullets lit up the sky and the Howard Johnson rooftop, eventually killing Essex.

Pitman's spontaneous, unauthorized excursion not only resulted in Essex's death but the helicopter took half a dozen rounds to its fuselage. Instead of Pittman receiving a medal for his actions court-martial proceedings were later instituted against him for unauthorized use of the helicopter. Louisiana Congressman F. Edward Hebert intervened on his behalf ending the process. Besides Pitman's three tours in Vietnam he would go on to be involved in the attempted rescue of American hostages in Iran in 1980. Pitman retired as a lieutenant general in 1990.

Unfortunately, where this could have been the end of the story and the shooting, the word was circulated that there was a total of two and perhaps three snipers doing the killing. The next morning Browder and others watched as a SWAT team descended from a second helicopter onto the roof. A storage shed on the roof was the supposed lair for the killer or killers. More shooting ensued and police officers started dropping. Mark Essex's body was found and it was determined that he was the lone gunman. An autopsy performed later would show that more than 130 rounds had hit his body.

Back in the Charity ER, Hollier was assessing about five wounded police officer patients lined up on stretchers. As Hollier approached Officer Guy Leblanc, whom he had known before the incident, he noticed Leblanc to be visibly upset. Trying to console the officer and tell him that his injuries weren't too serious, the officer said, "Larry, we f---ed up. You don't understand, we were shooting each other. Bullets were ricocheting all over the place." The chaos on the roof and the erroneous reports of more than one sniper, along with poor to no communication between attacking forces, had caused a dozen police officers to be injured by "friendly fire."

About this time, then Governor Edwin Edwards arrived on the scene with an entourage of newsmen, the Charity Hospital administrator and assistant administrator. Hollier and Edwards knew each other and in Cajun French, Edwards says, "Larry, *comment ça va?* (How are things?) *Qu'est-ce qui passe ici?* (What's going on here?)Larry took the governor to the side and informed him of the recent events, telling Edwards about cops inadvertently shooting cops.

Edwards told Larry, "Come with me and don't say a word." Edwards then went from officer to officer consoling each one of them and thanking them for their service. "Son, I'm Governor Edwards. The people of Louisiana owe you a debt we can't repay. Now you get well." No mention was made of how they got shot. Edwards turned, winked at Hollier, and walked out.

When the smoke cleared including late deaths that would occur in the ensuing weeks to come, Essex shot a total of thirty-two people, killing ten police officers and nine civilians. A poor communication system between forces contributed to the chaos and injuries. There had never been a mass disaster drill at Charity Hospital. In a much smaller sense, almost every Friday or Saturday could resemble a mini-mass disaster.

On January 6 and 7, 1973, the residents, interns, and nurses of Charity Hospital, the uniformed members of the New Orleans Police and Fire departments, a rogue Marine pilot, and an unselfish young firefighter did what they had to do and what they had been trained to do. They took care of the wounded, dead and dying. Thirty-two years later the same cadre of nurses and physicians, although with different names and specialties, would go above and beyond to take care of those patients left behind at Charity Hospital during Hurricane Katrina.

The Upstairs Lounge

If 1973 hadn't started off with enough excitement and killing, it would only take another six months for more carnage to come through the ER doors of Charity.

In July 1973, a crime was committed against the gay community in New Orleans that would go unparalleled in this country until 2016, forty-three years later. The Upstairs Lounge was located on the second floor at 141 Chartres Street in the French Quarter. The old wooden three-story building was once an old home, dating back to 1848. A single front entrance led into a foyer with a wooden staircase rising to the second floor. All the windows were secured with bars, a very common finding in many New Orleans homes, not limited to the French Quarter.

Earlier in the night one of the patrons, Rodger Nunez, was thrown out of the bar. While in a drunken state, he kept getting in arguments and fights with other patrons. He swore out loud that he was going to "come back and burn the place down."

Later, around 8 p.m. the night of the twentieth, someone rang the door buzzer to the lounge. Upon answering the door, the bartender was greeted with massive flames and the smell of lighter fluid. The place went up like flash paper. The bartender knew of a hidden back door that led to the roof of the floor below. He was able to lead about fifteen to twenty people to safety by jumping to another roof and then climbing down to the ground below.

Despite the escape of those inhabitants, thirty-two young men died as a result of the fire. Nunez was arrested, questioned, but never charged. He had a psychiatric history and subsequently even admitted on four separate occasions to starting the fire. In November 1974 he committed suicide.

Mo Bethea was in the operating room that night of the twenty-fourth. His junior resident came in and told him they were admitting a burn patient to him. Mo kept operating. A little while later he got admitted another burn patient, and another.

Although it wasn't opened yet, a new burn unit had just been built on the second floor at Charity. Prior to this there was no consolidation of burn victims. They were scattered all over the surgery or pediatric wards in random fashion. There was also no isolation from infected patients with other conditions. A patient with severe burns could have easily been placed next to a patient with an open infected wound. With the arrival of the burn victims from the Upstairs Lounge the unit was opened early. It couldn't handle all the patients and filled up quickly. Even though the excess patients had to be transferred to other hospitals in the city, Big Charity was again at the epicenter of a major New Orleans disaster.

Third-Year Resident, 1973–1974

Tulane 14-LSU 0

As great is the change from being a senior medical student to becoming an intern the change from being a second-year resident to the third-year is even greater. A considerable increase in responsibility comes with this title. You still answer to your chief resident but have much more authority and independence with regard to cases you operate on. You are in charge of one of the four general surgery services at Charity and have under you a first-year resident and two interns, one assigned to the male patient's ward and one for the female patients and pediatrics.

Bill Woolverton (Wolf) and John Gage (Johnny Baby) were my chief residents.

Drs. John Gage and Bill Woolverton.

Both had already been in the service. Wolf, besides having spent a year in the "dog" lab at Tulane had spent two years at the Cardiovascular Research Institute under Julius Comroe.

He could quote the literature on pulmonary diseases backwards and forwards. His lab coat was always crammed with the latest reprints on the surgical literature. He taught us how to manage our own ventilator patients. Pulmonary resistance, PEEP, shock lung and expiratory volume, to name just a few, were terms that were dropped more than bowel sounds and blood loss. I learned more pulmonary physiology from Wolf than I had in medical school.

He and Dr. Drapanas would try to out-joust each other on rounds, going back and forth quoting article after article, trying to one-up each other. Drapanas usually won.

John was close to being surgical royalty. His father and Dr. Alton Ochsner had been best friends and inseparable. John's middle name was Ochsner. The two of them gave me an incredible amount of leeway and freedom when it came to doing cases. It was a year full of learning and responsibility. We worked hard but it was fun. We were on top of the world.

July 6, 1973 was my first day on call as a third-year resident on a male admit night at Charity. It was the Friday night of a long July 4th weekend. It was a full moon and it was a payday. To those working in hospital ERs, these events are "harbingers." Full moons are a certainty. Paydays bring out the worst in the knife-and-gun clubbers. There is likely to be a wreck somewhere, a major shooting or there will be several admissions with the same crazy injury. Despite what was about to unfold during the next 24-hour period, the prior weekend in New Orleans had already been one of a major tragedy, the previously discussed Upstairs Lounge fire.

Taking charge of my service July 1, I did assume the care of one patient from the prior weekend. My burn patient had about 60 percent second and third-degree burns. Taking care of him demanded new challenges. Although the acute period of massive fluid resuscitation had passed, he still required careful fluid monitoring and routine burn care and skin grafting. Our burn patient, after a period of stabilization would later be transferred to one of the local hospitals at the direction of his family. Youth was in his favor.

Some years before, Tulane resident, Art Axelrod had made an observation regarding burns and survival. "Axelrod's axiom" stated that if the patient's age plus the percentage of body surface burned was greater than 100 percent, the mortality was the same. It didn't change the way you treated the patient, but it give you an idea as to the scope of what you were dealing with.

On that Friday, the sixth, I saw my first patient in the ER about 3 p.m. A young man had actually shot himself in the right thigh with a .22 caliber pistol. Most of the time the histories we obtained from GSW victims was that they "were on their way to church" or a "friend of theirs accidentally shot them." This young man really did accidentally shoot himself. He had a fantastic injury in that the bullet had passed between his femoral artery and vein, lacerating them both and causing an AV fistula (arteriovenous). It was a great case. AV fistulas have special hemodynamics unique to themselves. Acutely, arterial high-pressure blood passes through the communication into the vein and back up the venous system toward the heart as well as coursing down the artery in normal fashion. With time, however, arterial blood that would normally go downstream reverses its course and is "stolen" from the artery's distal supply and goes up the lower pressure venue system. A network of collateral (extra) vessels also forms around the fistula to bring blood to the affected extremity. When a mature fistula, one that has been present for a long time, is operated, it can be a major bloody procedure. When they're done acutely, it's just a matter of sewing the holes up.

The seriousness of chronic A-V fistulas was exemplified in Rudolph Mitchell. He presented in chronic heart failure because of the size and duration of his fistula, and Glenn Pennington and Bill Browder made the paper after his surgical repair.

Male Surgery Patient Honored at Farewell Party

Doctors and nurses wish Randolph Mitchell (seated) farewell. From left to right are: Dr. B. Browder, surgery resident; Mrs. J. Holifield, R.N.; Dr. T. Hoberock, surgery resident; Miss M. Matherne, R.N., and Dr. G. Pennington, surgery resident.

Drs. Bill Browder and Glenn Pennington with A-V fistula patient, 1972.

I closed this case up and went down to the ER to see what was next. I found an intestinal obstruction with a tender belly on one roller and a possible hot gallbladder on another. As I was talking with the first-year in charge of the ER, a gunshot wound to the abdomen rolled in. That solved the dilemma as to which patient to take next. That night we admitted thirteen patients. Not all required surgery that evening.

One patient with acute hemorrhagic pancreatitis was admitted, treated by my first-year and died before I even got a chance to see him. Every time I went downstairs there were patients lined up on stretchers on both sides of the hall between trauma rooms one and four. The third-year admitting females was just as busy.

We finished operating about 6 a.m. We made rounds on all our patients, new and old, and then went to the central elevators in the front lobby to meet our staff man. Our whole team then grabbed a quick bite of breakfast in the doctor's dining room before making rounds again on the entire service. We then went up to Grand Rounds in the Delgado amphitheater.

Saturday Grand Rounds, Delgado Amphitheater, 1970s.

Luckily, we didn't have any patients to present. About this time I was in a daze and was just going through the motions, having been up without sleep for more than twenty-four hours.

Grand Rounds finished up about eleven. My first-year and I saw a couple of the more serious patients one more time and wrote some orders. I went up to my room on the fourteenth floor. Len and I had some friends scheduled to come over for dinner that night, but I had to lie down even if just for a few minutes. Being exhausted, still in scrubs and with my lab coat on, I laid across the bed sometimes after noon.

Startled, I awoke. It was dark. I didn't know where I was. As I turned I fell off the bed. It was 8:30 p.m. that night. Using the phone in the room, I called home. I was greeted with, "Where are you? Merle and Terry are getting ready to leave." Sometimes there just isn't an explanation that will do.

Being able to schedule my own patients for surgery was a distinct advantage. The chiefs and third-years would meet every afternoon and make out the operative schedule for the next day. Although we had reserved operating rooms, they were never enough for all the cases that needed to be done. The general thinking was that if you were going to be on call in the hospital and there were no emergencies that had to be done, then operate on cases you couldn't get done during the day. Therefore, when you were on call at night you didn't hesitate to put a case on the emergency schedule whenever there was an open OR.

All of this was done of course, at the discretion of Miss Elaine, the night OR supervisor. She "ran the book." She was used to all the tricks residents over the years had used to get in an operating room. If it was an elective inguinal hernia that had been sitting on the wards for a couple of weeks, it would "incarcerate" (become trapped) requiring emergency surgery. One senior resident had a patient who needed an elective gastrectomy. He had been trying to get the patient on the elective schedule for some time to no avail. On a slow on call night he told his first-year to go to the blood bank and check out a unit of blood. A nasogastric tube was inserted into the patient's stomach and the blood was then injected into the patient's stomach—voila, a bleeding ulcer. He got on the schedule.

Stranger things happened around the end of June also. One thoracic chief resident had a young man on his service with coarctation of the aorta. He was scheduled to rotate off the service the next day and didn't want to miss doing the case, so he brought the patient to an emergency operation that night. The next day he was making rounds with the CV resident who was taking his place. When they came upon the recently operated coarctation patient from the night before, the new chief questioned the "emergency" of the procedure. "You'll get to understand how it works," he was told.

As a third-year resident I had my own clinic day once a week. The charts for the day were put in a shopping cart the night before. Most of the new patients were sent from the admitting areas or the ER. The rest were follow-ups from your previous surgeries. Medicine residents also had their own clinics. A key to the medicine clinics had been passed down from surgery chief resident to chief resident. Mark Kappleman and Mathis Becker used it to get into the medicine clinic one night. Rummaging around the pile of charts, they found the chart of a patient with a severe thyroid condition. After calling the patient and admitting her she underwent the necessary pre-op workup and surgery. As it turned out she was a patient of Dr. Kay Reeves, head of the endocrinology section of the medicine department.

Things would have gone undiscovered had it not been for the fact that Reeves happened to be seeing a consult on the same surgery ward that the now "post-op" thyroid patient was admitted to. She not only noticed and recognized the patient, but noticed the bandage on her neck covering her scar. Perhaps that is why I never had the key passed down to me.

During the months of July and August I did about a dozen gallbladder resections. Very few of them went as quickly as that first one that Buck Rogers had helped me do. In those patients that we were able to demonstrate gallstones in the common bile duct preoperatively, we would do a common bile duct exploration on them. All of these operations were done "the old-fashioned way," through a long incision under the rib cage.

Laparoscopic gallbladder resections, with their same day discharge, were about ten years away from becoming the standard of care. It was standard procedure to leave a soft drain at the site and then remove it over a couple of days. Patients were kept in the hospital at least five days after surgery. Dr. Drapanas started not draining them. A new standard was set and we stopped draining them.

We always saw a varied selection of gunshot wounds (GSW). Most often it just involved sewing up holes in the small intestine or doing colostomies if the large intestine was injured.

One evening in September, a forty-four-year-old man (JV) came in with multiple GSW to the abdomen. It had been suspected that he was involved in some kind of drug deal, but that really didn't matter to us—yet. At operation he had multiple perforations of the small intestine and stomach. His abdominal space was full of red beans and rice, a New Orleans favorite not limited to druggies.

We sewed up all the holes, resected some small intestine, irrigated his abdomen with copious amounts of bug juice and closed him up. Postoperatively he went into pulmonary failure. He had not aspirated, but he did require being intubated and being put on the ventilator. By now, the ICU had been moved to the twelfth floor. That would be his home for the next several weeks. He developed just about every complication one could have. He required prolonged ventilation and was on intravenous hyperalimentation. He also had high output renal failure, almost requiring dialysis. He became a living textbook of postoperative management of the acutely ill patient. We attributed his pulmonary failure to "shock lung," but we couldn't put a finger on any one thing to cause all his problems.

Over time, he gradually improved. Renal function returned to normal, but most importantly, his lungs healed and he was no longer in pulmonary edema requiring ventilation. When we were satisfied that he was eating well enough and was ambulatory, we transferred him down to C400B. He was in a corner bed.

Because of the complicity of the case Wolf asked me to present him to Saturday Grand Rounds. I had operated on him. I had taken care of him through shock lung, high output renal failure and managed his hyperalimentation, but I was still nervous. Wolf sensed it and gave me a piece of advice I never forgot. "Remember," he said, "you know more about that patient than anyone. Know everything in the chart and what happened and you'll be fine." I never forgot that advice whether presenting a case to a family at bedside or a paper to hundreds of physicians at a national meeting.

On the first Sunday he was on the ward, he had visitors. I was on call in the hospital when I was called to the floor on an emergency basis. He was in florid pulmonary edema and in shock. We reintubated him, placed him back on the ventilator and transferred him back to ICU. This time we drew some blood tests for a drug panel—it was positive. He had been given a "fix" and it did him in. Whether someone gave him a normal amount of some substance, and in his weakened condition, it was too much for him, or someone gave him too much of a bad thing and finished him off, we would never know. This "kat" didn't have another life.

Stab Wounds

The standard treatment for penetrating wounds of the abdomen on both the LSU and Tulane surgical services had universally been exploration of the abdomen. Often this resulted in a "negative lap." It gave the first-year residents and third-year residents needed experience in surgical technique, but quite often it was an unnecessary operation. The infection rate at Charity wasn't zero; hence, one ran the risk of subjecting the patient to an unnecessary complication also.

In early December 1973, Dr. Carter Nance of the LSU Surgical Service presented a paper to the annual meeting of the Southern Surgical Association on a prospective and retrospective study of patients with stab wounds to the abdomen. Selective observation was performed in 393 patients under a strict protocol. The results demonstrated a marked reduction of negative explorations. It also cut the complication rate in half. Although Tulane was hesitant, at first to adopt this method of treatment the results could not be denied.

As if Nance's paper wasn't enough of an event to usher in December, back on the uptown campus on a Saturday evening, December 1, the ground was shaken. LSU had only lost one game in a ten-game run going into the traditional rivalry game with Tulane. Tulane had lost two games. The historic Sugar Bowl Stadium, where Tulane played its home games, was rocked by a fourteen to nothing victory over the Tigers. No one left the stadium when the game was over. It had taken twenty-four years for "Hell to freeze over." One good friend of mine who owned a camera store on the West Bank took a picture of the final scoreboard and used the image on his Christmas cards that year.

The other cases that a third-year resident loves to perform are gastrectomies, stomach removals. Peptic ulcer disease was rampant in our patient population. Drugs like Zantac and Tagamet had not been developed yet. Not only did these patients present with chronic pain, but more likely we saw them with perforated ulcers or duodenal and gastric ulcers that were bleeding. If they had gastric carcinoma, or if possibly, they required a more complicated resection it would become a chief case.

Intestinal anastomoses are delicate procedures. If one is sewing an artery and it develops a small tear, you usually know it immediately when the clamps come off. Sewing the intestine requires sewing delicate layers together also. The tissue is fragile and bruises easily which can sometimes lead to impaired blood supply and an anastomotic leak after the abdomen is closed. All the suturing was by hand as there were no stapling devices available yet.

Not unique to Charity, but unique in the way it was described to us by the patients, was the "locks." "Doctor, I got the locks." If I heard it once, I heard it dozens of times. Intestinal obstruction, whether because of a prior operation and subsequent adhesions, because of a new tumor, or dead bowel, we saw them all. They presented with an enlarged doughy abdomen. Bowel sounds were absent or you might hear what sounded like dripping water in a tunnel. Often they had waited a long time to come in and when inserting a nasogastric tube in their stomach, you would get as much as a liter of dark foul-smelling fluid out. They were always dehydrated.

The worst of these were the "wintergreen cases." These patients had dead bowel and when we opened their bellies an odor coming from it would gag a maggot. A little bottle of oil of wintergreen was kept in each OR. The circulating nurse would dab a little of it on the front of your mask to help block the smell.

Lallie Kemp – "On the Road Again"

In January of 1974 we went on a three-month out-of-town rotation to Lallie Kemp. New housing quarters had been built, a very nice quadruplex that could house four families. We had an apartment as did the pediatric resident, the ob-gyn resident and the first-year general surgery resident. Having relatives in Independence made it nice for Len as she could spend time during the day with them. They also enjoyed babysitting our almost two-year-old son.

The chief resident still did the cancer cases, most of the colon resections and all the vascular cases. Different members from the staff in New Orleans would come up on a weekly basis. If one of the general surgeons was coming we would try and line up something they could help with and instruct on. If a plastic surgeon came, it would usually be a plastic case. The first month, among other cases, I did a couple of gastrectomies and a partial colon resection for bleeding diverticulosis. There were always inguinal hernias and appendectomies to do or help the first year and intern with.

Toward the end of the month Dr. Bob Ryan, head of the plastic surgery section was our visiting staff. He helped me do a wedge resection and flap rotation for a basal cell carcinoma of the upper lip on a fifty-six-year-old lady. These are very delicate procedures and one has to be meticulous about hemostasis and careful not to devascularize the flap. At Charity, the plastic surgery resident did these cases. So as a general surgery resident we didn't have a lot of exposure to them. They were very satisfying and the patients were very appreciative.

Ryan was a superb technician. As much as he was known for his surgical ability, he was also known to have the largest collection of oil paintings by a well-known local artist who lived on a plantation south of Alexandria. The artist, Clementine Hunter, would become incredibly famous and Ryan's collection worth millions. The collection has been on loan, at times, to what was then called the Delgado Art Museum in City Park in New Orleans. Yes, the same Delgado from the amphitheater.

In April we rotated back to Charity. A couple of very significant things happen in the late spring months. As a senior resident is getting ready to leave the program and either go out in private practice, go on staff, or go elsewhere for additional training, you are more likely to pass cases down. Such happened with me in April and May of 1974. I was doing more colon resections, gastrectomies and even a neck dissection for carcinoma, also involving a skin graft. As with the lip resection and flap rotation I had done earlier with Ryan, there was something very appealing in plastic surgery. It is very delicate and precise. A bilateral breast augmentation I had assisted Ryan with as an intern and these recent two cases, made me wonder if I should go into "plastics." Because of the amount of trauma we saw at Charity, the plastic surgery residents dealt mainly with reconstructive surgery, such as putting faces back together, plastic reconstruction for severe burn victims and some augmentation surgery. By this time, the silastic "bag implants" for breast augmentation had definitely replaced the earlier direct silicone injections that had been so glamorized by some Hollywood stars.

In March, a twenty-three-year-old-female came into the ER with multiple gunshot wounds. This patient and another young woman I had taken care of in the fall back at Charity pointed out the nondiscriminatory behavior of penetrating trauma. This gal must have really made someone angry. She had a bullet hole through her common femoral artery that we repaired. She had multiple perforations to her small bowel that we sewed up. The most challenging injury was the one to her right ureter. It's not easy to hit that little tube that's not the size of a pencil. Normally at Big Charity we would have called Urology to share in the experience. Since we did it all at Lallie Kemp, we cut out the damaged area and sewed the two ends back together.

The other young female, seen at Big Charity, had shot herself. She was about seven months pregnant probably in a period of prenatal depression and decided she didn't want the baby. She took a small caliber pistol and put it to her very protuberant belly and pulled the trigger. Wolf had seen her initially and had called the ob-gyn resident on call. The decision was made to take her to the OR. He wanted me to explore her with the gyn resident.

Fetal heart tones were still present and she wasn't in labor. Upon opening her abdomen the uterus filled up her whole belly. Her intestines were all pushed to one side and after running her bowel we found no other injuries. She did have a bullet hole to the fundus of her uterus. The gyn resident took a long sterile needle and syringe and tapped the uterus. He got back clear pink fluid. We discussed it.

If we were to open up the uterus and tend to the baby, it wouldn't have survived. There was no such thing as in utero surgery like there is today. If the baby was seriously injured it would not survive and nature would take its course.

We elected to do nothing. He sewed up the hole in the uterus and I closed up the abdominal incision. Time went on. Although it was one of those crazy Charity cases I forgot about it. One day about three months later I ran into the gyn resident who had operated on her with me. "Hey, you remember that pregnant woman we operated on a few months ago? One of my residents told me he recently delivered a little boy with a healed GSW to the calf." Sometimes less is more.

The other significant event that took place in late spring, was the yearly meeting held in Dr. Drapanas' office. Here, on a one-on-one basis, you would meet with the Boss and learn your fate for the following year. As I had shown an inclination to thoracic surgery, the natural progression would be to go into the "dog lab," the research laboratory area that occupied the whole ninth floor of the medical school. It contained facilities for all laboratory animals used by any of the research people, surgery or otherwise. When I was doing the hyperbaric oxygen cancer research under Dr. Kokame, the ninth floor was where the mice were kept and where I had my own room with a small hyperbaric chamber. Also, on nine was where the residents were doing "piggyback" heart transplants in dogs in the sixties.

Mathis Becker had spent a whole year working with Dr. Albert Hyman during his research year. Hyman was a cardiologist who had done the area's first heart catheterization. Becker branched out a little that year when he brought one of his own dogs to the lab for a spaying operation. When he followed that one up by spaying a neighbor's cat, he got in trouble and was given a cease-and-desist order.

Sitting in his well-appointed office, Dr. Drapanas told me I would be chief resident of the thoracic and cardiovascular service. I was taken aback. Although I really had no desire to do a lab year, I had to ask him about the lab. He said, "There is no more lab. There is no more funding for it. You will be at Charity for six months and then at Ochsner for six months." The elation and sense of accomplishment I felt was tempered by the fact that I really didn't know if I was ready for that much responsibility.

As a warmup, that June I was placed on the chest service. Becker was finishing up his training and getting ready to go into private practice back in his home state of Florida.

Drs. Mathis Becker and James Ciaravella waiting for staff, lobby of Charity Hospital, 1974.

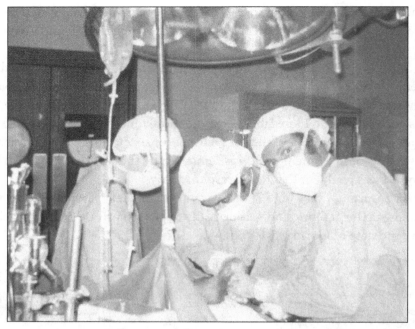

Drs. Becker, Ciaravella, and Todd in the OR, 1974.

Mathis helped me with all the non-cardiac thoracic cases and also my first pacemaker placement.

Cardiac pacemakers, 1974 and 2020.

There was no cardiac catheterization laboratory. Normally a portable X-ray unit called a C-arm would be used in the OR. Since these were not available we used the fluoroscopic equipment on the sixth floor. Those early pacemakers were the size of a cat's head biscuit. They controlled the rate in the ventricle only and had a battery life of one year. Technology of the batteries then improved to give them a two-year lifespan. As battery science has further progressed, pacemakers have diminished markedly in size, their life span has increased to eight or ten years and they pace both the upper and lower chambers of the heart (dual chambered). In actuality they are minicomputers.

Tulane surgery faculty and staff, 1974.

Part II
Advanced Training

Chief Resident, Clinical Heart Surgery, July 1974–1976

The American Board of Thoracic Surgery requires a candidate for the thoracic boards to have completed a general surgery residency and be board certified in general surgery before he can sit for his thoracic boards. Historically, all general surgeons at Charity were trained in non-cardiac thoracic surgery. We did whatever was served to us. On any admit night you had to be prepared to take care of abdominal and vascular, as well as thoracic injuries.

Many general surgeons even continued to perform thoracic and vascular surgery once in private practice. With thoracic boards already being in existence and vascular surgery boards being established in the late seventies, it would fall on the discretion of each hospital and their credentialing committees to determine who, if anyone would be "grandfathered" in. We were trained to do it all—punt, pass, and kick. As specialty boards in vascular surgery were established and as cardiac surgery became more refined requiring longer training, the triple hitters became phased out.

If one wants to earn their living at and be fully accredited to perform cardiac surgery, one must fulfill a minimum caseload of cardiac surgery cases. You do it; you do it again and again. By going right from my third-year of general surgery residency straight to being chief resident of the cardiothoracic service I was achieving my goal, sometimes I thought too quickly.

Of the many quotes credited to the famous surgeon and teacher, Dr. Theodore Billroth, there is one that is familiar to every cardiac surgeon in training or practice: "The surgeon who attempts to suture a wound of the heart may be sure of losing the estimation (esteem) of his colleagues forever." There are days in your residency and certainly days when you are in private practice that you wonder if you should have heeded those words.

On July 1, I was thrown right into battle. I had received a call from Huey Long hospital about a sixty-year-old man who had been in an automobile accident and had sustained a torn thoracic aorta. Significant in the history was that it had taken them about four days to suspect the diagnosis. The man was still in shock, bleeding into his tissues and chest and was close to death. I consulted with Dr. Bob Hewitt. The man was transferred to Charity. That night I did my first traumatic transection and dissection of a descending aorta.

Most of his ribs on the left side were broken into multiple pieces. Even the first rib was fractured, a sign of severe trauma. We had to use two chest retractors in order to keep multiple rib fragments out of the operative field and give us adequate exposure. There was a considerable amount of blood sequestered in his tissues, and his aorta was thinned out like wet tissue paper. Besides that, he had a coagulopathy preventing his blood from clotting. I had never operated on a human aorta before and wasn't doing a very good job. The key to any vascular surgery is the flexibility and manner in which the surgeon turns his wrist such that the needle and suture goes through the tissue as atraumatically as possible. I felt I was doing as much damage to him as the car accident had.

At one point I asked Dr. Hewitt if he wanted to finish the case. He said, "Jim, this man's fate was decided when he had his accident. Perhaps if we had gotten him a few days ago he may have had a chance. If you have to learn on a case, this might as well be your first." We replaced the torn portion of his aorta with a woven Dacron graft. We first had to pre-clot the graft. A suitable sized graft was selected. One end of the graft was clamped off and about ten to twenty milliliters of the patient's blood was thoroughly used to thoroughly coat the inside. This was done in a manner to get blood into the interstices of the graft. The blood-caked graft was then autoclaved. This process actually baked the blood into the graft and helped prevent bleeding by preventing oozing through the graft.

Despite our efforts at replacing blood and clotting factors, the patient never stopped bleeding and died later that night. Bob was right in everything he had said, but the patient still had died under my hand and I felt responsible. In the ensuing six months at Charity, before I rotated out to Ochsner Hospital, I did two more traumatic aortic dissections. Both of these patients lived.

At the weekly D&C conference I was asked to present the case. I took the blame using my inexperience as an excuse. Although Bob Hewitt came to my defense there were still technical things I could have done differently and improved on.

With regard to the "fault" scenario, a senior Ochsner cardiac surgery resident came to Charity for a period of time while the same level Tulane resident went to Ochsner's program. On one occasion a visiting professor was making rounds at Charity with the chairman, the Ochsner cardiac resident and one or two junior residents. They had just examined and discussed a patient's case that involved a series of very bad complications. While waiting for the elevator, the visiting professor asked the Ochsner resident why he thought the patient was doing so poorly. The resident thought a moment then said, "Well, sir, you can't make chicken salad out of chicken shit." The silence was deafening.

After the aortic dissection case, I knew I had a lot of things to improve on. I didn't want to let others and myself down. Bob Hewitt had an incredible amount of patience. After finishing Tulane Medical School and his residency training, he had been a distinguished trauma surgeon in Vietnam. He had also spent time at the Walter Reed Research Institute. His experience was extensive and he was extremely generous in sharing his knowledge. He worked closely with me that next six months. I valued his help and friendship.

During that first month I operated just about every day. I did an endless number of diagnostic endoscopies. Thoracotomies for lung cancer or severe infections were abundant. I did pacemaker placements, palliative shunts on infants with cyanotic heart disease, and over sewed blebs on patients with recurrent collapsed lungs. I even had to operate on a two-year-old girl with a sewing needle in the right lower lobe of her lung. Go figure.

During the summer months the Crippled Children's Program of Louisiana, as it was called then, would arrange for any children with congenital cardiac defects to be admitted to Charity or Ochsner Foundation Hospital and have a diagnostic cardiac catheterization and surgery, if needed. Even though we did a smattering of septal defects and patent ductus (PDA) closures throughout the year, those summer months were busier.

About the second week of July I would do my first open heart surgery as the primary surgeon. Lula was a nine-year-old girl with an atrial septal defect

(ASD). I had been an assistant on a couple of valves that Mathis had done back when I was a third-year, but this was definitely different.

Historically it was significant that some of the first open heart operations ever attempted were on ASDs before the heart-lung machine had even been perfected.

Bob helped me every step of the way. It was nothing like that first gallbladder Buck Rogers had helped me do. You did not waste a lot of time but each step was precise and carefully planned. Before I even made the incision I knew each step I would make. It was akin to a pilot's preflight check. You had to have everything on the operative field before you started. I would always look over the instruments at hand and check the back table. Nothing could be left to chance and I couldn't assume anything.

All the tubes that would connect the pump to the child were circled around me and placed on the table. Kathy, the perfusionist, was seated directly behind the pump and it was directly behind me. "Now make an incision in the midline about an inch below her sternal notch down to her xyphoid," Bob directed me. The Stryker saw we had at the time was no different from the cast saw down in the cast room in the ER, except it was sterile. A more sophisticated model came out later, as did the Sarns that I used the rest of my career.

A child's heart is smaller than your fist. If you let yourself start thinking about how many times a heart beats an hour, a month or a year it would drive you nuts. It's an incredible organ. But, sometimes, as with this little girl, one of the stages in development took a shortcut and left a heart defect.

A simple hole like an ASD is what you want if you have to have a problem with the heart itself. It's 100 percent curable. Before I retired I would see just about every congenital heart anomaly that had been diagnosed. I placed the tube in her aorta for giving the oxygenated blood back to her body from the pump and then the tubes for draining the darker, unoxygenated blood away from her body to the oxygenator in each of her vena cava.

The Harvey oxygenator was markedly improved over an older style Travenol bag oxygenator that I had seen in use not too long before. This was more compact and it was housed in a plastic cylinder about eighteen inches tall that mounted to a mast on the heart lung pump. There was still a direct blood-to-air interface. This caused some breakdown of the red blood cells (hemolysis), but was more efficient than what had come before it.

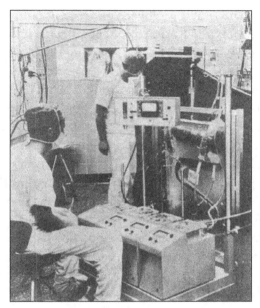

Travenol bag bubble oxygenator, circa 1960s.

Harvey bubble oxygenator, circa 1970s.

At the appropriate time I removed the venous clamps and allowed the pump to take over. Bob told Kathy to cool her down a little. This would be a means of lowering her metabolism and allowing her body to require a little less oxygen.

I placed an angled DeBakey clamp on her aorta and we snared down the tourniquets on her caval canulas. Her heart started to empty and slow. He instructed the anesthetist to rotate the table toward him a little. "Make an incision in the body of the atrium aiming toward her inferior cava," Bob instructed me. When I had the atrium open he inserted a small retractor in it for exposure and gently placed a suction device just below the level of blood that was coming up through the defect. I was looking inside her heart. She was still alive. Her heart had slowed almost to a stop, and Kathy and the heart-lung machine were a keeping oxygenated blood flowing to her brain and body at an adequate rate.

The hole was about the size of a nickel and shaped such that I could simply sew it up without using a patch. Just before I finished closing the defect, Bob instructed Kathy to rewarm Lula. I sewed up the atrium. I was impressed how Bob had used the sucker just enough to give me exposure but not let any air get to the left side of the heart. We placed a small air hole in her aorta, just in case, released her aortic clamp, and her heart started beating right on cue.

She would stay in the recovery room on the twelfth floor overnight. I found her mother on the ninth floor. She was very appreciative and cried.

As straightforward and usually predictable as were the repairs of an ASD, the tetralogy of Fallot offered more of a reconstructive challenge. You were reconstructing the inside of the heart.

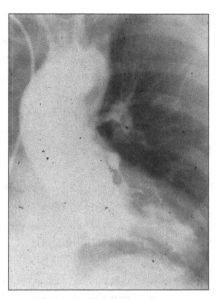

Tetralogy of Fallot angiogram.

They all had severe narrowing of the artery to the lungs (pulmonary stenosis), either valvular or subvalvular or both. They all had massive thickening of the muscle of the right ventricle (right ventricular hypertrophy) as a result of the right sided outflow obstruction and the heart trying to force blood to the lungs. All tetralogies had a large hole in the heart between the lower two chambers, a ventricular septal defect (VSD) that allowed unoxygenated blood to be directed to the body, resulting in a bluish discoloration (cyanosis) of the skin, which they all had. The cyanosis was especially noticeable in the lips and nail beds. This is the most common of the "blue baby" conditions a child can be born with. With this condition some children may live into their teens without early intervention.

That fall we had a young man with special needs present with tetralogy.

As I was doing the operation and sewing the patch into the heart to close the VSD, we heard a very loud *clunk* followed by "Oh, shit," from Kathy. It was not a sound normal to the operating room. It was a plastic container hitting on concrete. Bob looked up immediately and realized that the oxygenator had hit the floor. The metal bracket that held the oxygenator in its upright position had vibrated loose. At a flow of four to five liters per minute, air at once appeared in the tube bringing blood back to the patient. Bob grabbed the inflow perfusion tubing and tried to occlude it with his fist before we could clamp it, at the same time shouting to the perfusionist to turn off the pump.

The worst complication one can experience while on the heart-lung bypass machine is air embolus. The first organ the air enters is the brain. The air acts like a solid mass and occludes the flow of oxygen carrying blood. The complication was disastrous. We did everything we could to clear the lines, remove air from the heart, and complete the operation, but we knew it was futile.

Although the patient came off the pump, he succumbed a few days later. The manufacturers of the oxygenator came to New Orleans shortly thereafter to express their sorrow for what had happened. They should have expressed that to the child's mother and compensated her. Subsequently, the oxygenator was redesigned.

With the advent of membrane oxygenators, like I had worked on with Dr. Stanford at Wilford Hall this complication could definitely not reoccur. The major advantage of the membrane oxygenators was that there was no direct blood-to-oxygen interface; it was all done through a semipermeable membrane. The incidence of hemolysis seen with the old bubble oxygenators was greatly reduced and efficiency was increased.

One of the injuries we saw too often at Charity was the ingestion of lye and Old English furniture polish by children. In many homes in New Orleans, these items were kept under the kitchen sink. An exploring toddler would find the bottle, remove the cap, and ingest the sweet-smelling liquid. Besides the effect on the esophagus, they sustained a horrific inflammatory reaction in their lungs which could cause their death. If the child survived, they had severe inflammation and scaring of the esophagus. These children usually required having their esophagus surgically removed and replacing it with a section of the colon. Although a very big abdominal and thoracic procedure, it would allow them to eat and grow normally. We did a lot of surgery for the complications of those ingestions, both in adults and children.

Mediastinoscopy was another procedure at our disposal used not only in the staging of patients with lung cancer, but also diagnosing patients presenting with lymph nodes or masses in the central portion of their chests. If they had lung cancer and positive lymph nodes were biopsied at one of these procedures, they weren't a candidate for a lung resection. The one exception was squamous cell carcinoma. This was one of the more slowly growing lung cancers. When detected early it was usually confined to the lymph nodes and didn't spread via the blood stream. Again, I must emphasize, CAT scans had not been invented yet. With a CAT scan one could examine the chest non-invasively. They might still require a staging procedure, but the incidence of this was lessened.

I had always been fascinated by pulmonary surgery. The pulmonary lobes each have their own distinct blood supply and drainage as well as their own bronchial tubes. As everyone knows, the lung is like a sponge, but not as tough. Pulmonary resection requires a complete knowledge of anatomy of the chest, the blood supply of the lung, as well as the many variances one will definitely encounter. It looks nothing like the books.

As this year progressed, I routinely had members of the staff assisting me do lung cases. One particular patient had a carcinoma of the upper portion of his left lower lobe and was scheduled for surgery. Wolf was now on the Tulane staff and was going to help me do the case. "Call me," he said, "after you get him asleep and the chest is open and I'll come over". After opening him up I found that his mass extended into the lower portion of the left upper lobe. I called Wolf and asked if he was coming. "Why don't you go ahead and handle this one," he said, "You can do it; I'm tied up." I think that was his plan from the start.

Everyone has to have their first solo and it was my time. The patient's pulmonary function wouldn't allow him to have a pneumonectomy, so I resected his lower lobe and wedged the tumor from his upper lobe. He did well. I no longer asked for help in doing a pulmonary resection unless staff volunteered or insisted.

Another patient had been transferred form Huey Long in Alexandria. He had a proven carcinoma of his left lung, but would need a pneumonectomy. He had been bronchoscoped and the tumor biopsied. They had assured me that there was an adequate margin below the bifurcation of his trachea to do his resection.

The lesson to never trust someone else's bronchoscopy came to be at the hastening of this man's life. At operation we found the tumor to be too close to the carina. When I transected the left main stem bronchus and sent it to pathology we found ourselves with positive margins. Pulmonary staplers had not been invented yet. Perhaps they would have delayed or stopped the "blow out" and subsequent empyema he sustained a couple of weeks after the surgery. During the patient's post-op course I drained his empyema, did a rib resection and thoracic window, a procedure called an Eloesser flap.

We took care of him for several weeks knowing that there was no way he was going to close off that opening in his trachea with the tumor around it. He eventually died.

Again, in D&C conference, I had to justify his death. I had already discussed the failure to do my own bronchoscopy and the treatment of the empyema. When it came time to present the death it was almost expected.

I never did a pulmonary resection again without doing my own bronchoscopy. Had I performed one on him and done biopsies of the area, I would have found that he was not a candidate for a pneumonectomy or even surgery for that matter.

Later, in private practice, even if the patient had been worked up by one of the very capable and trusted pulmonologists I was fortunate to work with, I would still slip a flexible bronchoscope down the endotracheal tube and take a look before proceeding with any pulmonary resection.

In August 1974, most of the surgical staff went on vacation leaving Dr. Drapanas as one of the only attendings. The two general surgery chief residents and I would meet him in his office every Monday and plan out the cases to be done that week. I had another lung carcinoma patient (WL) who had been referred to me from the medicine service. I had scoped him and done a biopsy. The pathology report showed adenocarcinoma.

His pulmonary function studies were not excellent, but he had walked up three flights of stairs at Charity. This exercise proved to be a good indicator of pulmonary function especially when formal studies were done by a novice technician and compliance by the patient was inconsistent.

Dr. Drapanas told us to schedule all the cases we wanted to do on one morning and he would go from room to room and help us. I had my patient asleep and chest opened when he came in. This was only my third pneumonectomy and he could tell I was going a little too slow.

"May I show you something?" he asked. Now, what was I really going to say—no? He took some forceps and a pair of surgical scissors and in a few minutes he had made an incision in the pericardium, the sac surrounding the heart. He encircled the left pulmonary artery with a Dacron tape, as well as the left mainstream bronchus and pulmonary veins. "Why don't you transect those and sew everything up and I'll be back in a few minutes." He then left to go "assist" the chief general surgery residents, one doing a couple of carotids and the other an abdominal procedure.

I proceeded to put clamps on the pulmonary artery, pulmonary veins and bronchus and one at a time transected them and over sewed the ends. He came back later when the lung was out, shared some more advice and left.

Besides doing my first intrapericardial pneumonectomy, I learned many techniques that day that I would use for the next thirty-four years of my practice. The patient did very well; however, when the final pathology report came back the diagnosis had changed from adenocarcinoma to oat cell or small cell carcinoma. This disease spreads very quickly and survival is usually less than two years. Aggressive radiation and chemotherapy will usually melt away the tumor, but invariably it will return in an extensive way. Surgical resection was frowned on and not done at all for oat cell.

I saw Dr. Drapanas later that day and gave him the bad news. He couldn't have looked worse if I had sucker punched him. "We did a pneumonectomy for oat cell," he said in a very dejected way. The patient was discharged, received no extra adjuvant therapy and I saw him in post-op clinic a couple of times. That was in the summer of 1974.

Toward the end of July I had been seeing a young man in clinic with a severe pectus excavatum. This is a congenital condition that involves a deformity of the sternum and adjoining cartilage that are attached to the ribs. As the child grows, the sunken chest gets worse. The heart can be displaced with these conditions, but cardiac function and pulmonary function are usually normal. The surgery is mainly for cosmetic purposes. This patient desperately wanted surgery to correct his condition. Significant was the fact that he had previously had another congenital deformity cosmetically corrected. I was skeptical, but having never done surgery on a pectus, I remembered an old saying, "A case is a case."

One day that August while making rounds with Dr. Drapanas, I brought up the "pectus" patient. He told me to work him up, put him on the schedule and he would help me operate on him. I saw the patient back in clinic and told him our decision. He was agitated and brought up the fact that his chin was deformed and he was going to have it operated on also. Could both procedures be done at the same time? The red lights were now really whirring around. When next I saw Dr, Drapanas, he brought up the case.

"That patient ready yet?" he asked.

"Dr. Drapanas," I said, "there's something weird about that guy, and I'm not sure we should operate on him." He looked right at me.

"Jim, I learned a long time ago that when a chief resident doesn't want to operate on a case, don't do it. Cancel him." We did not commit an error in judgment.

Dealing With Death

In the fall we took a patient to the operating room with pure aortic valvular stenosis. The patient had massive enlargement of the left side of his heart as we could tell from his preop chest X-ray. The degree of the myocardial thickening present couldn't be over emphasized. His heart was massive. At operation, although this was my first valve replacement as the surgeon, the procedure was fairly straightforward.

The key to his survival would be how well we would be able to protect his markedly enlarged heart while sewing in the new valve. By sewing the edges of the pericardium (the sac surrounding the heart) up to the wound edges, one makes a "well" which will hold ice cold water. We did not have available to us sterile iced slush, a standard in today's operating rooms so a constant flow of iced cold saline was used to fill the well and bathe the heart. It was a mess.

Besides this we infused a cold solution of potassium, insulin and glucose (GIK) directly into his coronary arteries on a periodic basis. This solution was a precursor to the cardioplegia that is used to stop the heart today. Even this solution was not as cold as one would like but was the best that was available in that day.

In a normal scenario, when the valve is in place and after you have sewn the aorta closed, merely unclamping the aorta allows the patient's own warmed blood to reenter his heart and start the heart beating again. At worst it will fibrillate requiring the surgeon to electrically defibrillate the heart.

My patient's heart didn't even fibrillate. It was a rock. He had developed a condition called "stone heart." Nothing I did was effective in getting him off of the heart-lung bypass machine and he expired. This was hard, but it wasn't going to get any easier.

It wasn't that I hadn't had patients die already. The patient with the torn aorta didn't even have relatives accompany him. Neither did the patient who had the pneumonectomy. We were able to spend a lot of time with the mother of the young tetralogy patient. This was different.

I could not find the family. Within minutes of his being wheeled up to the operating room, his bed had been cleaned and a new patient had filled it. His family, if he had any, wasn't allowed to sit there. Where were they? There was no surgery waiting area on the twelfth floor and there was no ICU waiting room. Actually, the only waiting area in the whole hospital was the porches on either end of each floor and at the west admit area on the first floor.

It was like a bad dream. You were walking around in a wilderness calling out someone's name and you never got a response. I was actually frantic. I had to be the first to tell "this imaginary family" that their husband, brother, father was dead. I went down to the front lobby of Charity and even out to the front visitor's check-in booths on Tulane Avenue. No one had signed in for my patient. I retraced my steps to most of these areas a second time to no avail.

Perhaps I had not been conscientious enough before the surgery to be present during visiting hours. I had to try to do better.

Many years later in private practice it would be different. You always met someone. Any time you discussed the procedure and the risks you always saw to it that a family member was present. But on those rare occasions a patient died in the OR it was always up to you and you alone to make the "walk down the hall."

The walk from the OR, through the doctor's lounge down that hall that turned to the right before you got to the family waiting room. No matter what risk you had quoted, no matter what the procedure was and how sick the patient had been, it was during that walk down the hall I always reflected back to that aortic valve patient whose family I never found.

While in private practice, I would have one instance when I never met the family pre-op. I met with the patient several times over the course of his stay before his fairly routine coronary bypass operation. Most of his family was out of town. Because of my prior episode, I just did not want a repeat of that experience. He assured me they would be present after the surgery.

The case went fine without a hitch whatsoever. Upon entering the surgery waiting room, the "pink lady" volunteer ushered me over to a sitting area with five women of varying ages, all with very solemn looks on their faces. No one spoke. I introduced myself. Silence. Finally, one attractive lady sitting in a chair by herself spoke up. Using her hand, she gestured to each of the women, "Doctor, this is his mother, these are his daughters, this is his ex-wife and I am his next wife." You never hear it all.

Miami

American College of Surgeons

In October 1974, I had been allowed to attend the yearly Congress of the American College of Surgeons. This meeting was held on a rotational basis between Chicago, San Francisco and Miami. This year it was in Miami. The goal of every surgical resident was to become a Fellow of The American College of Surgeons (FACS). It was the notice to your patients, associates, hospitals that you had met the highest standard of training and passed your specialty boards in your field. One was required to complete a sufficient number of cases in various categories to be capable of handling whatever surgical case might come your way. The greatest advantage in attending one of these congresses was the specialty courses and fireside chats that were available. Lectures were given by surgeons who had written extensively on a problem or perhaps had developed the procedure or treatment on which they were speaking. You were hearing material straight from the horse's mouth.

Lectures could be held morning, afternoon and night. One would have to pay a fee to attend a series of specialty lectures, but the hours went toward continuing medical education hours we all were required to have. Len did go with me and as I remember most Tulane people stayed at the Fontainebleau Hotel on Miami Beach. We were in high cotton. I had signed up for a series of lectures on unusual surgical conditions, traumatic or other injuries one might come across that were just not commonplace.

In particular was a lecture on tracheal-innominate (T-I) artery fistula. This is a disastrous, rare, often not recognized complication that requires immediate surgical intervention. It occurs in patients who have had an indwelling endotracheal tube in place for a long period of time. The inflatable clear plastic bag that occludes the space around the breathing tube used to be stiff and required a high pressure to inflate it. High cuff pressures combined with the fact that the innominate artery coursed directly across the trachea behind the sternum could cause erosion of the endotracheal tube through the trachea into the innominate artery.

This artery is about the size of your finger and carries a significant amount of blood at a high pressure. When the fistula develops, the trachea can immediately be filled with blood causing the patient to drown.

Several weeks after returning from the Miami meeting I had just finished attending the weekly D&C conference. Before heading home I always made rounds on any patients I had in the ICU. There was a small room designated as a cardiac unit and it opened up into the main ICU reserved for general surgical patients. I walked by the bed of a young woman on a ventilator. Rod Jackson, one of the general surgery chiefs was standing next to her bed.

Quite noticeable, however, was the fact that bright red blood was coming from her tracheostomy wound and out of her endotracheal tube. The young girl had markedly advanced liver disease, was in a hepatic coma and had been intubated and on a ventilator for some time. The goal was to get her over this acute event for Dr. Drapanas to do a mesocaval shunt on her to treat her portal hypertension.

I told Rod that I thought she had a T-I fistula. He sort of agreed and when I asked him what the plan was he said they were going to let her go—die. I asked him if that was the Boss's decision and he said that the Boss didn't know about it. I said, "You'd better call Drapanas." Somewhat reluctantly he picked up a phone and called the surgical office. The one side of the conversation that I could hear after he had told Dr. Drapanas what was happening went something like: "You don't think we should—yes sir, yes sir he's here, yes sir, I'll ask him. We'll get it done right away." He then put the phone back on the receiver and looking at me asked me to help operate on her. I told him I'd be glad to help.

We quickly arranged for an operating room and took her to surgery. She was already intubated and asleep so it was just a matter of prepping her chest, doing a midline incision and splitting her sternum. Although I was intimately familiar with the anatomy of this part of the chest, I had never repaired a T-I fistula. It couldn't have gone any better. I clamped the innominate artery, took it off of the trachea, divided the artery and oversewed the ends. The hole in the trachea was repaired and adjoining tissue or muscle was placed between the trachea and innominate artery ends to act as a buffer.

I left knowing we had done something good that day. That time spent in a meeting a few months prior in Miami had been worth it. Unfortunately, the young woman succumbed to her serious liver disease a few weeks later.

Pulmonary and Cardiac Surgery, Ochsner Foundation Hospital

As extensive as the experience was these first six months, it was incomplete. I had not been exposed to any coronary bypass surgery. It wasn't even heard of at Charity. Dr. George Burch, cardiologist and chair of the Tulane Internal Medicine Department was a strong disbeliever in coronary bypass surgery.

The cardiology residents were not allowed to do coronary angiography; therefore coronary disease was not diagnosed. It was quite possible that some of the poor results that were had with valve surgery could have been because of coexisting coronary artery disease.

In January, I would be rotating to Ochsner Hospital for another six months of cardiac training. Dr. John Ochsner, Alton's second son, and Dr. Noel Mills were huge proponents of coronary artery bypass surgery (CABG). Dr. John had trained under Michael DeBakey in precoronary days, but had learned how to do them and do them well. Mills had trained at NYU under Dr. Frank Spencer, another huge proponent of CABG and an early pioneer of that surgery. Both were strong proponents of use of the IMA (internal mammary artery) as well.

I certainly would not be the first Tulane resident to rotate to Ochsner. Many had done so before me, but not all went on to do cardiac surgery. Some had done it for only a few months and could relate no particular experiences that they had. As it would happen after six months I would feel completely at home. There was a level of professionalism there that did not exist at Charity. This was not a resident run hospital. It was a private hospital that did train residents and fellows. Charity was a hospital built first to take care of the indigent, and secondly, its duty was to train doctors.

Ochsner Clinic opened in 1942, twelve years after Alton Ochsner's dismissal from Charity. Ochsner had received and declined an invitation to leave Tulane, this time to go to the University of Illinois. With the ongoing strife between the Tulane faculty and Charity Hospital, the Touro Infirmary agreed to give Tulane the use of ten beds for their private patients. This along with a relaxation of a previous ban of the Tulane staff doing surgery on private patients put Ochsner back in business even though he still couldn't operate at Charity. His fearless aggressiveness in tackling any surgical problem did nothing to hurt his reputation.

The LSU Medical School had been opened and receiving students but was having trouble passing its accreditation through the AMA Council of Medical Education. To this point, Huey Long and Arthur Vidrine hired the well-respected Dr. Urban Maes away from Tulane with the hope he would elevate their status and assure their getting approved. Maes agreed on the conditions that not only would relations between Charity and Tulane improve, but that Alton Ochsner would be reinstated to the staff at Charity. And, so two years after being barred from entering the hospital, in 1932 Ochsner was readmitted. One year later LSU received its accreditation.

Tulane's reputation grew, but so did Alton Ochsner's. Despite his growing successes he continued to feel that Charity was still imposing too many restrictions on Tulane. His main desire was for Tulane to have a university hospital. The administration did not think that this was feasible. The idea of a multispecialty group practice or clinic had already been proved workable with the start of the Mayo Clinic in the late 1800s. The Lahey Clinic had also recently been formed as well as the Henry Ford Hospital based on a similar model. Ochsner was determined to succeed with this idea in the South. He got together four specialists besides himself to do something, to join and form a clinic.

The concept was not well received by the physicians of New Orleans who labeled the founders of Ochsner Clinic "Judases." To further demonstrate their displeasure, on the Thursday before Easter of 1941 a bag of silver (thirty dimes) was delivered to the door step of each of the five founding physicians. Nothing would deter Ochsner from his goal. He was fearless when it came to tackling any challenge, from operating on the famed golfer Ben Hogan, to being summoned to Europe to do surgery on movie stars.

Built on Alton Ochsner's surgical reputation, the proximity to the Latin American countries and the fact that it was the only thing like it in the South, the Ochsner Clinic established itself as a destination hospital for health care.

One afternoon I went out to Ochsner's and its campus on the bank of the Mississippi River. I met with Mark Kappelman, the chest resident who had been at Ochsner for the preceding six months and who would be rotating back to Charity when I left. He told me that I needed to order some optical loupes as I would not be allowed to scrub on coronary cases unless I had a pair.

My six months at Ochsner would be divided into two months spent with John Ochsner, two months with Mills and two months on the pulmonary service, primarily with Dr. Hurst Hatch, the head of the pulmonary service.

Because I had waited too long to order my loupes they had not arrived when I was supposed to start. I was placed on the pulmonary service for the first two months. There was a wooden pigeon-holed consult box just off the main foyer of the hospital. If a physician wanted to consult another physician or surgical service, they filled out a consult slip and placed it in that particular physician's slot.

Dr. Paul DeCamp and Dr. John Blalock were two old school, Alton Ochsner-trained, non-cardiac thoracic surgeons on the staff. I would also be working closely with them doing chest cases. The greatest thing about the pulmonary rotation was the volume of surgery you were exposed to and got to perform. For the most part as a thoracic resident I did most of the cases. Significant also was that the clinic had the new flexible fiber optic bronchoscopes.

The patient was given a light general anesthetic and a special endobronchial tube was inserted into the trachea. This had a ventilating port on its side. The scope was threaded though the rear end of the tube and the anesthesiologist could still ventilate the patient through the side port. It was as close to a closed system that you could get, thus assuring proper oxygenation.

In contrast, at Charity the bronchoscopes were rigid and all the exams were done under local anesthesia. There we would anesthetize the throat with Xylocaine viscous and a sponge soaked in topical cocaine temporarily placed behind the tonsillar fossa. Sometimes a little intravenous Librium or Valium was given to relax the patient. Oxygen was connected to the side port of the scope and a lens was placed over the open end of the scope.

The advantage of the rigid scope was the ability to biopsy anything you wanted to with a larger biopsy forceps. There was no magnification as there was with the flexible scope and the lighting wasn't as good. Another drawback was one only had access to the main pulmonary branches. With the flexible scope a much more thorough exam of the bronchial tree could be performed. There was really no comparison when it came to exposure and visualization. When it came to a foreign body in the bronchial tree or the esophagus, for that matter, nothing was superior to a rigid scope.

Shortly after I started at OFH, a young woman presented with recurrent cough, fever and pneumonia. She happened to be the girlfriend of one of the medical staff physicians. They had expected Dr. John to scope her. He told me about her as the anesthesiologist was putting her to sleep. As I inched the scope down her trachea I found a great deal of pus in her right lower lung segments. After irrigating the area with saline and upon sucking the fluid out, I started seeing what turned out to be peanut fragments floating out of her bronchi. She evidently had been chewing peanuts, coughed and had aspirated some of the fragments. They swell in the lung and as small as the fragments are they can block up the air passages and cause pneumonitis. I removed everything I could see and she eventually got well.

Operating with DeCamp and Blalock was an experience. As progressive as things were at OFH with the technology and instrumentation available, those two didn't believe in using the electrocautery.

The chest wall muscles are very vascular. When one makes an incision through the skin, the fatty layer and the chest muscles, there are countless small blood vessels. Even though the cautery available to us at Charity in those days was very rudimentary, we could still clamp individual blood vessels and then one by one "zap" each hemostat. Besides the time saved, tying down to the point of a hemostat wasn't always effective. Later, the amount of blood saved by "cutting" or transecting these layers with a cautery was huge.

Decamp and Blalock, however, would not use the cautery and instead made you clamp every blood vessel with a small hemostat and then tie each one with 4-0 silk. The silk now came on a small plastic spool, which was a step up from the wooden spools of cotton they had been trained to use. Perhaps, they thought every case was a training exercise in how to tie knots; I doubt it. Time and blood were wasted.

They also did not believe in the use of Prolene, a polypropylene suture that was much less traumatic when sewing blood vessels. Bronchial and intestinal stapling devices were just coming into use in the mid to late portion of 1975. Whereas we were using monofilament suture to suture the pulmonary arteries and bronchi at Charity, DeCamp and Blalock would not use that either.

One day Blalock was helping me do a lobectomy. We had resected the lobe and still had clamps on the transected end of the bronchus. He had to break scrub and answer a telephone call. While he was gone, I sutured the bronchus with Prolene suture. He came back in and asked, "What's that?" "Prolene," Dr. Blalock, "It's a synthetic polypropylene monofilament and much less traumatic on tissues," I told him. He took a suture and put a few stitches in the chest muscle, just to try it out. With a "humph" he then removed it. I don't think he ever switched.

John Lockwood Ochsner, 1927–2018

John Ochsner was born in Madison, Wisconsin in 1927.

Dr. John Lockwood Ochsner.

The second of five children, he was raised in New Orleans when his father became chairman of the Tulane Surgery Department that same year. After receiving his medical degree from Tulane he began a surgical residency at the University of Michigan. Like many physicians of the time, his training was interrupted by the Korean War. By this time his former "babysitter," Dr. Michael DeBakey, who had been mentored by the senior Ochsner, had taken the position of Chief of Surgery at Baylor University Medical School.

It was a natural fit that John would now train under Dr. DeBakey in Houston. There, a like lasting bond would be formed with not only DeBakey but also with another cardiac pioneer and surgical giant, Dr. Denton Cooley.

Alton Ochsner, on assuming the chair of the Tulane Surgery Department at thirty-one years of age, became lifelong friends with Dr. Mims Gage. Gage, a Tulane graduate, was Matas trained and only a couple of years older than Ochsner. The two operated together on everything, reviewed and wrote on a multitude of case files from Charity Hospital and became lifelong friends. Ochsner had operated on Gage and Gage operated on Ochsner's mother, even transfusing her with his own blood. Gage's second son was named John Ochsner Gage, my previous chief and Ochsner's third son was named Mims Gage Ochsner. It was only natural that Mims Gage was John's godfather. The senior Ochsner had trained a young Michael DeBakey.

Following John Ochsner's training at Baylor he was asked to stay in Houston. In those days being DeBakey trained, he could have punched his ticket to go anywhere. He was inclined to stay until the director of the Ochsner Clinic flew to Houston and met with him.

"John, you will be a great surgeon wherever you practice, but there is only one hospital that has your name on the front of it."

John Ochsner was born to be a physician, he was born to be a surgeon and he was born to be Rex, King of Mardi Gras, all in the footsteps of his father. He did excel, where his father didn't, in becoming one of the leading cardiac surgeons of not only the South but the country. The rest is history.

In March, I finally got to rotate onto the cardiac service. Dr. John and Noel operated every other day. One would have the only cardiac operating room one day and the other would see clinic and make rounds. On any given week your surgeon operated Monday-Wednesday-Friday and the next week Tuesday-Thursday. One of my duties was to check the consult box, see the patients, work them up from a surgical standpoint and then present them to Dr. John or Noel.

I had answered the consult of an elderly gentleman who needed a valve replacement. Even though I had discussed his condition with him and gone over the whole procedure including risks, I told the man that I would be bringing Dr. John Ochsner to see him and discuss the surgery. Later on entering his room and after introducing the two, his response was, "Who are you?"

"Ochsner, Dr. John Ochsner," Dr. John repeated.

"I don't know who you are," he said. I jumped in and told him, "Ochsner, you know his name is on the soap and floormat." Dr. John gave a grin. I had no idea at that time that the name recognition was one of the reasons that had been responsible for luring him back to New Orleans.

I would see each and every patient Dr. John received a consult on. At Charity anyone was an eligible patient. We never looked at age. One day I was surprised after presenting him a candidate for bypass surgery when Dr. John said he was too old and turned him down. I was learning. The operation was not wildly accepted so I filed the experience away. That patient was sixty-five years old. I would never have thought that before my career was over I would be destined to successfully operate on three ninety year-old coronary bypass patients.

Coronary Arteries

I had never scrubbed on a coronary bypass operation. Basically you were doing microscopic surgery on the surface of the heart. The loupes took some getting used to. The closest thing to them was my binocular microscope I used when I was a freshman medical student. But now the lenses, the little telescopes, were attached to the front of a pair of glasses. The distance between the two lenses was measured to the exact distance between your two pupils. The length from the end of the lens was measured to the operative field and didn't vary. And the depth of field, a term known to every photographer, was less than an inch. With the glasses on, your world was about two inches in diameter.

The coronary arteries lie under a transparent layer around the heart, the epicardium, and most of the time they are easily visible. Most vessels are miniscule and form a huge vascular tree buried within the muscle of the heart. The average diameter of the vessels on top of the heart is about 1.5–2.0 mm. The needle holder we used was completely different and it resembled a long pair of tweezers. It was spring loaded and had a lock.

The other major difference was the suture material. You've probably heard it called fishing line. Well let me tell you, you have never caught a fish that small. We used 6-0 Prolene on the vein to coronary anastomoses and 7-0 on mammary artery to coronaries. It was delicate and to an observer one might have thought we were sewing with air. With regard to size, the closest thing I could compare it to was a hair; it was that fine.

The learning process was slow. Dr. John was not only assessing me on how I did the little specifics; it was the whole picture you presented to him that he was judging. Several cases later, we had come off pump, he had left the room and I was closing. The venous canulas had been removed. After the patient had enough of the pump blood transfused back to him,

I was taking out the aortic canula and had not secured the sutures down enough. It was bleeding. I put in a couple of more stitches and it continued to bleed. Had I torn the aorta? I heard a voice from over the screen. It was Dr. Welborn, the head of anesthesia, "Do you want me to get Dr. John?" "Not yet, I got it, gimme a pledgeted suture." I put in the mattress suture and the bleeding stopped. Then I heard another voice, "Everything OK, Jim?" It was him. The confidence I got from that one incident was invaluable. As glad as I was that they had called him, I was just as glad that I had handled it and he knew that I could do it.

Depending on how he thought your progress was going, on every case, he might let you do a little more. He taught me how to sew blood vessels, how to move, what to hold, what not to hold. Forget about the pictures in the books. If you want to hold the needle backwards and upside down when sewing in sutures on a mitral valve, do it. Whatever works for you, you do it, but do it right. I would use those techniques I learned from Dr. John, and Noel, on the next 4,000 pump cases I would do through my career.

"Bull Pen"

In the spring of 1974 back at Charity a teaching parody was done on Dr. Alton Ochsner's well-known bull pen. The event was held in the Delgado amphitheater on the twelfth floor at Charity, the same location where regular bull pens were held. Dr. Drapanas first came out and explained how the great names in surgery were going to comeback from a time long past and discuss a case presented to a modern day Tulane medical student. Dr. Drapanas then came out dressed as the "Typical Conservative Tulane Medical Student" beads and all.

Most of the attending staff and senior residents participated, but were adorned with wigs, mustaches and spectacles to represent Matas, Gillies, Osler, and other greats from a time long past.

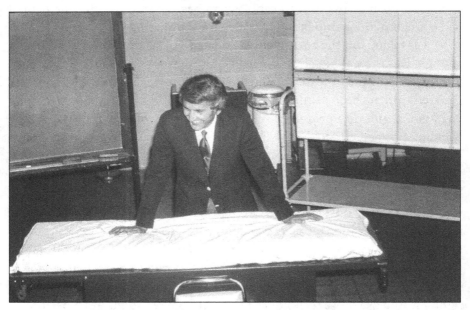

Drapanas introducing staff bullpen, Delgado Amphitheater, 1975.

Drapanas as a Tulane medical student, 1975.

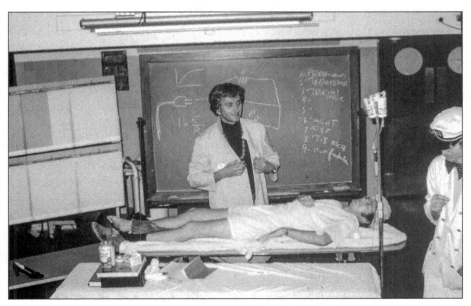

"Student" Drapanas examining patient.

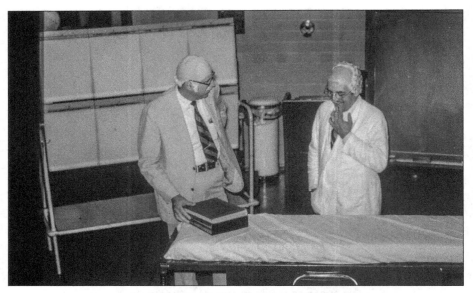

Drs. Bob Ryan and Jim Dowling doing bullpen, 1975.

The first two months of operating with Dr. John were like a flash fire. He never stopped. He was a whirling dervish in the operating room and it was seldom that he did an operation the same way twice. He did what the anatomy or condition gave him and wasn't afraid to jump into anything.

Like his father, he was somewhat of a showman and flamboyant. He could talk the talk and he could walk the walk. Whereas Noel limited his case load mainly to involve cardiac surgery, Dr. John did peripheral vascular surgery, lung surgery and whatever else came his way.

In March of that year, one of the first cases I did with him was a pacemaker placement. It wasn't just any ordinary kind of pacemaker. The patient was a twenty-five-year-old woman with heart block. We were going to put an atomic pacemaker in her, a Medtronic Model 9000. A limited number of these had been implanted starting in 1973. It was thought that with the average survival of a normal pacemaker being one to two years, the atomic pacemaker could last a patient their lifetime.

One of the main drawbacks in using one, however, was that at the time of death, the pacemaker had to be removed and returned to the manufacturer.

If the patient died at a hospital other than the one that had implanted the pacemaker, this could cause some logistical problems.

The case was scheduled in the afternoon on a day we had clinic. After lunch I hurried down to the OR in an attempt to do and finish the case before he got there. As he scrubbed in he said, "Got here kind of early, did you?" With a grin under my mask I told him he had gotten there a little late.

No matter how you screwed up at the operating table, he always forgave you. He might scream, rant and carry on about what a dumb thing you had done, but ten minutes later it was all over and he'd take you to get a cup of coffee. No matter what your error was, he never brought it up again.

Noel Mills and Terry King, the senior Ochsner pediatric cardiologist, had been doing laboratory research on transcatheter closure of atrial septal defects (ASD). If Dr. John had an ASD closure in the operating room, Mills and King would both come in and study the anatomy. There is no uniform size of a septal hole, but they had a device with them they'd been working on that resembled a small double umbrella. Noel would scrub in and would size the device against the defect.

On April 8, 1975, a seventeen-year-old girl became the first successful patient to receive a transcatheter closure of an ASD. King and Mills had done the procedure in the catheterization lab with the operating room on standby. That evening, not only the local 5 o'clock news covered the event, but so did the national news media and the next day it was in the paper.

John started receiving calls from his surgical colleagues from various parts of the country. "Why hadn't it been presented to a scientific meeting or in a medical journal before going straight to the press?"

There is no question that they had performed a "first." In today's era of sensational twenty-four hour on end news coverage, it hardly even seems mentionable, but then that type of "advertising" was frowned upon. The furor subsided and they actually did several more successful "umbrella" implants.

In early May that spring, I was called to Dr. Drapanas' office. It was that time again to find out what your assignment would be for the next year. He told me that I was staying at Ochsner for another six months, which would mean that I would be there for a whole year. I was to be the first Tulane thoracic resident to spend one year at Ochsner and the first Tulane resident to do two consecutive years of clinical cardiac surgery. Prior to that, the year spent in the lab doing canine heart transplants or other research had sufficed for the American Board of Thoracic Surgery's two-year requirement to be Board-eligible. He told me the requirements had changed and one now needed two full years of clinical cardiac surgery.

May and June were spent on Noel Mills service. Noel was an excellent cardiac surgeon. He had been trained in coronary surgery at New York University. However, he and Dr. John couldn't be more different, not only in their personalities but in their methodologies.

Noel was very programmed and specific in every move he made. He also was not as flexible or forgiving as Dr. John. If you ever made a mistake, he never let you forget it. He was shorter than average and with his red hair the Ochsner residents nicknamed him the "Banty Rooster." He would peck and peck and peck at you. The cardiac cases we did were the same, but Noel didn't do pulmonary surgery.

Dr. John and Noel were big proponents of using the IMA to graft to the LAD (left anterior descending artery). When doing a case, with Dr. John, the resident usually harvested the saphenous vein, while Dr. John took down the mammary artery and cannulated the heart or he would have us cannulate the heart for bypass. He might allow us to stand on the right side of the table and do the cannulation or if we were on the left side we might do some anastomoses from there. There were also cases which he would let me do in their entirety.

Noel insisted that we took the IMA down and he harvested the vein. His thinking was that if you injured the IMA while taking it down, you knew it right away and couldn't use it. If one were to damage the vein, it might be possible for the vein to incur a subintimal tear or other injury that would not be recognized at the time of implantation. The damaged reversed vein would then sustain early vein closure and a subsequent late poor result.

Noel had a routine, in that after he harvested the vein, he would clip it inside a sterile towel dampened with antibiotic solution and place it on the back table. On one occasion when he was doing a case he asked for the vein graft. The scrub nurse couldn't find it. Things were getting so tense that Noel broke scrub and looked for it himself. He found it in the trash can. The circulating nurse, thinking it was a used dirty towel, had thrown it away. Carefully, he unfolded the towel, revealing the still-sterile vein, which we then sewed in.

In those early days of coronary surgery we really didn't know how long the revascularizations would last. We actually told some patients that they were cured and would not need further intervention. This was erroneous thinking mainly based on the fact that the operation hadn't been done long enough. It has turned out that, on the average, a vein may last eight to ten years. Even though many grafted vessels lasted longer, I used to give my patients that range. They never held it against you if the grafts lasted longer.

In the seventies, widespread use of the internal mammary artery wasn't widely accepted. Although papers were being published showing its efficacy and the advantages of using an artery, mainly higher patency rates than a vein, the naysayers were publishing also. There were articles published not advocating its use because of the extra time it took to harvest it or possibly removing the blood supply of the chest wall. None of these arguments held up.

With time, however, it became the standard for CAB grafting everywhere, as did the use of a free grafted radial artery, when feasible.

In June, when I was on the second month of my rotation with Mills, Dr. Drapanas was killed. Most of the personnel at Ochsner did not know Drapanas. Dr. John did, however, and I remember him telling me the news. He was very serious, more so than I'd seen him in the few months I'd known him. I really don't know what kind of relationship they had, if any, but I think he knew what effect it would have on the school.

My course for the next six months of my Ochsner rotation and the six months that would follow when I returned to Charity had been determined. Drapanas had seen to that. Being away from Charity during that period actually made it easier for me as I wasn't directly subject to the confusion of leadership that was transpiring down on Tulane Avenue.

During the month of August, I did a rotation with the two pediatric cardiologists. They, like the Charity cardiologists were examining children referred in from the Crippled Children's Clinic with congenital heart disease. Mostly, I spent a lot of time in the cardiac X-ray suites where the cardiac catheterizations were done. I was able to catheterize a few of the older children, but mainly it was diagnosing the variety of congenital heart cases that presented.

Every child who had a cath had some form of heart disease. That's why they were there. It was definitely a skewed population. The problem with my point of view was that during this period Len was pregnant with our second child and due to be delivered the following month. I didn't see how it was possible for her to be born with a normal heart. I hadn't seen one in a month and I actually lost sleep over it.

Since Len had undergone an emergency C section at Wilford Hall during her first pregnancy, the second delivery was scheduled for September 4. I told Dr. John that I was going to be with my wife that day and would not be able to assist him. He said that would be fine; I should just do what I needed to do.

Susan was born that morning. Mother and daughter were doing fine, so later that day I sought him out to tell him the good news.

He said, "Congratulations, now I want you to help me do a case."

"What is it?"

"She's an old patient of my father's. She needs a cholecystectomy and common bile duct exploration, I haven't done one in quite some time and I need you to help me." We did it and it never stopped amazing me that there were no limits to what he would try.

In the fall there were several meetings that Noel attended where he presented papers. He booked himself out of the clinic and operating room for almost the entire month of October. Likewise, Dr. John booked himself out of seeing patients in the clinic during that period. This meant that he planned on operating every day. Besides my normal duties in making rounds and caring for postoperative patients, I spent the night in the hospital each day we did a pump case.

The ICU at Ochsner was one large room. We generally kept our cardiac patients along one wall separated from general surgery patients only by a space in the middle. At the end of the room there were two "sleeping rooms." For the better part of a month one of those rooms would be my home away from home. Many nights I was so tired I didn't even close the door to shut out the noise coming from ICU.

From the beeping alarms on ventilators, the constant whir of the Emerson suctions used for chest tube drainage to the occasional overhead page from an operator, it all became white noise. A nurse might come in at night and kneel beside the bed, "Mrs. Barton's urinary output in bed four has dropped off. Would you like me to give her twenty of Lasix?" Or Mr. Stewart's chest tube drainage is still 100 milliliters and hour." "Give him fifty of protamine." Some mornings after getting up I would review a chart and find a verbal order I had given that I did not remember at all.

There was nothing sacred about weekends. The first week I got home on a Thursday night as we didn't do a pump case that day. I got home Saturday after a Friday night at the hospital and when a dissecting aneurysm came in on Sunday I was back at the hospital. This went on for a month. After a week of not being home, Len would bring our two kids to the hospital so we could have dinner in the cafeteria and they could see their daddy. At the end of thirty-one days I had spent five nights at home.

During the year Dr. John had two distinguished visiting professors visit the clinic. The first was Dr. James Hardy. Hardy was chairman at the University of Mississippi Medical School and a pioneer. He had published a major textbook on the complications of surgery, but more significantly he had performed the first lung transplantation and also the first heart transplant, all in the same year. However, the reputation that preceded him was one of a fire-breathing dragon in the operating room. That boy was said to have a temper. The day before his visit Dr. John informed me that he had scheduled an aortofemoral bypass for Dr. Hardy to do and he wanted me to help him. I was panicked. Although I had done a few, the thought of operating with him terrified me.

When it came time to make an incision, he told me to stand on the right side of the table, the surgeon's side. He was going to assist me. I started an incision down the midline of the patient's abdomen, but I wasn't quick enough for him. "Let me show you something." Now where had I heard that before? He took the scalpel and with one swoosh, like Zorro wielding his saber he sliced from skin all the way through to inside of the belly. There was no way whatsoever that he was not going to cut some bowel in half, but he didn't. He helped me do the rest of the case and after he helped me do one limb of the distal anastomosis, he dropped out. It had been a good experience.

The second visitor that year, although I never saw him, was Dr. DeBakey, or as Dr. John referred to him, "the old man." DeBakey's wife, Diana, had died about three years before, at the age of sixty-two, ironically of a sudden heart attack. He had just remarried—a thirty-three-year-old artist—in August.

He was in New Orleans on a visit and came to see and have lunch with Dr. John and his mentor, the senior Ochsner. We had a case that afternoon that I had started, so when Dr. John scrubbed in he couldn't stop shaking his head. "I can't believe the old man; I just can't get over it." He continued, "He's old enough to be her father, he's wearing elevator shoes and he's passing out coins with their picture on it."

What made the contrast of the "new" Dr. Michael DeBakey compared to the "old" was not only his nicknames, "Black Mike" or "the Texas Tornado," but the intensity with which he had lived and operated. Dr. John told stories from the time when he was a resident at Baylor. He had to have made rounds on every patient before DeBakey got to the hospital at 6 a.m. The patients weren't confined to one or two floors or wards. They were all over the hospital.

Dr. John had telephones installed in the stairwell at each floor level. He would see all the sicker patients and then run down each flight of stairs to the phone. A prearranged call to the floor nurse would tell him if he needed to see a particular patient or if he could just get pertinent information over the phone.

I had also heard the story how one day DeBakey and his whole entourage, were making rounds. After a patient had been presented, DeBakey turned to a senior resident and asked him the result of a very esoteric lab test. Of course the resident didn't know the answer so Black Mike fired him on the spot.

DeBakey and his first wife had been to a meeting in Hawaii. They had spent no time away from the hotel during the meeting. On the day of departure at the airport, they were told that their plane would be delayed for several hours. It was only natural for Mrs. DeBakey to suggest that they could now do some touring and see the Island. Nope, Black Mike insisted they go back to the hotel where he checked back in and went to his room to work on another paper. There was no end to DeBakey stories.

In November Noel returned from his trips and things got back to normal. Dr. John then went to a meeting in California. We had been working up a patient who needed several coronary grafts. In those days we could keep a patient in the hospital as long as we needed before surgery. Postoperatively, they might be intubated and on the ventilator for a day or two until stabilized. When to discharge them was strictly at the discretion of the surgeon with input from the cardiologists. There was no insurance "gatekeeper" telling you to get your patient out of the hospital. There also was no same-day admission for cardiac surgery--or any surgery for that matter, as there is today.

Dr. John wanted to operate on the patient the same day he got back from his trip and actually wanted him ready on the operating table when his plane landed. As we were discussing the timing of all of this I asked him when he wanted me to bring the patient to the OR. He thought for a minute and said, "Put him and the table and get started when I fly over Denton."

"Denton, Denton what?" I asked him.

"You know, Denton Cooley in Houston. Get started when I fly over Denton Cooley in Houston." He decided on an approximate time that would be appropriate and left.

When I went to schedule the case Dr. Welborn, reminded me that Dr. John was out of town. I said that I knew that, but he wanted the case ready when he walked back into the clinic. He was very skeptical hearing this from a resident and voiced his objection. I acquiesced but reminded him that if the case wasn't ready like he wanted he would have to deal with Dr. John. He consented.

Now, I never wanted anything to happen to Dr. John. He had treated me very well and it had been an incredible learning year for me. We became good friends and would play a lot of golf together in years to come, but it wouldn't have bothered me for one minute if that plane had been delayed. I wanted to do that case by myself.

The Ochsner chief cardiac resident, Nelson Ancalmo, knew the situation and had agreed to assist me if Dr. John's plane didn't get in on time. On the day he was scheduled to arrive, I had the patient brought to the OR and placed on the table. As time got closer to his time of arrival at the airport, I told them to put him to sleep. We got him prepped and draped, I harvested the saphenous vein from his leg and then helped the intern close the incision. Hmm, no Dr. John. Moving up top I made the chest incision, split his sternum, inserted the Favaloro retractor and took down his left IMA. I then prepared the mammary. Still no Dr. John. Now, I couldn't just let him sit there, so we had anesthesia heparinize him and cannulated, ready to go on bypass. No, JO. I was preparing to take the venous cannula clamps off and go on pump, when a voice from over my shoulder said, "You ready yet?" I looked around and he was leaning against the OR door, dressed in scrubs, drinking a cup of coffee. You gotta love it.

Years later when Dr. John was elected to be president of the American Association of Thoracic Surgeons, I received a call from one of his friends and members of that elite organization who had to introduce him. He knew of my association with Dr. John and wanted me to share some stories with him. The story about the floor mat and Denton Cooley were just two I had to relate to him.

As the end of calendar year 1975 and my stay at the Ochsner Clinic grew to an end, I reflected on how eventful the year had been. A young giant of a surgeon, with whom I really had limited direct exposure in the operating room, had been taken suddenly from us. Drapanas had instilled in me techniques, knowledge and an attitude of the right way to do things that would stay with me forever.

Dr. John Ochsner, on the other hand, was fueled with the fact that not only was he local, but he was "surgical royalty" in New Orleans. It seemed that he took more of a personal interest in me.

Before I left OFH, after making rounds one day, he took me aside and we sat down. He asked me what my plans were down the line. He implied that they were looking for another surgeon, but also mentioned that he didn't think Noel was ready for a third person. At the time I wasn't really sure what he was getting at. He told me to stay in touch, but he also strongly insisted that if I ever needed him he would be available for me.

As a resident being mainly interested in my own little world, I wasn't fully able then to understand the dynamics at play. He knew things were unsettled at the medical school and there would be a leadership problem. I think he really wanted to be involved with the school in a serious way. During his training he had two giants in the surgery field leading way for him, his father and DeBakey. He had accomplished everything his father had, and more. Was the position as chairman of the Surgery Department at Tulane one of his unfinished goals?

Later a quote was attributed to him that read "Surgery is an art as much as a science—-you have to improvise almost every case—no two cases are the same—it's like opening up a package; it's always a little different."

Mary Jane Ray

Alton Ochsner was the driving force of the clinic. As his reputation was growing, a young girl had been born in Jackson, Mississippi whom he would soon meet. For the first four years of her life she had been labeled as a "failure to thrive". She was from a well-respected family and her father was a successful attorney. Her parent's Mayo-trained physician referred her to Rochester, Minnesota where the diagnosis of patent ductus arteriosus was made.

Her mother, Mary, researched the condition as if she was studying for her boards. She read and scanned all the American and European literature available and knew Mary Jane needed the surgery. A close family friend and noted author knew of Alton Ochsner's reputation. "Why don't you go see him," he advised, "it'll be close to home." They met with Ochsner on more than one occasion and even at her young age Mary Jane remembers Ochsner speaking "to her" and not "about her," how personable he was.

On her last visit before the surgery he asked her if she wanted him to get her anything. "I'd like a chocolate pie," came from the mouth of the little red-headed charmer. "I promise you will have a chocolate pie," Ochsner told Mary Jane Ray.

On August 20, 1947 Alton Ochsner assisted by Michael DeBakey, who soon would be leaving to head the surgery department at Baylor Medical School, operated on the young girl. Before she left her Jackson home she had been showered with gifts for fear she would not survive and they would never see her again.

Growing up in New Orleans in the shadow of Tulane, Charity and the Ochsner Clinic with a father who not only had trained at Tulane but knew Alton Ochsner, personally, I had heard the events of the operation. I had actually met Alton Ochsner while accompanying my father on rounds at Hotel Dieu Hospital. The story had been told and retold about how DeBakey had put his finger through Mary Jane's aorta. "Don't move a muscle," Ochsner told him. Whereupon Ochsner placed a purse-string suture around DeBakey's finger allowing the young DeBakey to withdraw his finger without significant hemorrhage.

Years passed and I would spend a whole year in training at the clinic that bore his name. I would meet him again on a couple of occasions while making rounds with his son, John.

In 1980 we moved to Shreveport to practice. Being new people in town we were invited to a couple's house one night for a dinner party at a beautiful, landscaped home in one of Shreveport's finest areas. The husband was an ophthalmologist and his attractive Southern belle red-headed wife was from Jackson, Mississippi. "I hear you are a cardiovascular surgeon," were her introductory remarks. "Where did you train?" After I told her, she came out with it,

"I had heart surgery by Drs. DeBakey and Ochsner when I was a little girl." Things hadn't clicked yet because I actually didn't know the actual patient's history, but I did know that heart surgery wasn't being performed when she was a child. I persisted, "Where's your scar?" "It's around my left side and my mother had always told me that something special had happened during the operation and I could have died."

It had taken thirty-three years and I was talking with living history. She was indeed the same patient. My meeting Mary Jane had made up for me not talking with or questioning Alton Ochsner.

MARY JANE RAY—Lovely lit[tle] daughter of Mr. and Mrs. Bob R[ay,] 380 Iroquois Street, has recently [re]turned from a New Orleans hospit[al] where she underwent an operati[on] for a serious heart ailment. She [is] completely recovered and is n[ow] able to welcome friends at the ho[me] of her parents. Mary Jane, who h[as] been ill all of the four and one-h[alf] years of her life, is beaming w[ith] pleasure over her restoration [to] health.

Mary Jane Ray.

Mary Jane had formed a company where she would design and artists would paint and decorate pediatric wards of hospitals. In 1978 she actually had a job at the Ochsner Foundation hospital where upon she met and reintroduced herself to her hero, Dr. Alton Ochsner.

Cardiothoracic Surgery Service – Charity

In January 1976 I went back to Charity armed with eighteen months of cardiac surgery experience. I had a new confidence in my ability with a desire and need to do what I had been trained to do for the past year, coronary bypass surgery. Two more very significant things had happened in 1975, besides Drapanas' death, that would distinctly affect my training. Dr. George Burch, Musser Professor and chairman of the Tulane Department of Medicine had retired and Dr. Bob Hewitt had left the school to go in private practice in New Orleans.

Burch had been chairman of the Department of Medicine at Tulane since 1947, twenty-eight years. A noninvasive cardiologist, he was noted for his research in heart disease and measuring central venous pressure as an indicator of heart failure. His main interest was in electrocardiography and his published books on EKG were textbooks we used in the classes he taught us as medical students. His *Primer of Electrocardiography* had been printed in nine languages. He was the first to create a section of infectious diseases at Tulane.

As a student, I heard him quite often say that medical students shouldn't have summer jobs working at hospitals, they should sit under a tree and read a book. Even though tuition in those days was low, not all medical students could afford to do that. Despite his interest and knowledge in diseases of the heart, he was not a proponent of surgical correction.

When I was a medical student, Dr. Burch had held a weekly conference in the second-floor auditorium at Charity. He would have patients presented with various medical conditions. One of the more common medical conditions seen in the young female population at Charity was lupus. His conclusion as to what caused this condition was not an autoimmune disease, but the widespread use of Massengill douche powder. Every woman who was presented to him that had lupus used it.

Another favorite exercise was to have a patient with valvular cardiac disease presented to his Saturday morning lecture. Quite often, and I saw and heard it happen, he would take a preop heart valve patient from the surgical wards and discuss the case. He would describe the murmur, review the various EKG changes, and take the patient's history. At the conclusion of this he would ask the patient what they were doing in the hospital. The answer would be "Sir, they gonna do a heart operation on me." Burch's usual response to this was to tell the patient that if she let them operate on her she was going to die.

It was not uncommon for us to come to a ward the morning of surgery and find that our patient had deserted. There is no question that the patients we operated on were usually Class III or IV. They were all in congestive heart failure with end stage disease and consequently, their mortality was high. However, what Burch was doing, and this was well known, was to take the less critical cardiac patients and send those to Dr. John Kirklin at the University of Alabama.

Burch touted Dr. Kirkland often saying how good a surgeon he was and what good results he had. Kirklin definitely was a leader and pioneer in cardiac surgery, and an excellent surgeon. However, by sending the lower risk patients away Burch did nothing to enhance the development of cardiac surgery at Tulane and in New Orleans.

Burch's students from the class of 1974 had subsequently published a little four-and-a-half-inch square red covered book titled "*Quotations of Chairman George.*" Does that ring a bell similar to a publication of a noted Chinese dictator? Some of Burch's quotes published in the book were:

> "Cardiac cath—you know, I gotta laugh. I could have told you she had left ventricle failure. She didn't need a cardiac cath, she needed a doctor";

> "If the country threw away transplantation and dialysis and studied urinalysis, it would be a helluva lot better off"; and

> "I'm not anti-surgery, I'm just pro-patient."

I did not miss Dr. George Burch's presence. He had outstayed his welcome and his ideas and teachings had not kept up with the times.

However, I would miss Hewitt's departure. His move into private practice and off of the full time staff left the Tulane Surgery Department without a full-time cardiothoracic surgeon. I was determined not to be deterred. Dr. John had offered and I planned to take him up on his offer to come and help me at Charity.

When I came back I had a meeting with all the third-year and first-year residents. I asked them to take careful histories on any patient they saw in clinic or they had on their ward with a nonlife-threatening disease, especially the patients with vascular disease. Review what medications they were taking and if any of them were taking nitroglycerine for angina, I wanted to see and examine them.

The first patient they found was CH, a sixty-two-year-old female with angina. I consulted a cardiology resident I knew who had progressive thinking. I asked him to do a coronary catheterization on her. Burch's successor, Dr. John Phillips, was more progressive in his thinking and did not discourage his residents from doing cardiac caths.

After the study was done I called Dr. John and asked if he would review the cineangiograms with me. He agreed and I made the drive down Jefferson Highway. He advised me to not do anything fancy, do the two vein grafts and get out. "She'll be fine," he said. On January 27, 1976 I performed the first reversed saphenous vein aortocornary bypass graft on the Tulane Surgery Service at Charity Hospital. The patient did especially well.

I listed that case on the weekly Bugle and was asked to discuss it at D&C conference. It was a straightforward case with good results, but the response was muted. I was approached by Dr. Bill Collins.

Collins was a non-cardiac thoracic surgeon who Dr. Drapanas had hired to staff residents at one of the in-town private hospitals. The rotation to the private hospital was not beneficial. The rotation was discontinued and he was back on the full-time staff at Tulane.

He told me that he wanted to help me do the cardiac cases. The situation was a sticky wicket. I mentioned to him that Dr. Ochsner had volunteered his help. "We don't need him over here," was his reply.

It was obvious that Collins was threatened at the possibility of John Ochsner coming to Tulane. He had actually been hired by Drapanas for a job that no longer existed. Although he finished his military career in a senior position, he was mainly an administrator, not a practicing surgeon. If Dr. John were to develop a persistent and reliable presence on the Tulane staff, would Collins even be needed?

And then one must consider the other side of the dynamic. Did Dr. John want to further follow in his father's footsteps and be chairman of the Tulane Surgery Department? Without a doubt, he was the leading cardiac surgeon in the state. He had the whole Ochsner Foundation Hospital behind him. Hell, his name was on the building! But did he want more? Also, it's possible he just wanted to be wanted, for Tulane to ask him.

When Ted Drapanas was being recruited as the new Henderson Professor and Tulane Surgery department chairman, I was told that a meeting with the senior and still ever-present Dr. Alton Ochsner, was part of the interview process. Had some deal been struck? At that time Dr. Charles Pearce was the senior, cardiac surgeon on the Tulane staff. Bob Hewitt had just returned from military duty in Vietnam. Pierce had bridged the gap from the outdated intramyocardial Vineberg procedure to the gold standard direct coronary revascularization procedure and developed a very successful private practice in New Orleans.

Drapanas gave Pierce a choice: academics or private practice, "town or gown?" His choice was to leave. A few years hence three different Tulane- and Charity-trained cardiac surgeons would join Pearce's team and become the leading cardiac team in Orleans Parish. There was an obvious void at the school.

In March, our residents found another patient. This was a forty-year-old female (LF) who needed a triple bypass. I was emboldened by my first success and wanted to implant an internal mammary artery (IMA) in her. The problem was that Charity did not have a Favaloro retractor.

This was a special device that was clamped to the left side of the table after the chest was opened. Two rake-like arms were then placed under the left sternal edge, attached to the support and the left hemisternum was then lifted to allow exposure underneath the rib cage. The internal mammary arteries were imbedded in tissue on either side of the sternum. This vessel arose as a branch off of the subclavian artery and had branches that supplied each rib and the muscles between each rib.

Although it carried a lot of blood, it was an auxiliary artery and removing it would not be consequential to the patient. The area it supplied had a dual blood supply.

Dr. Akio Kitahama was my third-year resident at that time. Akio had been a fully trained general surgeon in Japan. He was working at the Japanese National Cancer Center in Tokyo as a member of the liver cancer team. Dr. Drapanas had been an invited guest speaker to the Japanese Cancer Society and they met through the president of the Society. Akio, like his Japanese predecessor Tomoo, also wished to be able to write FACS after his name. He was an excellent surgeon and resident.

As I discussed my plans with Akio he said he would hold the sternum with two ordinary rake retractors. I cautioned him about the task he was volunteering for, but he was determined.

On March 23, we did the first internal mammary artery graft to a left descending artery ever done at Charity on the Tulane or LSU service. Our successes were being recognized by the cardiologists because in April our service was consulted by the medicine service to see a thirty-one-year-old male on one of the medicine wards. We had not only opened the door to coronary bypass surgery but had actually busted it down.

Cardiology had consulted us to do coronary bypass surgery on one of their patients. The fact that this patient was an inmate at the Orleans Parish Prison and was handcuffed to the bed did not deter us. We did his double bypass operation on April 6, 1976. These patients had done well. The cardiologists were being better prepared for their eventual trip into the outside world of private practice, we were doing cardiac cases and the anesthesiology residents were getting to do hearts. Life was good.

I had to be selective about who I would let put the cardiac patients asleep. Mohammed Naraji was a very capable Adriani-trained chief anesthesia resident and would later become head of the department. We had a good relationship, and whenever possible I tried to get him to do the cardiac cases.

One interesting case was a man (JS) we took care of with an empyema. I had done a thoracotomy and decortication on him in May. It was customary to see him in clinic postoperatively for a couple of visits just to make sure he healed appropriately. On his last visit, I told him he was discharged and didn't need to come back.

He said, "Doc, you mind if I ask you about a problem I have?"

"Of course not, what's bothering you?"

"Well, when I exercise," he said (holding his fist over his chest) "I get this pain in my chest, that feels like an elephant is sitting on it."

I couldn't believe it. He was describing classical angina pectoris right out of Major and Delp's book on physical diagnosis. I admitted him and asked the cardiologists to work him up. He had triple vessel coronary disease. I did a quadruple bypass on him, including another IMA.

During that six-month period we did a total of six coronary revascularizations. We had set a new standard for coronary surgery at Charity. The cardiology fellows were doing procedures and getting experience in things they needed to be able to do when they went into private practice and we were doing successful heart procedures.

That spring, Bob Hewitt, who was still seeing patients in the Crippled Children's Clinic, informed me about a thirteen-year-old boy (EM) with a huge ASD that we needed to operate on. It sounded fairly straightforward, but it wasn't. When younger, he had a serious lung infection and a tracheostomy had been performed. It had become a permanent tracheostomy with a mature stoma. In effect what he had was a hole just above his sternal notch that connected directly to his trachea. If he put his finger over the hole he could talk and even breathe through his mouth.

Dr. Burch had seen him in clinic at some earlier point and even though EM had a huge ASD, he said it was too dangerous for him to have his heart fixed and it would kill him. His weight was that of a six-year-old, but otherwise he was a nice kid with no other problems.

The tracheostomy stoma posed somewhat of an access problem with an increased risk of infection. We had the anesthesiologist intubate him directly through the stoma. We prepped everything including the endo-tube, but when we draped the operative field, we used a "steri-drape" that was adhesive on one side, with the bottom edge of the steri-drape stuck just above his sternal notch. A normal, but lower, skin incision was made and the rest of the operation was straightforward.

That summer and several months after we had operated on him, I saw Bob. He had seen the young man in clinic and said that not only was he doing well, but his tracheostomy had been allowed to close and he had gained about twenty pounds. It wouldn't be the last time I saw EM.

During my first six months on the cardiac service we had several occasions to do valve replacements. In 1971, a new valve, the Bjork-Shiley (B-S) valve had been produced. This valve was a tilting disc valve. A flat disc floated between wire struts, which allowed the disc to tilt open to almost ninety degrees. It was made of a substance called Delrin.

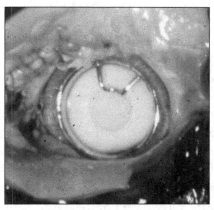

Heart specimen with Bjork-Shiley Delrin aortic valve, 1974.

The disc valve was trying to replace what had been the standard until that time, the Starr-Edwards (S-E) ball valve.

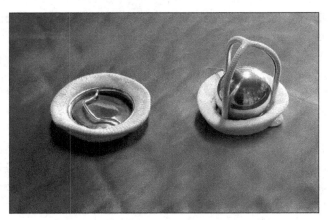

Bjork-Shiley and Starr-Edwards heart valves, 1975.

The S-E valve had a ball in a modified cage of steel that allowed the ball to go up and down depending on the pumping of the heart. Blood would come through the opening and then go out around the ball. The ball valve was a very hemolytic valve and a very thrombogenic valve, it caused clots to form.

Over time the S-E valve had undergone many modifications from the composition of the ball to the composition of the struts. Initially the struts were bare; clots formed. Then the struts were covered with a thin woven Dacron material; the material disintegrated and embolized. Then the covered struts had an inner "track" inserted on them which gave some protection to the covering. No matter how the valve was constructed clots still formed and required the patient to be on a strong blood thinner, forever.

One other hemodynamic drawback of the S-E valve was the outflow area, the amount of blood it let go through the opening. In a patient with a small aorta, no matter how big the valve orifice was, the effective opening was only the area around the ball when it was at the top of the cage. Although the disc valve was slightly better when it came to thrombogenicity, the patient still required a blood thinner. The main advantage of the B-S valve was that the outflow was much better and offered less resistance.

None of these early valves were perfect and many modifications were made to the disc over time. The decision to use a mechanical versus a tissue valve was based on several factors, the main one being the compliance of the patient. Could he or she be relied on to take the blood thinners? If the reliability of the patient was in doubt, a tissue valve (the pig valve) would have to be used. This valve was constructed of several components from different pigs to make one valve. In actuality it looked just like a human valve and with the exception of the first six weeks, did not require long term blood thinners. The problem was that it had a finite life span and would have to be replaced.

Simply put, as I would hear Dr. Dwight McGoon later tell patients, "Mechanical valves are thrombogenic, and nonthrombogenic valves aren't durable."

NTL (Tan) was a twenty-eight-year-old Vietnamese male who was sent to us by the medicine service with severe mitral valve disease. He was one of the first cases I had done after returning to Charity from Ochsner. By the looks of his valve, he had rheumatic fever as the etiology of his mitral insufficiency. We replaced his valve with a Hancock valve. This was one of the first pig valves that had been developed. The operation went very well and he was discharged without complication.

Two to three months later I was approached by one of the medicine residents who had been involved with Tan's case. He told me Tan was back in the hospital with endocarditis, a serious infection probably of the valve. He told me that he had been having chills and fever and that although the results of his blood cultures had not returned yet, he was sure of the diagnosis. I felt very bad about the news, but somehow, inside of me, I didn't think that he was infected.

I went to see him on the medical ward. He did not have a murmur and he really didn't look sick. In reviewing his chart and his temperature graph, I noticed that he spiked a high temperature every afternoon about the same time.

I reflected back to when I was an undergraduate student, and was a zoology major, I was fortunate to do several extra credit projects under Dr. Andrew Arata. Arata was from New Orleans; he was a mammalogist and a great guy to work under. His specialty was bats. He had since left Tulane and taken a position with the World Health Organization doing research in Africa.

I happened to be in the student lounge one day when he walked in. As we sat over a cup of coffee, he told me he had not been feeling well and came back to New Orleans to see my father, who happened to be his personal physician. With Arata's history of working in Africa, the first thing my father did was to order a blood test for malaria. It turned out to be positive.

Knowing that Tan was from Southeast Asia, I ordered a malarial blood test on him. Later I received an excited call from the medical resident telling me that, indeed, Tan had malaria. Sometimes it's better to look for zebras rather than donkeys.

The remaining six months of my formal thoracic residency was filled with a myriad of cases that I would see later in private practice. There were more lobectomies and pneumonectomies, chest wall resections for malignancies, drainage of empyemas as well as lung decortications for the complications of empyemas.

The congenital heart cases were abundant also: coarctation of the aorta, operations for pulmonary stenosis, closure of septal defects and pulmonary artery bandings for neonates with too much blood flow to the lungs. There is no telling what other conditions we could have found if we'd had a CAT scan or MRI available to us then.

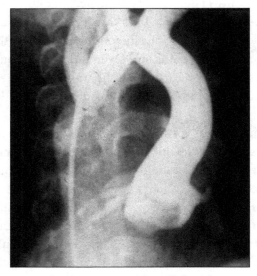

Angiogram: coarctation of the aorta.

Our team still did many diagnostic bronchoscopies and esophagoscopies. Pacemaker placement was not recommended as much as it is today because of the lack of twenty-four-hour outpatient monitoring capabilities. It was not until the late eighties into the nineties that the cardiologists took over pacemaker implantation and cardiologists specializing in electrophysiology emerged. I needed these cases in order to be able to sit for my thoracic boards. More important, I needed to be proficient at them.

The lack of diagnostic modalities was brought home with one special case. A sixty-four-year-old lady (MD) was diagnosed with a posterior lung mass on her chest X-ray. Her physician had found it as an incidental finding as the mass was asymptomatic. We ordered tomograms on her, but they didn't help us that much other than tell us that the mass was in the posterior portion of her left lung.

At operation I explored her with Akio hoping that she would be a candidate for a lung resection. To our surprise we found a descending aortic aneurysm. The aneurysm was stable and showed no sign of leakage, but it was large enough that it had to be resected. We were not prepared to do a graft interposition at that time so we closed her up.

I discussed fully with the patient and her family what we found and what was involved in resecting her aneurysm. Basically the technique is the same one that we used to treat an abdominal aneurysm. The technique was originally proposed by DeBakey and later described by Dr. Creech. However, the main difference is that the surgeon is clamping the aorta very high up in the chest, thus stopping the blood flow to all the organs in the abdomen, most important of which are the kidneys. The other critical fact is that the blood flow to the spine can be interrupted leaving the patient with paralysis secondary to ischemia (lack of oxygenated blood) to the spinal cord.

There are three ways to do these: clamp the aorta, open up the aneurysm, sew in the graft rapidly, with no distal protection and pray; second, one can perfuse the patient through the groin using the heart lung machine. This affords good blood supply to the kidneys and lower portion of the body. We would have had to schedule this with the heart lung pump and find staff to help us. The third option is to use a Gott shunt. We had used these when I was at Ochsner with good success.

This shunt was a long plastic tube about an inch in diameter that was tapered on either end. The upper end of the shunt is placed through a small incision into the aorta or subclavian artery on the heart side of the upper clamp. The other tapered end is placed into the descending aorta below the clamp. The other advantage of the Gott shunt is that the inner wall of it is coated with heparin, a powerful anticoagulant. A large dose of heparin then does not have to be given systemically, thus lowering the incidence of postoperative bleeding.

Our patient had excellent anatomy distal to the aneurysm which allowed us to be able to use the aorta in her chest rather than use the femoral artery in her groin for the distal insertion. Mark Kappleman had returned from his cardiothoracic rotation at Ochsner and was now chief resident in General Surgery. I discussed the case with Mark and he volunteered to help. The operation went very well. The hooker to the whole procedure had to do with what we found when we put her to sleep.

While she was flat on her back and before we turned her on her side, we could see a pulsatile mass in her abdomen. She had an abdominal aortic aneurysm also. To repair the abdominal aneurysm first would have placed a marked increase in pressure in the walls of her thoracic aneurysm. We had to do her chest first, let her get over that operation and then bring her back for the abdominal procedure.

Postoperatively, although she did well, she was very slow to walk. This wasn't from a neurological standpoint. She was overweight and had led a very sedentary life. She knew she needed another operation.

Thoracic incisions were and still are painful. Two more things we didn't have then were aggressive physical therapists to walk and exercise your patients. It was all up to the interns and medical students. Physical therapy for routine postoperative patients didn't exist. The other thing which would have been a big help was the use of a thoracic nerve block with an indwelling catheter. These became popular in the early Nineties and made a huge difference in the postoperative pain incurred by thoracotomy patients.

After a couple of weeks in the hospital, Mary was still not ready for the next procedure. She wanted to go home. I agreed to let her go realizing that being around her family and home surroundings would do her more good than harm. I let her go on one condition. I would give her a week and when I had an open bed I would call her, she would be readmitted and have the abdominal aneurysm resected. She fully agreed and understood the risks of not treating her aneurysm at all.

One night about a week later, when I was on call, a bed came open. I called her, but she told me she was babysitting her grandchildren and she couldn't come in until morning. I told her I would have an intern meet her in the admit room at 10 a.m. She failed to show the next morning. When I called her house, her daughter sadly told me that she had died that night. I was too late.

I thought this case over and over in my mind as to what I should have done differently. If I had forced her to stay in the hospital, I don't think she would have agreed to proceed. To have done simultaneous procedures on this lady would have been more than I think she could have withstood. With the pain from a thoracic as well as abdominal incision she might never have recovered. Perhaps this is one of the few instances of "patient error." The disease won. As a surgeon you cannot force a patient to have an operation. You can suggest, strongly recommend, and present the pros and cons to the best of your knowledge and experience. It was a difficult lesson learned.

Even when I was in the private practice, knowing the risk of someone not having a bypass operation for serious triple vessel disease or left main disease, I could not tell them "they had to." Yes, I did have one or two patients refuse to have same stay surgery and "have to" go home after their cardiac catheterizations. Some died before their scheduled readmission. We don't always have the ultimate plan or answer for everyone.

Diagnostic Scopes

Bronchoscopies, esophagoscopies and mediastinoscopies are a group of procedures that are mainly diagnostic. The mediastinoscopy is the only one of these that is an operation.

Done under general anesthesia, it involves a small transverse incision just above the sternal notch. The surgeons index finger is used to develop the space in front of the trachea, behind the nominate artery and between the lungs, the mediastinum. A metal scope is then inserted once any lymph nodes are palpated and a direct biopsy can be performed.

In my day, this modality was extensively used to diagnose lung cancer, stage it and diagnose various infectious diseases of the chest. An infection in this area is rare because it can only be accessed by surgery, but when it occurs, it is disastrous and potentially deadly.

I was doing a mediastinoscopy one day in the "heart room." The patient was thought to have sarcoidosis, but a biopsy was needed to rule out other diseases. We had finished the biopsy and sent the specimen to the lab. I had just finished a row of subcutaneous stitches when the head circulating nurse for the Delgado operating theater came into my room. She wasn't there to tell me what a great job I was doing.

In her hand she held a large paper disc that was basically a circular graph. The graph was an automatic recording performed by the autoclave when any instrument or instruments placed in it had been sterilized. This procedure assures that instruments are, not only sterile, but that no disease is transmitted from one patient to the next by any surgical instruments.

Operating room nurses can be tough. Their emotions are left at home because they can't let them interfere with their job. They are invaluable and over the years I was very fortunate to work with some of the best at several great medical centers. In order to become an OR supervisor you have to earn your job and this one hadn't started yesterday. She was upset.

"Dr. Ciaravella, your instruments aren't sterile."

Boom! *Why don't you just blow up the room,* I thought.

"What do you mean the instruments aren't sterile?"

"The graph shows that proper temperature was never reached, the autoclave didn't work," she replied. Now, these things aren't in the book, any book. It doesn't happen or isn't supposed to.

There's a moment in time when you're sort of frozen and not sure what to do. First, I took a culture from the used scope and sent it to the lab. That wasn't an immediate solution but might help me later. Then, using a second scope, this time sterile, I decided to reopen the wound and irrigate the area with copious amounts of antibiotic solution.

We had the anesthesiologist start an intravenous prophylactic antibiotic drip. Before closing I inserted a small rubber Penrose drain as deep into the chest as my finger and the scope had explored. I then loosely closed the wound. If he was going to get an infection, I wanted to know it as soon as possible.

The next day there was a small amount of cloudy drainage from the drain site. We cultured it again and he was treated appropriately. Although his hospital stay was a little protracted, we had avoided a major catastrophe.

"I've Got a Tumor in My Heart"

During that spring one of the most interesting cases a cardiac surgeon can do was brought to us, a left atrial myxoma. This benign tumor of the heart grows from the wall between the two small pumping chambers (the atria) into the left atrium. It usually hangs from a stalk and is called pedunculated. Quite often they can break off pieces. They then present as an embolus to an extremity or possibly the brain. The surgery involves opening the right atrium, cutting out that part of the septum containing the tumor and closing the hole with a patch.

One of the most famous stories about an atrial myxoma concerned one that had been sent to Dr. Creech by the chief surgeon at the Public Health Hospital on State Street. The patient had a large pedunculated atrial myxoma that, when the patient was sitting up, would occlude the outflow of blood through the mitral valve and cause the patient to pass out. Dr. Creech was cautioned and appraised of the situation. He passed on the information to his chief resident. The resident made the admitting room personnel aware to call him as soon as the patient arrived.

Unfortunately, when the patient did arrive, the resident was scrubbed on an emergency surgery that lasted a long time. Things got busy in the West Admit area to the point that there was not enough room for all the stretchers. During evening shift change the new medical resident in charge told his nurses to put any patient that was on a stretcher into a wheel chair, thus allowing more patients to occupy the same space. When they arrived at the myxoma patient they were met with a great deal of resistance, so much so that he began repeatedly screaming, "I've got a tumor in my heart." What then followed was a consult to psychiatry. The psych resident naturally admitted him to the third floor, as you can guess, against his will.

Later that evening when the chief resident came back to find his patient, he was able to successfully retrieve him.

Although the year was coming to an end we were staying busy. As a final send off two cases presented themselves that we had to do. The first was a two-month-old infant with a myriad of problems. She had a large VSD (hole between the two major pumping chambers), a severe long segment coarctation of the aorta and a PDA. She wasn't thriving and definitely wasn't going to live if we didn't do something. Ideally we would have liked to correct everything at one operation. To patch her VSD required her to be on the heart-lung bypass and at her age and weight she probably would have needed profound hypothermia and circulatory arrest, a technique I would not do until later. Although the VSD and the PDA could be closed at the same sitting, not addressing the coarctation would make the whole procedure fruitless. It was decided to attack everything from the left chest. We would close her PDA, band her pulmonary artery, thus restricting the amount of high pressure blood going to her lungs, and sew in a long patch to relieve the coarctation. Despite our good intentions and technically a good operation she did not survive.

We had hoped that by palliating her, it would give her heart time to rest and her body to grow before attempting the next stage of the procedure. Perhaps this was one of those shoulda, woulda, coulda moments. It is always easy to second guess yourself.

Within two days of the infant's surgery we did a "blue plate special" on a forty-four-year-old female. Surgeons use this term anytime you "fix" several heart conditions at one sitting. In reality, the two month old was a mini blue plate special. Ida needed an aortic valve replacement and a double aortocoronary bypass. For lagniappe she also had an ascending aortic aneurysm that needed repairing. It's a big operation and definitely one where all the problems have to be corrected at once. The biggest factor in her favor was that the formula and the technique for the administration of the cardioplegia had definitely been improved. The operation went well and I could now move on to my chief and final year as a resident.

I had just done two very major operations for completely different reasons on two different very sick patients. The child had died and the adult had lived. The adult was actually relatively young for the amount of disease she had. The child had three different conditions, each separately could have been curable, probably not needing further surgery. If you start thinking about these things it can really get to you. Obviously, if some technical error is made by you or any of the team you know where the blame lies. But when things are done exactly as planned a death is hard to accept and understand. Some things are meant to be and are completely out of your control.

"Doctor, It's a Miracle"

New Orleans is a very religious city. The Catholic population, percentage wise, could possibly rival the Vatican. Many incredible things happened at Charity, especially the good things. Patients with stab wounds to the heart that were sewn up and walked out of the hospital, or with multiple GSW's to everything that shouldn't have made it, but did. There were patients with complication after complication who stayed in the hospital for months and still survived.

We often heard the term "miracle." I'm not trying to be skeptical. I am not a disbeliever; just possibly I don't remember seeing any. More likely every patient I saw was a miracle.

When Gary Dotson was a senior resident, one busy Saturday night a young child was brought into the ER after being a passenger in a serious car accident. The child was bleeding internally to the point that it needed emergency surgery. Gary explained the situation to the family and was told that because of religious convictions, the child could not be given any blood.

If you are a surgeon and have an active practice the odds are that at some point you will have to deal with the "don't give him any blood" scenario. I was in similar situations as a resident and would be in another one later in my career when a child needed emergency cardiac surgery. When time permits, the surgeon contacts the hospital attorney who in turn gets a court order from a judge and the administration of blood is left to the discretion of the surgeon.

Gary did not have the luxury of time late on a Saturday night. As fate would have it, the child had a ruptured spleen with massive intraabdominal bleeding. Gary administered the needed blood and undoubtedly saved the child's life. When he left the OR to go talk with the family, he was confronted by the whole congregation. He gave them the good news about the child coming through the surgery. No one asked him if he had given the child blood and he didn't volunteer any unasked information. A "miracle" was born.

Every resident does remember their first gallbladder. I certainly remember the one "Buck" Rogers helped me do at Lallie Kemp. Butch Knoepp definitely remembers his first.

It was at the end of Butch's first year of residency at Big Charity. His third-year resident was going off to be chief at Lallie Kemp and was going to help him do the case. At operation, after making the incision, Butch's chief explained that with any elective abdominal operation, when feasible, it was standard practice to explore the abdomen to determine if there was any additional pathology.

From the assistant's side of the table, through the right subcostal incision, the third-year reached his gloved hand in the belly and systematically explored-- "normal spleen, liver's okay, stomach, bowel—wait a minute, she has an aneurysm. Butch, look, you're going to do the gallbladder and postop you explain to her what she has and that she's definitely going to need to get it fixed. Have her call you and you present the case to your next chief and he'll be very appreciative," was the third-year's direction.

The case proceeded as scheduled and the patient did well. During her recovery period Butch explained the finding of the aortic aneurysm, the risks associated with not fixing it and the plan over the next couple of months. The patient was grateful.

Sure enough, sometimes around August of that year, the patient was re-admitted and Gary Dotson, Butch's new chief was told about the case. The case was scheduled with Dr. John McDonald as staff, Gary as the surgeon and Butch assisting. Upon opening the patient, this time through a proper midline incision, no aneurysm was found, nada, zilch.

Again, post-op the duty fell on Butch to explain to L.D. the patient, that her aneurysm was gone. Now, in today's litigious society, the first thing that a surgeon might have done is call the hospital attorney and your malpractice carrier. Not with this patient, "Doctor, it's a miracle! I've been praying to Father Seelos for a miracle and he's answered my prayers."

Father Francis Xavier Seelos was one of twelve children born to his parents in the Kingdom of Bavaria in January 1819. In his early twenties, following his time in the seminary, he asked to be transferred to the United States to care for the German immigrants.

In 1866 he was assigned as pastor of the Church of St. Mary of the Assumption in New Orleans. Seelos spoke fluent English, French and German and heard the confession of whites and blacks alike in all three languages. Unfortunately, after less than a year in New Orleans at age forty-eight, he succumbed to yellow fever, the disease that ravaged so many of the parishioners that he cared for.

At that time and until today in New Orleans, the Church of the Assumption houses the National Shrine of Blessed Father Xavier Francis Seelos.

Butch accepted her comment and belief of the "miracle," but mainly was quite relieved that the patient wasn't irate about the unnecessary operation she had just undergone. Time went by. Butch became chief resident at Huey Long Hospital in his hometown of Alexandria and the story was largely forgotten.

One day, the hospital operator paged Butch: "Dr. Knoepp, there's a man here with some papers for you," she said. Butch accepted the envelope adorned with the Papal seal from the Vatican. In it were papers for him to fill out documenting that this would, indeed, be Father Xavier Seelos' third documented miracle which would lead to his sainthood.

This time Butch declined to be involved and forwarded the papers on to his former third-year resident who had started this ball rolling in the first place.

On April 9, 2000 in St. Peter's Square, Pope John Paul II beatified Father Seelos, known as the "cheerful ascetic," making him one step away from sainthood. That is the rest of the story, believe what you will.

Lagniappe – Dr. Rowena Spencer, 1922–2014

John Sanders, T4, got on the elevator at Touro infirmary one afternoon in 1967 to go work up his new medicine patient. A little lady, grayish hair pinned in a bun on the back of her head, got on behind him. Not visible in the bag she was carrying was a container full of powdered Ivory Snow soap. Stuffed in John's brown three-quarter-length lab coat bearing the Tulane Medical School patch was a glossy paper-bound blue spiral reference book.

"What's that Goddamned little blue book in your pocket?" she asked, as if he was taking his oral exam for the medicine boards.

"It's called *Medical Therapeutics,* Dr. Spencer," John replied.

"Humph!" She retorted. "I guess it replaces that Goddamned little black book."

That would have been a mild introduction to any of us on a first encounter with Dr. Rowena Spencer.

Rowena Spencer was born in 1922 and raised on a plantation outside of Utility, Louisiana, in Catahoula Parish.

Dr. Rowena Spencer.

Approximately 200 miles north of New Orleans, this now defunct town carried a population of about eight. When one examines the many "firsts" that Rowena achieved, it is not surprising when her family history is examined. Her father was one of Louisiana's first orthopedic surgeons. Not only that, but the women who had come before her, in her family had very progressive ideas with regard to business, higher education, and medical careers.

Her great uncle Judge William Brainerd sired two daughters. Both received doctoral degrees and both taught at Sophie Newcomb College in New Orleans. Another female leader in her family was her great aunt, Sara Tew Mayo, who also had received a medical degree and returned to New Orleans to help establish what would later become the Sara Mayo Hospital.

Earning money as a babysitter helped Spencer pay her way to an undergraduate education at Louisiana State University in Baton Rouge, the state's first coeducational college.

Perhaps the most outstanding medical school in mid-1943 with regard to innovative pediatric surgery was Johns Hopkins University.

Dr. Alfred Blalock, working with his assistant Vivian Thomas, had been trying to perfect a laboratory model to study congestive heart failure. Using the right subclavian artery, they created a connection to the right pulmonary artery to increase pulmonary blood flow in attempt to create pulmonary overload and pulmonary hypertension. Also in that era, Dr. Helen B. Taussig, pediatric cardiologist at Johns Hopkins, had a profound interest in congenital malformations of the heart. These "hopeless" cases to Taussig were a "jigsaw puzzle."

Hearing of Blalock's laboratory experiments that increased pulmonary blood flow, Taussig approached Blalock. The results of this association would change "blue baby" surgery for ever. Vivian Thomas created many of the instruments that Blalock used and Thomas himself actually performed the shunts on laboratory animals.

On November 29, 1944, Dr. Blalock, assisted by Dr. William Longmire and Dr. Denton Cooley, with Vivian Thomas looking over Blalock's right shoulder, and Helen Taussig also a witness, performed the first subclavian to pulmonary artery shunt in a live patient. This operation would forever be known as the Blalock-Taussig shunt.

Rowena Spencer was one of four female medical students at Johns Hopkins during this period. During her four years as a medical student and her fifth year as Johns Hopkins' first female intern, she would befriend Vivian Thomas. The bond formed by the two was natural. Thomas, an African-American, an incredible technician and an innovator in his own right, was required to enter the hospital through the servant's entrance and was not allowed to accompany Blalock to the dining room or other facilities. Thomas was subjected to the racial discrimination prevalent of the times. Spencer had likewise been subjected to discrimination, not because of race, but because of gender.

As a female medical student, she was not allowed to examine male patients and was forced to stand behind a screen as others examined them. While taking a medical art class, she was not even allowed to study and draw male anatomy in the morgue. As a senior student she was prohibited from examining male urology patients.

Besides Cooley and Longmire, other notable residents at Hopkins during those years were Mark Ravitch, Dwight McGoon, and Henry Bahnson, who would later mentor Theodore Drapanas. Nine men trained by Blalock, including these, would go on to be chairmen of major medical school surgery departments and notable surgeons in their field. It was only right that Spencer would be associated, in time, with this group. It is likely that the only thing that prevented her from achieving the same notoriety the others received was her gender.

In the 1970s, Dr. Spencer was the first full-time female surgeon on the LSU staff; however, she was a frequent visitor to Tulane surgery conferences. These were mainly Saturday morning Grand Rounds in the Delgado amphitheater on the twelfth floor at Charity. If she staffed a Tulane resident's case at Charity, she would then attend the Friday afternoon D&C conference at Tulane depending on her schedule.

Besides her private practice in the city, she was readily available at any time, day or night, elective or emergency, to assist both Tulane and LSU residents with any type of pediatric case at Charity. To say that she was generous with her time was a severe understatement. She could be gruff, rude or might just ignore you, but it seemed to me that she always had a twinkle in her eye. Her demand for absolute perfection, which she demanded from anyone around her, came only from the standards she had set for herself.

Any ill patient has a margin of error built around them. The older the patient, to a point, and the less serious the procedure, the bigger the margin of error. With pediatric patients and especially neonates, the margin of error is as large as the delicate skin surrounding their body. The smallest error or in the case of a neonate, the slightest drop in temperature, could prove fatal. Unfortunately, as late as the seventies these facts were only known by a few.

The subspecialty of neonatology had not been fully developed. There was also no pediatric surgery training program at Charity Hospital in the seventies. What's more, during that period there was probably no formal pediatric training program in the Deep South. Other than sightings at Grand Rounds, my only exposure to her before the spring of 1974 was when I was on an in-town surgery rotation at, Baptist Hospital. She was not banned from the surgeons lounge, but she wasn't welcome. She drank coffee in the nurse's lounge and if she wanted to do a case she was told she had to wait. When she left the lounge I could hear the male surgeons voice their opinions of her. "Who does she think she is?" and that was mild.

On any particular twenty-four-hour Charity Hospital admit day, the third-year resident admitting females also admitted pediatrics. Pediatric cases were usually done by the third-year or senior residents and depending on the case, Dr. Spencer was available to assist.

One night during my third year, a four-year-old boy was admitted with a gunshot wound to the upper left side of his abdomen. This child just happened to be in the wrong place at the wrong time. The knife-and-gun club happened to be in session and it further exemplified their nondiscriminatory actions.

Dr. Spencer assisted me as we explored the boy, removed his spleen and repaired a hole in his diaphragm. She didn't breathe fire from her nostrils, she wasn't demanding, she was respectful to even a mid-level resident and we got along fine. She cradled that little boy on the operating table before and after the procedure as if they were the only two people in the world. Nothing was going to hurt that child again.

As fate would have it, at this one and only place called Charity, another young boy, a three-year-old, was admitted the same night following an auto accident. The child had been riding in the back seat with his mother. The force of the accident threw the mother on top of her son and the force of the impact ruptured something in his belly. X-rays in the emergency room showed free air under his diaphragm, a pathognomonic sign of an intraabdominal injury needing surgery.

Spencer and I discussed the case. She reasoned that he had a blow-out of his colon. For some strange reason I had actually been reading my surgery text and had read a section on traumatic bowel injuries. The most common injury was a blow out of the jejunum a few inches from the duodenum. I played the odds and told her what I thought his injury was. It turned out that I was right. She accepted the finding of her missed guess gracefully. I sewed up the hole, irrigated the abdomen, and closed. It seemed she looked at me in a different light. I had earned some respect from her. Thereafter, she helped me do several elective pediatric cases from congenital hernias to pyloric stenosis to tracheal anomalies.

When Bill Blackshear was a senior resident, Dr. Spencer asked him to assist her with a private case at Touro Hospital. Following his internship, Bill had been in the US Navy for two years stationed in Southeast Asia. He was battle tested and well prepared to operate with her. The case went well and she was very appreciative to the point that she sent him a check as an assist fee. He never cashed the check. In fact he framed it and kept it. She didn't hesitate to let him know how displeased she was at him not cashing her check.

Bill Browder had been on call for "peds" the same evening as the annual Tulane Surgery party. He saw all of Dr. Spencer's patients then checked out and went to the party. A short while later Dr. Spencer arrived.

"Dr. Browder, how are you?" she said to Bill.

"I'm doing fine, Dr. Spencer. I just made rounds on everyone."

"Interesting," she replied, "I just came from the OR operating on one of *our* patients."

Now a little flustered, Bill answered, "I'm not on call, Dr. Spencer."

"It's a good thing, Dr. Browder."

She could just as easily go into a rage, as exemplified by a time when a resident rolled an X-ray machine over her foot in the OR. Witnesses say the screaming and cursing went on for five minutes. Not only was the intelligence and the legitimacy of the resident's birth questioned, but every expletive ending in "-ing" was used on him.

Butch Knoepp did multiple rotations on Dr. Spencer's service. After one or two rotations when he kept showing up again, she commented to Butch, "You again?" Butch didn't back down, "I'm afraid so Dr. Spencer, you keep firing people."

Later, when Butch was a cardiovascular surgeon in private practice in his hometown of Alexandria, he had seen a patient who needed surgery. The patient told Butch that he had a relative in New Orleans who was a physician and asked if he would mind if the relative called him.

In time Butch received a call from Dr. Spencer. On finally realizing to whom she was talking to, she commented, "You slimy SOB, how are you?" Butch had been approved.

Sometimes her temper was inappropriate to the point that she attempted to carry out retribution. When he was a resident, Steve Golladay had been assigned a very complicated project by Dr. Spencer. It involved constructing a detailed three-dimensional study of the abdominal vasculature of a six week old fetus. Steve's goal was to become a pediatric surgeon and he had already been accepted to a pediatric surgical fellowship at Spencer's alma mater,

Johns Hopkins University. Golladay spent countless hours on the project as well as spending one hundred dollars of his own money for material, which amounted to about 20 percent of his monthly salary. When Spencer saw the finished project, she was so displeased she threw the project on the floor and called him a slimy bastard. If that wasn't enough she tried to have his fellowship cancelled. Golladay succeeded in getting his fellowship and ultimately became chief of Pediatric Surgery at Arkansas Children's Hospital and then LSU Medical School.

One spring afternoon of 1974, my wife and I were in the front yard of our duplex townhouse in New Orleans East. As we watered the grass and talked, our son played nearby. As we looked up I saw a moving car rolling over something in the street. Just inside the right front tire, I saw blood and blond hair. It wasn't a dog. It was my son.

As we ran screaming to the scene of him, lifeless in the middle of the street, I shouted to a neighbor to call an ambulance. Although he had a pulse, he wasn't breathing, and I had to give him mouth-to-mouth resuscitation. He started breathing but didn't open his eyes. His left eye was swollen shut, he was scraped and cut all over and blood matted his blond hair.

The ambulance arrived quickly and I told them to take us to Charity Hospital. The driver said that Methodist was only about a mile away. "Take us to Charity!" I insisted.

As we sped down I-10, with the siren blaring, cramped in the back of the old Cadillac station wagon-style ambulance, I knew there was nothing Len and I could do but wait. Len cradled our son. My mind wandered to a time when I was a senior medical student on an out-of-town surgery rotation at Lallie Kemp. A logger had gotten hit in the head by a tree that he was "topping." He was knocked out. He had a lucid interval and was then brought to the hospital unconscious. He had to be transferred to a neurosurgeon in Baton Rouge, but because he wasn't breathing, an endotracheal tube had been placed and someone had to accompany him and squeeze the ambu bag. This would be the only way he could receive oxygen and have a chance to live.

I drew the short straw. It was night and the fifty-seven-mile long jostling journey went quickly. In Baton Rouge I assisted the neurosurgeon in lifting a skull flap. The patient had sustained a tear in his middle cerebral artery from a fracture resulting in a large subdural hematoma. I learned later that the patient didn't survive. I could not help but wonder if this ride would have the same result.

As we raced to Charity, I had the driver radio ahead to have Woolverton and Gage, my chief residents, waiting for us. Once in the ER, I knew I needed Dr. Spencer. I called her office and told her receptionist my name and asked if I could speak with her. She came to the phone immediately and I froze. The emotions of the moment wouldn't let me speak. She knew something was wrong and asked, "Do you need me?" That's all she said, "Do you need me?"

She came to the ER and took charge. She called Dr. Blackwell Evans, a Tulane urologist she trusted. The four of them took my son to the OR. His spleen was ruptured and the top of his left kidney was severely damaged. They did what was necessary to repair everything. He stayed in the Pediatric ICU for the next four days until he woke up. She saw him at least twice a day.

One Sunday afternoon she came in wearing bib overalls with a hammer hanging from one of the loops. She had been to her cabin in the Slidell area doing some work and stopped in on her way back home. You can take the gal out of the country but can't take the country out of the gal. Our son went on to fully recover and was discharged from the pediatric ICU directly to home.

On Saturday mornings during Grand Rounds in the Delgado amphitheater, she would always sit to the extreme right on the first row next to the right wall. Her head down, she would knit. Very seldom would she look up at anything but a case that might hold her interest, of course pediatric in nature. Dr. Drapanas and other full time staff would also occupy spaces on the long solid curved wooden oak benches, but they would be on the first or second row and in the center of the semicircle.

One particular day a pediatric case was presented. After a lengthy presentation by the senior resident and an equally lengthy discussion by the staff, each contributing their two cents, Dr. Drapanas asked Dr. Spencer if she had anything to contribute. She took her time to look up and when she did she said, "I didn't come her to talk, I came to sit and knit." Silence fell on the assembled. She put her head down. Still silence. And after what seemed like an eternity, but really only a few seconds later, she raised her head and offered an expert opinion to the problem that had been presented.

Dr. Rowena Spencer was a pioneer. She had trained at a time when she wasn't supposed to. Women had rights. They had the vote and "equality," but female surgeons were unheard of, nor accepted. While at Hopkins, she was not allowed to examine unclothed male patients. She had successfully separated conjoined twins but wasn't made to feel comfortable to sit in the surgeon's lounge and enjoy a cup of coffee.

I have since read that much later in her career, a conflict with a nurse caused her to be removed from the staff of a local hospital. I don't know the circumstances or the facts. I do know that she was one of the finest surgeons I ever had the privilege and honor to operate with and learn from.

I have also had the privilege to work with some great nurses—and some who weren't too great. Is it not inconceivable that she ruffled the feathers of a nurse who wasn't meeting her standard of patient care with one of "her kids" and she let her have it broadside?

Ironically, the discrimination that had been used against her for most of her career could have been working for someone else against her again. At one point she went back to Johns Hopkins. When asked what it was like and what she did, she said, "Well, (I went) to see Vivian."

Unfortunately, I was not aware of the history surrounding Rowena Spencer when I was a third-year resident. At that time I didn't know a Blalock-Taussig shunt from a garden hose. It wasn't until two years later that I would be performing them as well as total corrections for tetralogy of Fallot as well. If only I had asked her what it was like meeting and working with Vivian Thomas or for her to tell me about Alfred Blalock and Helen Taussig. I guess I just I should be grateful for what exposure I did have to her and the fact that she was available when I needed her.

Chief Resident, General Surgery, 1976–1977

The goal of any resident is that last year, the year before you leave to start your practice. It is why you put up with the on-call sleepless nights, the verbal abuse from superiors or public admonishment of your errors. It's what the whole thing has been about. And the ultimate goal along that journey is to be chief, especially at Charity. I had achieved that goal but it was anticlimactic.

It may sound ungrateful. It may sound like I was not looking forward to the role I was about to play for the next year. But, in fact I had achieved my real goal. I had completed two years of cardiothoracic surgical training. I had held those beating hearts in my hands. I had stopped them and started them up again. And now I was to hold stomachs, colons and broken livers? There was no comparison. It really didn't hold any interest for me.

Did I really need to stay another year? In order to sit for my thoracic surgery boards I had to have passed the general surgery boards. In order to sit for the general surgery boards I had to act in the capacity as chief resident. I had researched this, in depth. There was no getting out of it.

July 1976 started a whole new year and brought a series of challenges I hadn't expected and really wasn't prepared for.

There were four of us who were senior residents. Two fellows were in their fourth year. They were each assigned to a service, but were not acting as chiefs.

Bill Browder had been scheduled to do a year in the lab in 1975. He was to work under Dr. Drapanas, doing portal hypertension research. Drapanas' untimely death put Bill in limbo. Although he was on the payroll, there was no place for him in the general surgery rotation. He had no place to work. By strictly a chance meeting he became acquainted with the chairman of the physiology department, Dr. Nicholas DiLuzio, who was doing research on a substance called *glucan* and needed a research assistant.

Glucan was used in defense mechanisms against bacterial, fungal and viral diseases. It was also found to be of some benefit in inhibiting tumor growth. It turned out to be a perfect solution for Bill. He would be salaried by Tulane Surgery, yet spend a year in the physiology department working with DiLuzio. Bill and I would be co-chiefs for our last year.

Bill Blackshear was another senior resident. Bill had a partial Berry Plan deferment, like mine, and had reentered the program after serving in the navy for two years. He saw action in Vietnam and Laos, initially, and was then stationed at the Naval Academy in Annapolis as a medic. While spending time with Bill over the phone collecting data for this book, I asked him where he did his military service. When he told me, naturally I asked if he "saw action." "Yep," he said, "I was shot at."

When I was in the heat of a different kind of battle as a surgery resident taking care of sick and injured, it's a shame I was too focused on my own personal endeavors to realize that one of my fellow residents had been in a real life-and-death battle where he was the potential target. It had taken more than forty years, and maybe a little maturity, to see Bill in a different light.

Ruary O'Connell rounded out the group of four senior residents at Charity. Ruary entered the program as a third-year resident, transferring from Ireland. As it turned out, he filled a vacancy that became open when a second-year resident decided to play the guitar for a living rather than be a surgeon. Do you think he knew something we didn't know—the guitar player not Ruary?

For the first six months I was in charge. I made out the schedule and tried to handle the little disputes that arose. In fact, Browder and I worked very closely in making decisions. I was a couple of years older than Bill and had more surgical experience because of my two years doing cardiac surgery; however I strongly valued Bill's judgment.

The problem with my having to do six months as chief meant that I would not be doing any cardiac surgery. Over the past six months after coming back from Ochsner, I had done twenty-four pump cases, consisting of valve replacements, congenital hearts, and the six coronary bypass operations. The only hope of getting back to doing cardiac surgery was a three-month cardiac surgery rotation I was scheduled to do in January 1977—or so I thought.

I really didn't need any more abdominal surgery cases on my résumé, so I had an idea. I sat down with my third-year residents and said, "Look, I haven't done any general surgery cases for two years. For the first month or so, I might do some cases that you would normally do at your level. I don't think it will take me long, but I need to refamiliarize myself with these cases if I'm going to help you. If you find me two vascular cases a week to do, I'll help you do all the other cases."

Colon resections, gastrectomies, thyroid surgery, and others were all considered "chief cases," and normally a third-year resident would not be doing them until just before his senior resident was getting ready to leave, like Mathis Becker had done with me.

The residents were great. Every week I did major vascular cases: carotid endarterectomies, femoral-popliteal bypasses, aortofemoral or-iliac bypasses and abdominal aneurysm resections. I helped the third-years do anything else and they in turn passed down occasional gallbladders to the first-year residents. We all were busy and although I wasn't doing hearts, I stayed proficient with vascular cases and the occasional chest case.

Assistant Clinical Director

Besides my duties as chief resident I also received an appointment as an assistant clinical director (ACD) at Charity. With the title came some additional pay. But, along with the title also came some, not always, pleasant duties. Charity's uniqueness, being shared by two medical schools, contributed also to some unique problems. The fact that every other night was staffed by a different school's residents was only part of the problem. The complications in management centered around the fact that the patients couldn't always select what night they were to become sick or need medical attention.

The duty of the ACD was to solve those problems, be a mediator. Charity's main function was to take care of sick patients. Sometimes residents lost sight of this. Of all the minor disputes I had to deal with, one particular case comes to mind which exemplifies the need for a mediator.

I was on call a Tulane admit night and was also on call for ACD. A patient came into the (medical) admit room with an LSU number. The patient was a severe diabetic and metabolically was out of control. He had elevated blood sugar, renal dysfunction and high blood pressure. Straightforward so far? Nope, there's more. Besides the medical problems he was febrile. His fever was coming from gangrene of the leg and he had undergone prior surgery by the LSU service.

The LSU medicine resident didn't want to admit the patient because of the gangrene. And the Tulane orthopedic resident didn't want to admit the patient because of the severe medical issues. Besides, he was an LSU patient. A case that fell under the "monster rules" if there ever was one.

Actually, I saw the solution to be quite easy. Tommy Hawke was my third-year that night and I had brought him down to the admit room with me. Although it would have fallen completely under my authority to order one of them to admit the patient, I didn't want to create that hostility. I told Tommy to admit the patient to our service. That got him in the hospital. The LSU medicine resident would be consulted and he was told to take care of the diabetic and blood pressure problems. After twenty-four hours we would consult LSU orthopedics and transfer the patient to them. Problem solved and patient received good care.

One day in my ACD roll I received a call from a nursing home located just south of Baton Rouge. The administrator had a very obese patient he wanted to transfer to Charity for a "fat" operation. In that day bariatric surgery, as it is known today, was a complicated operation. There were no stomach bandings performed or gastric pouches done laparoscopically. The operation of the times was an ileojejunal bypass.

The effect of this procedure was basically to short circuit just about the whole small intestinal tract. Although weight loss was dramatic, when they survived, persistent diarrhea was a major concern and the complication rate at Charity had almost been prohibitive.

I asked the hospital administrator what the patient weighed. He told me that the highest their scales went up to was 450 pounds and he had topped that. I was very reluctant to accept this patient.

I had never forgotten a patient who had been operated on when I was a first-year. The patient had required prolonged mechanical ventilation to the point that because of a need for ICU beds, he was transferred down to C400A. A ventilator patient on a general ward was not good. Large brown metal privacy screens were placed around the bed. The wards did not have those sliding curtains one sees today. After a few days of this the attending nurse complained that the alarm on the ventilator kept going off. In fact what had happened that no one recognized was that the patient had died and the ventilator couldn't expand his stiff lungs.

In my head I saw this scenario all over. I told the administrator that I would get back with him. Dr. Krementz was the acting chairman. In the most negative tone I could, I presented the patient to Krementz. "We are a major referral center and a teaching institution." He replied, "Transfer the patient."

I called the administrator back, informed him of the decision, and told him they could transfer him.

"We can't transfer him; we don't have any means to transfer him," was his reply.

"Well, just put him in an ambulance." Then the words came that I feared. "He won't fit in an ambulance."

"Won't fit? Well, put him in the back of a truck," I impatiently told him.

"He won't survive a trip down there in the back of a truck, its ninety-five degrees."

Remembering my Air Force days, I recalled the military ambulances, the "cracker boxes," the forerunner for every ambulance on the road today. I asked him if he knew any military people or National Guard Reserve Center personnel. I was sure they would help him "get rid of his patient."

In preparation for this impending saga I put on my ACD hat and did two things. First, I went up to twelve into an empty OR. Operating tables aren't that wide and they are not made for comfort. We were going to have to weld two beds together in order to accommodate our forthcoming event. I didn't tell the OR crew anything until I saw the white of his eyes.

Going back down to four I found the nursing supervisor and told her of our intentions. She took me to one of the smaller wards in the front corner of the hospital. It was an eight-bed ward and this particular one only had a couple of patients on it. She agreed to transfer those patients to other wards.

The arrival day came. I had the ambulance truck bring the patient to the back loading dock. This is where the big scales were that weighed produce for the hospital as it was brought in. The big boy tipped in at 600 pounds. We had welded two beds together upstairs on four and he was brought right up. The wards did not have doors. In my attempt to keep it from turning into a side show we got more metal screens to block the gawkers' view.

Routine lab and studies were drawn and finally after a waiting grace period, I went in to talk with him. Because of his size he couldn't walk and there is no telling how long it had been since he had even been out of bed.

I introduced myself.

The first words out of his mouth were, "What am I doing here?"

"Well, sir, they have sent you down here to have an operation to help you lose weight."

"Operation! I'm not having any operation!" was his wonderful reply. I discussed further with him what they had told him of his transfer, details and the purpose of the operation, and other facts that he really wasn't interested in. I really didn't want to leave anything unsaid in case later on he changed his mind or the situation was presented to him in a different, more complete manner, making me look like I hadn't done my job.

I reported my findings to Krementz. As a senior member of the staff, he had been around the block and wasn't about to talk anyone into surgery. He thought a moment, "Why don't you see if the LSU metabolic research unit will take him?" Krementz's fourth-floor cancer research unit in the LM building was right above the LSU unit on the third floor. He knew this and at the time, I didn't even know that unit existed. They sopped that patient up like red eye gravy on a sour dough biscuit. I think that was the biggest bullet we ever dodged, pun intended.

A few years later the duties of the ACD got expanded to include talking with the news media. The amount of crime and gunshot wounds in New Orleans had risen to a significant level and giving weekly trauma reports seemed to be something of a news interest. One of my third-years, Martin Evans, was also appointed an ACD when he was chief resident. One night when he was on call, his pal and co-chief resident, the aforementioned Dr. Hawke, was operating on a severe GSW. The patient was bleeding out and required massive transfusions.

The blood bank, still under the direction of Dr. DeJongh, had been moved downstairs a couple of floors off of the twelfth floor. DeJong had a rule that no more than two units of blood could be checked out at any one time. One of the interns had been running up and down the stairs carrying blood from the blood bank to Tommy's operating room.

Tommy had the circulating nurse page Martin and begged for him to do something about his need for more blood. Wearing his freshly polished assistant clinical director's hat and cloak, Martin went to the blood bank and grabbed ten units of blood for Tommy's case. DeJongh later beeped Martin telling him that he had stolen the blood and that he wasn't allowed to do that, that there were rules.

Martin told DeJongh that he was the administrator of the hospital that night and that he was fired. The next day Martin got called to the surgery department chairman's office.

"Did the Tulane chief resident really fire the head of the blood bank?" Martin was asked.

"Yes, it's a stupid rule, but he can be rehired, but with a new policy." was his reply. Trying to conceal a grin and amusement at the situation, the chairman cautioned Martin about firing someone who was a department head, an LSU professor and a state employee, but agreed the policy needed changing. Subsequently it was.

Another ACD had gotten a call to the ER about a patient who had expired and was found on the back ramp. What was unusual was that the deceased had stamped on his forehead in red letters: "NOT AN EMERGENCY." The heavily inebriated individual had come into the ER on multiple previous occasions and was repeatedly sent out. The last time the patient returned the impatient resident stamped the patient's forehead. The rejected patient went out the back doors coded and died on the ramp. A little Betadine was used to erase the evidence off of his forehead and he was transferred to the morgue.

An unpleasant duty required of the ACD had to do with bed management in the ICU. There were a finite number of beds available and usually too many patients who needed them. Most of the time transferring patients out of the unit was handled by residents within their own service. In other words, the resident might have to choose which of his patients would get to stay and who would have to be transferred out. Patients on ventilators usually took precedent as far as needing a bed, but sometimes even a patient on a ventilator might have to be sent down to a ward.

Besides the training programs for physicians, Charity also had an oral surgery training program for graduate dentists. Overall they were really a good bunch of guys, but conflicts arose in the management and treatment of patients seen in the ER with regard to maxillofacial and mandibular fractures. Someone gets in a fight down at one of the Crescent City's never closing bars and now you have a broken jaw.

Plastic surgery, ENT and oral surgery all wanted to treat them, and they all did it well. Early on it was a matter of who could out hustle who when it came down to getting the case and a lot of times that's where the ACD came in. Then a simple rotation was set up which meant that the oral surgeons only got one out of every three cases. In actuality, out in the "world" the oral surgeons were going to be doing many of these cases.

Then it happened. Problems arose in how the oral surgeons managed their fracture patients in the operating room. Stabilizing these jaw fractures required wiring them together, similar to braces a teen gets because of tooth malalignment. The difference begins in what happens with the rubber bands or where the wires are put. With a jaw fracture, the physician does not want the lower jaw to move so the bone can heal. This requires wiring the lower jaw to the upper jaw, thus splinting it. The result is that the patient can only eat a liquid diet.

Whereas the plastic surgeons and the ENT residents didn't affix the last set of wires to the lower jaw in the recovery room until after the patient woke up, the oral surgery residents finished everything in the operating room—-with the patient asleep. And that's where the problem came in. Unfortunately, the anesthetics in that day were accompanied by a fair amount of nausea and sometimes vomiting. On more than one occasion a wired-up oral surgery patient would be sent to the recovery room, wake up with nausea and with his mouth wired together, vomit, aspirate and die. That problem was soon corrected.

Trauma

In the second week of July, a seventeen-year-old (RG) came into the ER after he crashed the motorcycle he was driving. His leg was broken and he had a torn popliteal artery. Motorcycle accidents are horrible. Even though

229

those were days that didn't mandate the wearing of helmets, he was lucky that he didn't have a head injury.

One of the most common injuries a motorcycle rider incurs is a posterior dislocation of the head of the tibia from the end of the femur. When this happens it usually tears the popliteal artery, the major artery that runs behind the knee. This is bad enough and it has to be repaired. The thing that makes this injury even worse, however, is the fact that the accompanying popliteal vein is often torn also. When this happens it also has to be repaired. It cannot be ignored.

Injuries like this have a 50 percent amputation rate of the lower leg. Quite often the venous injury is ignored or not recognized and disaster results. Besides a severe fracture of his tibial head, RG had torn both the artery and vein.

Operating with one of the orthopedic residents, I did a saphenous vein interposition graft to the popliteal artery and repaired the popliteal vein. The "orthropod" resected bone and stabilized the joint with rods and other hardware that they use, the Erector Set type stuff. The young man did well. He'd had a close call and could have lost a leg and was lucky he didn't have other major injuries.

The next day did not go as well. I was doing an elective esophagoscopy with the rigid scope on a forty-six-year-old female with a severe esophageal stricture, narrowing. I had anesthetized her oropharynx with topical cocaine solution and some Xylocaine Viscous. She was also given a mild sedation. Things happened very quickly and to this date I wish I had done something different.

I received an emergency page from my wife at home. Normally you wouldn't even answer a call from home, but this was different. Len had been at her part-time job doing psychological testing and Dorothy, our housekeeper and babysitter was at home with our almost four-year-old son. Yes, the same one who had been run over by the car.

A man had come to the front door and tried to force his way in the house saying he had "come for the boy." Dorothy was a large lady, and using her weight to advantage, she shoved the door closed on his arm, causing him to retreat. Even though Dorothy was "old school South," she didn't defer to anyone. She lived in one of the housing projects off of Orleans Avenue, a tough neighborhood. When I used to take her home after she babysat for us, she wouldn't let me drive her to her building. "I'll get out here and I'll be all right," she'd say, patting her purse with her Saturday night special in it.

At the same time Dorothy slammed the door on the first guy, his partner had jumped out of their car and tried to bust open the gate to our enclosed wooden fenced-in back yard. Nikko, our Australian Beagle (all bark and no bite), started barking like crazy and scared him off. I hung up the phone and hurriedly finished the esophagoscopy.

The patient jumped at the same time I was advancing the scope. I felt a slight give. Thinking I had dilated her stricture, I withdrew the scope, told the first-year to write some orders and hurried home. In my haste I had unknowingly perforated her esophagus.

Things were as well as they could be at home. The police and my wife were there. Dorothy gave them a description of the man and for most of the evening we tried to figure out not only who would want to kidnap our son but why. It was a very unsettling feeling.

If that wasn't bad enough, later that night I got a call from the third- year on call at the hospital that my esophagoscopy patient was in distress. They had obtained a chest X-ray showing fluid and air in her left chest cavity. This was an ominous finding.

I hurried back to Charity and took her to the operating room fairly sure of what I would find. She had a hole on the left side of her esophagus just above the esophageal sphincter. The amount of inflammation was incredible, especially considering the fact that the perforation had only happened a few hours earlier. Knowing she had a severe stricture, I couldn't simply close the perforation.

I was torn feeling needed at two different places at the same time. Would those men come back? I had left Len at home alone with our son. I couldn't dump the case on Browder. I should have called an attending for help. Instead, we did what would later commit her to a colon interposition by sewing over the esophagus, draining her esophagus out through her neck and performing a feeding tube gastrostomy. We irrigated out her chest with copious amounts of antibiotic solution, placed a couple of chest tubes and closed her chest.

She did well, but the following Friday at D&C conference, I caught hell. I had committed an error in technique by perforating her and an error in judgment by not calling for help. I thought the presence of her severe stricture would have precluded a simple closure of the perforation I had caused. It seemed like colon interpositions around Charity were almost as common as gastrectomies. I had seen and done so many it just seemed like the most expeditious and safest thing to do. I was wrong.

Bill Collins seemed to relish in my being roasted. He had assumed a position of authority by default. Most of the comments centered on why I did not just sew up the hole. The other comments had to do with other procedures I should have tried rather than committing her to a colon interposition. They were right. They were all right. The circumstances surrounding the case really weren't important. I felt they were personal and I wasn't going to bring them up. I should have stopped the procedure and come back to fight another day.

Over the next couple of months the third-years, Martin Evans, Tommy Hawke, Dick McCormick and others, had done a great job finding cases. Both Bill and I had our own clinic day on Wednesdays. Other general surgery services or the medicine residents could refer in any elective case they wanted for us to evaluate. My initial request to be able to do two vascular cases a week turned into my averaging twice that many. I did numerous carotid endarterectomies, femoral to popliteal bypasses, aortoiliac and aortofemoral bypasses, as well as the occasional chest case.

Of all the cases I had helped Dr. John do, I think the repair of an abdominal aortic aneurysm (AAA) was something that impressed me and stayed with me the most. The process, the anatomy and the methodology was just about perfect. Whereas the internal anatomy might vary a little, I think it was the one procedure he did the same, time and time again. It was a ballet of maneuvers, control, sewing and timing.

I ran the memorized images of him doing one in my head time and time again. Circling the aorta with a tape, opening the sac and sewing up any perforators, selecting the appropriate size graft and sewing in that most important first stitch. That special stitch you started with that you would never see again. The one that assured there would be no leaks while suturing the graft in. And then sew like the wind so they can't even see your hands move. Many years later in private practice, Dr. Robert Barrett would call that a "no leak 'um.'"

Later in my career, the greatest backhanded compliment I would ever receive would come from a crusty scrub nurse at an "across town" hospital where I seldom did cases. I had received a consult on a patient with an aneurysm who had requested me but, because of insurance reasons had to be done there.

The patient was asleep and being prepped on the table. As I was checking the back table, asking the scrub nurse about the instruments and grafts that she had available, sort of my "pre-flight" check. I was receiving curt "yes" and "no" answers from her highness. I knew that she knew what she was doing, but I was getting the feeling that she didn't think I knew what I was doing.

Robert, an LSU graduate and Jacques Wheeler-trained vascular surgeon, and I started in on it. Within just a few minutes we had explored the abdomen, opened the retroperitoneal space, encircled the aorta with a tape, freed up an area at the bifurcation where to put the distal clamp, selected a graft and had the anesthesiologist administer heparin. I asked for the DeBakey aortic clamp and she said, "You all have done a couple of these before, haven't you?" As if on cue, Robert and I answered simultaneously, "First one I've ever seen."

Matas' first subclavian artery aneurysm repair involving intrasaccular suturing, rather than simple ligation, demonstrated as much how they should not be handled as how they should be done. Creech's paper in the Annals of Surgery put it in neon lights in the surgical community. Many non-medical people had never heard the word aneurysm.

It wasn't until Michael DeBakey made the headlines in 1964 by operating on the abdominal aneurysm of the Duke of Windsor, that it became a household term. With the advent of the CAT scan aneurysms could be diagnosed and measured accurately. Prior to this there were two ways to make the diagnosis, if it hadn't ruptured, that is. A pulsatile mass in the abdomen just above the navel was diagnostic if the impulse was transmitted to the side (laterally) as well as to the front. A lateral abdominal X-ray would usually show a calcified rim in the wall of the aneurysm. If an ultrasound was available, which we didn't have, it was a huge aid. If any of these qualifications were met and there was a high suspicion of an aneurysm being present, the patient was brought to surgery.

Quite often a patient would present with peripheral vascular disease as his main complaint requiring an abdominal arteriogram and an abdominal aneurysm would be found incidentally. With the use of the CAT scan to measure aneurysms the diagnosis became a lot easier and definite criteria were established. After DeBakey's performance with the duke, the medical community coined a term for the size of his aneurysm—a "Duke 1." It had been rumored that his aneurysm was not that big, but he was the duke and ex-King of England.

In August I was referred a seventy-five-year-old man with bilateral iliac artery aneurysms as well as an abdominal aneurysm. Sometimes you have to be careful what you wish for. I would get to do my first aneurysm but it would involve a "Y" graft rather than a simple tube. I'd have to get control of the major blood vessels deep in his pelvis. They just take time and it's a lot of sewing but luckily they weren't leaking and it wasn't an emergency. Iliac aneurysms actually are deadlier than the abdominal kind as they tend to rupture earlier with much less warning. Despite his age, the patient did well. He was motivated and his attitude helped him get over the surgery a lot quicker.

Besides the vascular cases, I was still doing thoracotomies for lung cancer, infection and trauma. My ill-fated esophagoscopy of the second week of July had given me a new respect for the term "speed kills." The flexible esophagoscope had finally made its way to Charity. Commonly referred to as the "long black snake," it had excellent optics and illumination. It was less traumatic to the patient even in the hands of the inexperienced. It came with a bite block but sometimes the medicine residents would forget to use it. So, it was not unheard of that year for an anesthetized but awake patient during a period of anxiety to bite into the scope, thus ruining a several-thousand-dollar instrument.

As good as the new scope was, the rigid scope was still superior for the removal of foreign bodies. I could remove large chunks of swallowed meat that got stuck at the opening to the stomach, occasionally dentures that got swallowed, and the best of all—a toothbrush. A glass-paneled cabinet in the ENT procedure room displayed the various foreign bodies removed using the scopes.

The third-year residents I had on my services were highly qualified. I tried to give them as much latitude and responsibility as I could. Because of the volume of cases we dealt with it did not take long to be able to tell which of them could stand alone and which of them, perhaps, weren't prepared to move forward.

One night after my team and I had been on call, I was home asleep. It was about 2 a.m. and the phone rang. It was GT, a third-year who had been on call with me the night before. Unbeknownst to me, he had admitted a lady with a tender belly, and an acute abdomen.

Growing up with a general surgeon as a father, all my life he had preached to me, sometimes even at an unusual time such as studying for a tenth grade biology test, "Never let the sun set or rise on an acute abdomen!" If I heard it once, I heard it a hundred times. Both he and my mother were devoted opera lovers. I had known all my life that one of their idols, the famous tenor Enrico Caruso, had died of an undiagnosed ruptured appendix. I later learned that one of my heroes, Frederic Remington, had also died of same.

GT was perplexed. He thought his patient had an acute appendix, but not only had he not pulled the trigger and operated on her, he hadn't told me he had admitted her. And, if that wasn't bad enough he was unsure about what type of incision to make. As I lay in bed we discussed the types of incisions he could make, something he should have easily known at his level of training. I told him that if there was any uncertainty as to the diagnosis, a midline incision would give him access to solve several findings.

We hung up and I lay there knowing what I had to do. Before I could get out of bed, Len threw in her dollar's-worth: "You *are* going aren't you?" I got dressed and headed down to Charity, hoping along the way that the patient would be alright until I got there, but also worrying about GT and his lack of decision-making power and judgment. The patient did, in fact, have an acute appendix. It hadn't ruptured and he took care of it.

Doctor's wives are amazing people. Although a lot of couples meet in medical school now and form "two-doctor" marriages, back then it was not that common. Out of the whole cadre of residents I worked under, with or above, I only knew of one of the junior residents who wound up marrying another physician. There were many more who had a nurse for a wife, including Dr. Drapanas.

Most wives seem to assimilate an incredible amount of medical knowledge from their husbands over time. Wives are often asked by their friends for medical advice. My wife is no exception, to the point that one of her nicknames is "Dr. Len." I do caution her on her giving advice, even today. She has learned that sometimes the best advice she can give one of her friends is "get a second opinion."

GT finished out the year and was senior resident at one of the satellite hospitals. He actually was accepted to a fellowship in thoracic and cardiac surgery but was released after a few months. He left New Orleans and practiced general surgery with a general surgeon in another Southern state. Shortly thereafter he committed suicide. Could I or the powers in charge at that time have prevented that end? There really weren't any warning signs. In those days it was unheard of us to get psychiatry consult on one of our own. I didn't find out until later that Drapanas had done it. If I or others had known that then could we have prevented a suicide? We'll never know. He was in a very demanding profession that he wasn't suited for.

Penetrating Wounds

The New Orleans "knife-and-gun club" was always active. Any night you were on call you were subject to many types of penetrating injuries. Historically, over the years we had seen many more knife wounds than GSWs. We referred to two types of knife wounds—stabbings and "juggings." A stabbing was done usually, with a downward thrust. This motion would result in wounds to the head, shoulders and neck area. There is a thin muscle layer beneath the skin of the neck area above the clavicles extending up below the jaw, the platysma. Any knife wound that penetrated the platysma was automatically brought to the OR. There are countless blood vessels in that area, the most significant being the carotid arteries.

A small puncture wound could inflict considerable damage if it hit the right spot. Stabbings also inflicted wounds to the chest. Most of the times, if these penetrated the chest cavity they could be treated with a chest tube and drainage only. Lung injuries from stabbings usually healed on their own. If there was persistent bleeding from a stab wound to the chest possibly requiring a blood transfusion, the patient was brought to the OR. The most common injury I saw from these were lacerations or transections of the internal mammary artery or intercostal arteries. They were easy cases to fix but still required a thoracotomy.

Steve Harkness relates a situation he was placed in within the first few days when he was a third-year resident at Lallie Kemp. As it turned out he was the most senior resident in the hospital for that period of time. Overnight on June 30 of each year you are automatically promoted or transformed to the next level and expected to handle the situations that befall a resident at that higher level. Ready or not it was a transformation we all went through. As I had experienced my first day as a chest resident, Steve was about to experience this change firsthand.

On July 4, a young warrior came into the Lallie Kemp ER with a stab wound to the chest. Steve placed a chest tube which should have expanded the lung and sealed the leak. The patient kept bleeding— and bleeding. He exceeded the accepted amount of drainage of 250–300cc per hour.

Steve called the chief resident at Big Charity. After telling him that he had a patient who needed a thoracotomy, he told him he was putting the patient in an ambulance with an intern and sending him to New Orleans. "You can't do that," was the reply "we're too busy here, you operate on him." Steve told him that he'd never done a thoracotomy. "Do one today or bury him!" was the reply. The patient was taken to one of Lallie Kemp's two ORs, given a general anesthetic, turned on his side and prepped. Steve then rigged a bent wire coat hanger such that it would hold the phone and hang close to the operative field so they could talk back and forth. Steve was then "talked through" the thoracotomy and subsequent removal of the injured portion of the lung, all via long-distance call from seventy miles away.

"Juggings" were a different matter. If a patient came in who had been "jugged," the knife (or shiv—if they came from Parish Prison) was used in an upward motion or inserted from the side. Most commonly these resulted in abdominal wounds or groin injuries.

A stab wound to the groin came into the ER at Charity one night. The patient was unconscious from massive blood loss. John Church was the first-year on duty and was unsuccessfully trying to start an IV when the chief resident approached him. "Have you ever done a thoracotomy?" he asked.

After John's negative response, he was told, "Take this scalpel and make an incision, with one cut, from the top of the sternum to the xyphoid." They then split the chest, and John was told to place a catheter in the right atrium through which they administered massive amounts of fluid and blood in an attempt to save the patient's life. The man then went into cardiac arrest and was resuscitated. As it turned out he was a severely mentally deranged individual who had actually stabbed himself.

That week one of headlines in the *Times-Picayune* newspaper featured an article stating that "Tulane surgeons save boys life in ER with open heart surgery." At the year-end party and award ceremony John was given the "Dudley Do-right Judgment Award."

In that period from 1975 to 1976 we started seeing more GSWs than stab wounds. Not only was their aim getting better but they were using higher-caliber weapons.

GSWs to the clavicular area were especially challenging. The subclavian artery and vein course right behind the clavicle. It's a difficult area to approach and get control of the bleeding blood vessels. A "trap door" approach was the incision of choice. An incision was made in the midline, from the sternal notch down half way through the sternum. Two more incisions were made, one straight across the sternum, through the anterior portion of the chest between the ribs, and a second one paralleling this one but just above the clavicle, going toward the shoulder. A retractor could then be inserted, affording exposure to the injured area. They were potentially fatal, very dramatic injuries with dramatic repairs.

Several years later in my first year of private practice in Shreveport, a GSW to the left subclavian area came into the ER. The LSU Hospital had not yet been designated as a Level 1 trauma center yet so often the closest hospital was used for any type of trauma. I happened to be on call that night.

Once in the OR, I proceeded with the repair I had been trained to do at Charity. Although, I didn't know it at the time, the anesthesiologist had been an LSU graduate and had also trained at Big Charity. The nurses had never seen that injury or the approach and just about questioned every move I made, especially when I asked for the sternal saw. The development of Level 1 trauma centers and specialized training programs for trauma specialists is a major advancement. Charity would have easily had that designation in the sixties and seventies even though it did not have an OR in the emergency room area.

Carotid Surgery

Carotid surgery at Charity proved to be somewhat of an enigma. Carotid occlusive disease was and is the number one cause of strokes. Any patient having had a stroke or a patient found to have a murmur in the neck on physical exam would then be considered for a carotid angiogram. Today the sophistication of ultrasonography has markedly enhanced the diagnosis of carotid lesions. Most patients with normal pathways of blood circulation in the brain have cross circulation between the left and right sides of the brain. Smaller arteries in the back of the neck, the vertebral arteries, also aid in "collateral" circulation to the brain.

In order to do the surgery, the carotid artery has to be clamped shut, the vessel opened and the arteriosclerotic layer removed. During the operation, the major flow of blood is stopped from going to the brain. An age-old dilemma in doing carotid surgery is whether to shunt or not shunt the patients. Basically this involves placing a small plastic tube temporarily in the blood vessel to reroute the blood.

Historically, on the Tulane Service most staff surgeons had advocated shunting. Dr. Drapanas did not shunt. In an attempt to find an answer as to which was best, I undertook the task of reviewing all the carotid endarterectomies done by the Tulane Service at Big Charity, Huey P. Long Charity in Alexandria and Lallie Kemp Hospital in Independence.

Lallie Kemp had the smallest volume of surgeries when compared to the surgeries done at the other Tulane out-of-town rotations, other than when Don Palmisano was chief. As an incentive, he told the medical students on rotation there that they would receive a bonus in their grades depending on how many patients they found with carotid murmurs. The number of arteriograms being done skyrocketed, and Palmisano did more carotids that month than were done at Big Charity.

I wrote up a couple of pages of pertinent questions I wanted answered. Starting out at Charity, I worked with the record library to get me a list of all carotids that had been done. The most famous person in the record library was the "Dragon Lady." Her duty was to make sure that the house staff properly signed their charts and operative dictations. Failure to do so would result in your paycheck being withheld.

239

Early in the study the charts were fairly well organized and a lot of them were kept in the hospital. However, older charts were kept in a deserted building on Canal Street which she had given me access to. On the second floor I found charts, lots of charts, probably thousands of charts in stacks on the floor. Somehow there was some kind of organization to the process and I was able to find most of what I was looking for.

I went through the same process with the record librarians at the two outlying hospitals. Being smaller facilities, it was a much more organized process. The other senior residents were very generous in covering my service on the days that I went to Alexandria and Independence. Although the hour and half drive to Independence was manageable in a day, because of the length of the trip to Alexandria I elected to fly.

The flight to Alexandria was notable. Royal Airlines was a small airline actually owned by people in Shreveport who had been instrumental in starting Delta Airlines. That's where the similarities stopped. I was checked in at the Royal Airlines desk at the New Orleans Air terminal by a young man who took my small overnight bag. He gave me a boarding pass and said, "Come with me." We walked through the terminal out to a twin-engine, six-passenger plane. He then took my bag and stowed it in a hatch. He ushered me to a seat; I was the only passenger. And you guessed it—he secured the door, climbed up into the pilot's seat, and flew the plane.

When all the data had been collected, I had reviewed about 300 patient charts. There wasn't time for me to summarize the results and come to conclusions before the end of June. I took all the data with me to Mayo's where I summarized and analyzed it. A statistician I was working with on another paper was kind enough to assist me with the data from the Charity paper.

The overall findings were interesting. There really was no difference in the non-fatal complication rate between shunted or non-shunted cases. The overall complication rate was prohibitively high for both groups. It seemed like the main cause of this was the fact that patients with developing strokes were being brought to the operating room and operated on as an emergency procedure. Operating on these patients with impending strokes didn't prevent their stroke; it made them worse. While a fellow in Rochester, Minnesota I had analyzed all the data and written the carotid paper.

On a subsequent visit to New Orleans I visited the surgery department with the paper in hand hoping to get it published. I was told by then-chairman Dr. Watts Webb to discuss it with the staff attending, who just happened to be Rod Jackson, the same one with whom I operated on the innominate artery fistula. The results never got published.

Jackson had also distinguished himself when he was a resident at Lallie Kemp. He had caused a complete disruption in the operating room when he embarrassed the operating room crew.

Following an operation he had scrubbed on, he removed his gloves, concealing a gauze sponge. He discarded both gloves containing the sponge in the trash. Everything used at the operating table is counted. Sponge counts are like a religious ceremony. Instruments, needles, laps, and sponges are all counted—twice. No foreign body is left behind intentionally.

In 1974, a new synthetic material had been invented, PTFE. Chemically it stood for polytetrafluoroethylene, or what everyone today knows as Gore-Tex. Initially, it was developed as a conduit for use in vascular surgery. It had a distinct advantage when used in small-vessel bypass over the customary Dacron grafts because it was made down to a diameter of only four millimeters. Traditionally the patient's vein was used for vascular bypass in the legs, but in 1975 Gregory and Wheeler in Virginia performed the first femoral-popliteal bypass using Gore-Tex.

An alternative was now available for the patient who had poor veins or had undergone a prior vein stripping. The use of Gore-Tex was then expanded to renal-failure patients who needed vascular access for dialysis. As third-year and senior residents at Charity we would do these fistulas on the chronic renal-failure patients.

Although both LSU and Tulane had kidney transplant programs, the bulk of the dialysis patients were treated at a dialysis center on Tulane Avenue near Hotel Dieu Hospital. It was felt by Dr. McDonald, the Tulane renal transplant surgeon, that the nephrologists were not sending the volume of patients for transplant but rather were keeping them to dialyze in their center. It was a point of conflict. With the amount of trauma at Charity and the inherent mortality, it would have seemed there would have been enough donor material. We did a lot of fistulas and were even starting to use Gore-Tex for them.

In January 1977, Alton Ochsner's dream of a Tulane University Hospital came to reality. Built directly across the street from the medical school and connected by an enclosed pedestrian bridge, it allowed the staff of the school to see and treat their private patients entirely "on campus."

This new addition meant that residents and interns would also have to cover the patients done at the Tulane Hospital in the form of assisting the staff. A whole new service was created.

The new service set up was called a trauma service. It had a senior resident, third-year resident and an intern. During the day their duties, besides tending to trauma, were to be available to assist staff at the Tulane Hospital with any of their private cases. They were also on call for any trauma case that came through the doors through the night. Henceforth, for instance, if you were on Service III admitting males and a GSW victim came in to the ER, you would have to call the trauma team to take care of them.

It may seem like a decision that was looking to the future, because, today, in all major medical centers it is standard to have a trauma service. Were the powers to be looking that far ahead? Were they really that innovative? What it meant, also, until enough time passed in the rotation, was that some residents would not participate in the surgery of or caring for any trauma patients. This was happening to a surgery program that saw more or certainly as much trauma than any hospital in the country.

Days were slow. In the beginning the number of general surgery cases done at the University Hospital was few and far between. The surgical subspecialties were using the facility also.

At this time there was still no certified cardiovascular surgeon on the full-time Tulane Surgery faculty. Even though I did assist on a few of the private cases, most of the time the third-year resident or intern was assigned to do them. As major as these changes were, they really weren't going to affect me for another three months. I was scheduled to rotate back on the CV service the first of January.

Thoracic Surgery

One day Dr. Collins met with me. "You're going to be on the cardiac rotation this period, but you're not going to be doing any hearts. We have to learn how to do them," he added. At that first coronary operation he scrubbed on, it was obvious he had never performed or even seen one. He told me that during his training he had done a few non-pump mitral valve operations. What he was referring to was an old, out dated procedure where the surgeon performed a "finger fracture" for narrowed, calcified mitral valves. I also remembered that he had been the one who would not let me ask John Ochsner to come assist me.

In fact what he was doing now was trying to learn how to do modern-day cardiac surgery at the expense of the resident and the patient. I would still be doing all the non-cardiac thoracic cases, but he and Rod Jackson, now on the staff, would be doing all the hearts.

I was devastated. I was planning a career as a cardiovascular surgeon. I was the first Tulane resident to do two full years of clinical cardiac surgery and had brought coronary bypass surgery to the Tulane Service at Charity.

During that first couple of months on the thoracic rotation I performed over a dozen thoracotomies varying from complete lung removals, lobectomies, and thymus gland tumors to more empyemas. Since I had more experience with the congenital cases I also did several shunts for children with complex congenital conditions as well as repairs of coarctation of the aorta. I was determined to keep busy and try to make the hand I had been dealt better.

The results coming out of the CV operating room were not good. The mortality rate was high. One patient blew his aorta out on the way from the OR to the recovery room and there were other problems. We all have them. I'd just felt betrayed.

By this time, the department had hired a full-time pediatric surgeon, Dr. Bill Buntain, a quality person and surgeon. The previous few months he had helped me do some complicated, non-thoracic pediatric cases. I needed a sounding board and felt that I could discuss my feelings with him. I found myself, on more than one occasion, in his office feeling sorry for myself.

Bill had trained at the Mayo Clinic. He told me of a program at Mayo's he thought was perfectly suited for my situation. They accepted four fellows each year in what they called a "Special Fellowship in Cardiac Surgery." It was only for cardiothoracic surgeons who had finished their complete training, were board eligible, and wanted extra training and "polishing up." As he described it, it sounded perfect.

I applied to the program and had Buntain and Dr. John write letters of recommendation for me. I asked no one else on the Tulane staff for a recommendation and told no one else about my application. The natural paranoia of my 100 percent Sicilian self was not without basis.

Things had been said by Collins that, at times, made me wonder if I should ask Dr. John if I could transfer my residency to Ochsner. It would not work. I had to finish my chief year at the hospital where I had started. A few weeks after I mailed in my application I received a reply asking that I come to Rochester for an interview. During this process, I discussed my intentions, or hopeful intentions, with Len. "You want to do an eighth year?" she gasped. "In Minnesota?" We discussed it and I realized that it was the best course.

I weighed my options. I could have just set up shop in New Orleans.

My father had a very large general surgery practice. He was willing to feed me cases and we would have made a good living, but by the end of that June I would have not done a cardiac case for a year. My self-confidence was low. I thought of staying on the staff. That way I could get some more experience and assist in teaching the residents.

To that point I went to talk with Dr. Krementz. "You need a gimmick," he said, "You need something to make you stand out." You could have knocked me over with a feather. A gimmick! Wasn't the number of cases I'd done, the number of hearts and seven years at Charity enough of a "gimmick?" Besides, there had been numerous other chief residents who had stayed on the staff for a couple of years after their training. I definitely wouldn't have been the first to do that. I now knew I had to move on.

One of the senior residents covered for me and I flew to Rochester, Minnesota. The Mayo Clinic, or WFMC (World Famous Mayo Clinic) as it was often referred to in the news, was an impressive monument to its storied history in not only cardiac surgery, but medicine as a whole.

The Mayo-Gibbon pump was the first heart lung machine. The Plummer building was named after the same Plummer associated with esophageal and thyroid disease and the list went on. Interviews had been scheduled with several of the cardiac surgeons. I explained my situation and why I wanted to do a third year of cardiac surgery training.

On my last appointment I met with Dr. Robert Wallace who, at the time, was head of the section of cardiac surgery. As it turned out he was DeBakey trained and had been a contemporary of and friends with Dr. John. "We haven't gotten your letter of recommendation from John," was one of the first things he said. "I'll call him when I get back." I told him as we parted.

As soon as I got home from Rochester I called Dr. John. Within ten days I had my acceptance letter for a Special Fellowship in Cardiac Surgery at the Mayo Clinic. I shared the news with only a couple of people, Browder being one of them. The sense of relief, as well as the immense feeling of satisfaction that came over me would be hard to describe.

Even though it meant another year, it was a big step. It would not only round out my training but seal it with not only the training I had done at one of the finest teaching programs in the country but the world's most famous clinical program.

One night Martin Evans and I were on call. I was in my room on the fourteenth floor when I got a call from the OR supervisor. "Dr. Evans needs you in OR four," she said. Already in my scrubs, I grabbed my coat and raced down the stairwell to twelve.

"Whatcha got, Martin?" I called to him through the opened OR doors. He was holding both hands down in the wound as if applying pressure to something.

"Got a GSW to everything and also his aorta," he replied. "You want to see?"

"Sure," I said. With that Martin released his arm pressure and a visible column of blood made itself visible above the edge of the patient's opened abdomen. I scrubbed in. It was a mess.

This fellow's girlfriend had shot him one time with a .45 caliber pistol from his left side. The bullet had entered his flank, going first through the spleen, then the splenic flexure of his colon, numerous small bowel loops, the head of the pancreas, gallbladder, and liver. It even managed to go through the colon again. There was fecal contamination everywhere. The major bleeding was coming from the midline deep in his abdomen.

With Martin continuing to hold pressure, from the left side of the table I got control of the aorta right below the diaphragm and then had another vascular clamp ready to place right above the aortic bifurcation. I applied both clamps, Martin released his pressure and withdrew his hands and—blood continued its attempted journey to the ceiling. "Martin, it's not the aorta," I said. The massive bleeding was coming from a bullet hole right through the junction of his superior mesenteric vein and portal vein.

We all know how important the heart and brain are, but let me tell you, this is where you live. It's almost like "no man's land." Lots of stuff in a very small area and stuff you really can't do without. We repaired the veins. It stopped the bleeding and this allowed us to stabilize his vital signs. Because of the number of bullet holes in his colon we did a transverse colectomy. Next we repaired some holes to the small bowel. We were obviously saving the hardest part of his repairs, the pancreatic injury, for last.

We started sewing, trying to piece things back together. It wasn't working. We tried something else—that didn't work. By this time it felt like we had been operating on him forever. I told Martin I was going to call the staff for some advice. We weren't getting anywhere and I had sort of learned that sometimes no matter what I thought, there was no gold "S" on my shirt.

Breaking scrub I went to the anesthesia office and called Marty Litwin, who was on staff call. He answered the phone from a dead sleep. I apologized for the call and explained the situation. He made a suggestion and I told him we had already tried that. He made another suggestion and I repeated same. He made a third suggestion and when I told him that we had tried that too; he told me to try it again, it had to work. I scrubbed back in and told Martin what had transpired. "Let's try it again, Martin," I said.

With no result other than more frustration I went back out and called Litwin again. This time his wife answered. When I asked to speak with him, she said that he was on his way.

"Oh, he's coming here?" I replied, which in fact is what I wanted.

"Yes," she said. "He said that in all your years of residency this is the first time that he knew of that you had ever asked for help, so you must really be in trouble."

Marty showed up and scrubbed in. He then realized the extent of the problem. We fashioned a Roux-en-Y pancreaticojejunostomy. The tissues were not ideal and very damaged, but it was the best we could do. I knew this case would be discussed at D&C conference at best as just a case, but more likely when he started having complications and again probably when he died. I wanted all the help I could get from the head of the table.

We irrigated his abdominal cavity with gallons of antibiotic solution, placed retention sutures, and closed his midline fascia. We left the subcutaneous tissue and skin open packed with antibiotic soaked dressings and sent him to ICU.

His girlfriend, the alleged shooter, came to see him every day and sat by his bedside. About ten days later we reexplored him because of a very febrile course. We drained a subphrenic abscess and a cul-de-sac abscess. He went on to develop massive necrotizing fasciitis. Despite more debridement and antibiotics he expired of massive infection and sepsis.

The variety of thoracic cases along with the vascular cases continued. Browder was chief and had been since January. I tried to disassociate myself from the cardiac surgery results, but the other residents made a point of keeping me posted whether I wanted to be or not.

In April two very significant cases presented themselves. EM was the young man with the permanent tracheostomy that Bob Hewitt had helped me repair an ASD on one year earlier. It was not surprising that he now came in with severe tracheal stenosis.

It was amazing how much he had grown in just a year since his heart had been repaired. Hewitt again helped me with the operation. The portion of the trachea that is usually narrowed in these cases actually lies behind the sternum.

One might think it necessary to split the sternum in order to repair them; not so. By placing a rolled-up sheet transversely under the shoulders, it allows the head to fall back and elevates that portion of trachea up into the neck. The trickiest part of the operation involves the anesthesiologist. Even the smallest endotracheal tube will not pass through the narrowed area. Ventilation has to be done carefully. After the area is completely dissected free and exposed, the trachea below the narrowed area is transected completely. A sterile endotracheal tube is then inserted into the cut end of the trachea and non-obstructed ventilation can proceed. The stenotic (narrowed) area of trachea can now be completely resected and the two cut ends sewn back together end to end. This is an operation that demonstrates beautiful anatomy and a cure for the patient.

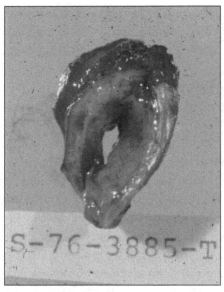

Resected tracheal stenosis.

Randy Owens

Over the course of the past seven years I had come to know many of my counterparts on the purple-and-gold side. We would never operate together, but there were occasions where you might be in the dining room or waiting for an OR when you might have a chance to chat and compare cases.

Randy Owens was the LSU cardiac resident. Besides being a regular at Joe's, he also loved to fish. Grand Isle, Louisiana, was often referred to as "the end of the world." The road ended right at the Gulf of Mexico. Bordered by Barataria Bay, an area made famous by the pirate Jean Lafitte, it was a fisherman's paradise. One could fish and crab in the brackish water of the marshes or fill up the boat with redfish and speckled trout out in the Gulf. Randy loved to fish there.

On April 17 he was surf fishing when a man and his son got caught in a riptide. Owens let a bystander hold his rod and reel. Using the line as a tether he made his way out to the couple. He let them use the line to help pull themselves to safety and avoid drowning.

When it came time for Randy to do the same, the line broke. He was swept away and drowned. The death was felt throughout the whole of hospital. Mother Charity had tragically lost one of its own children. The LSU house officers planned a traditional marching funeral from Charity to Joe's. Dr. Cohn got wind of it and vetoed the parade part of it. It didn't stop the celebration of life at Joe's.

During the spring all the residents were notified that we would be taking a standardized in-service exam. This was a first for the program. We had been "tested" every admit night with varied types of trauma, any 7 a.m. case doing a gastrectomy for carcinoma with a staff attending present, or on a bad Friday afternoon in D&C conference. When we were making rounds with an attending or Dr. Drapanas, a question would most often be answered by quoting the author who wrote the original paper on the condition or operation. Most of the time you would have that reprint folded in your pocket along with numerous others. In medical school you studied the texts. In residency, I found out, I should have.

After the exam I was summoned to Collins' office to find out the results of my exam. "You failed your exam; you will never pass your boards!" I was told. Was he getting enjoyment out of this or was it just my paranoia again? I think coming from anyone else's mouth it would have felt different, maybe softer or with some empathy.

"You better do something about it; you *will not* pass your boards." I heard it again. He wasn't going to tell me what I could or couldn't do. He had already told me I couldn't do anymore hearts and his results were worse than mine.

Of course, probably years later I have reflected back realizing (unknowingly) what a great favor he had done for me. I was very concerned and angry, but angry at myself and angry enough to do something about it. I left his office and took the back elevators down to the first floor, marched into the Tulane Medical School bookstore and purchased the two-volume set of Seymour Schwartz's *Principles of Surgery,* the ugly yellow books. Along with that, I got a handful of those yellow "Hi-lighter" marking pens, the fat ones.

That night, at a desk set up in the same room with my daughter's crib, I started studying. I started at the introduction and then into page one. I read and highlighted every word that remotely seemed important until I got through the last page of volume two.

This went on through the first three or four months of our time in Rochester.

The house we had rented had a finished basement, something you never saw in New Orleans because of the high water table. I had set up a study area down there. After highlighting both volumes, I then went back and, filling numerous legal pads, transcribed everything that was marked bright transparent yellow. Into Rochester's winter months, clad in a sweater and down jacket to offset Rochester's minus-degree temperatures, until I took the written part of my Boards in Chicago, I studied and restudied all my notes. They went everywhere with me.

Spending every other night in St. Mary's Hospital babysitting our post-op hearts was not spent idly. I was determined to pass my written boards.

Eric Ross

The medical term pulmonary embolus has become a household term, known by just about everyone. Most commonly referring to a blood clot traveling to the lung, an embolus is anything traveling in the blood stream. Deep venous thrombosis (DVT) is the most common etiology causing blood clots to go to the lung. On two separate occasions Mathis Becker and I witnessed a different kind of blood vessel embolus.

Becker had a narcotic agent come into the Charity ER one night with a GSW to the abdomen. When they explored him they found an injury to his inferior vena cava, the major vein draining all of the blood coming back to the heart from the lower half of the body. They could not find the bullet. Unlike in every Western you've seen, physicians don't go hunting for bullets if they are not readily available. If you did find one you were expected to mark it and turn it over to the authorities. You would then probably find yourself testifying in a courtroom. "Doctor, is this the bullet, with your mark on it, that you took out of agent so and so?"

If the physicians taking care of our twentieth president, James Garfield, had not been so overzealous in trying to find his bullet, he might have lived out his presidential term after his assassination attempt from what should have been a non-fatal injury.

Postop, Becker and his team got an X-ray demonstrating the bullet had "embolized" to the heart. They got two operations out of that one.

One spring night Martin Evans and I were again on trauma call. Eric Ross was a recent graduate of the accounting program at the University of Florida. He had taken a job in New Orleans and he and his girlfriend (Donna) had recently moved to the Crescent City. The Freret bus line, affectionately known as the "Freret Jet," runs from Broadway through the Tulane campus past Fortier High School and ends near downtown.

One night the couple was riding on the bus, sitting in an area between the front door and the back door that opens on the right side of the bus. At one of the stops closer to town, a young "night fighter" jumped out of the opened rear door of the bus, at the same time grabbing Donna's purse.

Chivalrous Eric jumped up from his seat, ran to the open door shouting at the thief to stop. The thief, still running, whirled around, and with a .22 pistol fired one shot at Eric.

Now, as a kid growing up in New Orleans, I spent just about every Saturday at the Fox Theater's matinee near the corner of Gentilly Boulevard and Elysian Fields Avenue, three blocks from my house. I watched Roy Rogers and Gene Autry make this Hollywood shot dozens of times. Whether they were shooting guns out of the black-hatted bad guy's hands, shooting hats off of heads, or placing a warning shot between another bad guy's feet, they never missed.

Neither did the young punk with the stolen purse. Eric was rolled into the Charity ER with a GSW to the abdomen exactly in the midline between the bottom of the xyphoid and the belly button. With two guns and twelve shots, I don't think Roy could have made the exact same shot at that distance one time.

Eric was in excruciating pain and in shock as he was wheeled into the Charity ER. An IV was rapidly started, blood was drawn for a type and match and I ordered some low titer O negative blood. We wheeled him directly to the ER X-ray room. Before a film could be taken, his blood pressure started bottoming out. I made the decision to take him directly to the OR. No time was wasted as there was none to waste.

While we prepped and draped him, I said, "You got this one, Martin, I'll help you do him. With one fell swoop of the scalpel, Martin exposed his

251

abdomen. There was blood everywhere, but it was mainly situated in the retroperitoneal space, the lining of our abdomen, the protective envelope, if you will, that covers just about everything. Most of Eric's blood volume was in that potential space from below his diaphragm to his inguinal ligament. We knew that the bullet had probably gotten his aorta. Besides a perforation in a small bowel segment, there was a hole going right through his duodenum into his aorta.

We didn't have any vascular clamps on the field and there wasn't time to get any. I took two "sponge sticks," four-inch-square gauze pads folded in a special way, held by a ring forceps, and placed one above the injury site and one below in order to shut off aortic blood flow. That's one of the tricks you learn along the way and you don't even remember who taught it to you. "Okay Martin, open up the aorta, sew up the back hole then the front incision and let's get out."

With the improvised "clamps" in place, Martin made an incision in the aorta through the bullet hole.

"There's only one hole!" he exclaimed.

"What, are you sure?"

Sure enough, the bullet had embolized, been taken down stream with the aortic blood flow into one of Eric's legs. What a case! "Sew him up, Martin, sew him up!"

This was the first time Martin had been placed in a really bad situation with an aortic repair. A quick image went through my brain of the first aorta I had tried to sew on with Bob Hewitt. That patient's fate had already been determined. His chance of survival was zilch. We were not going to let this guy die and I didn't want Martin to fail like I did. He was destined to become a very successful and noted board-certified vascular surgeon. "I can't," said Martin, "you do it."

I kept my right hand in its position occluding aortic blood flow from filling the opened aorta. Martin took the sponge stick from my left hand and got distal control and I sewed up the opened aorta with my left hand. Martin repaired the two perforations of the duodenum and the other small bowel holes while we waited for the portable X-ray to come.

The student X-ray tech placed the plate in the table and took the film. Because of the size of the bullet we reasoned that it probably wouldn't get lower than just below the knee where the popliteal artery splits into three smaller branches. The tech returned with the film showing the bullet to be exactly where we thought it should be. Unfortunately, in her excitement, she had forgotten to label the film left or right.

"I think it's in the right leg," she said.

"Are you sure?"

"Yes, I think that's the right leg." was her response again. Hoping that we might be able to fish the bullet out with an embolectomy catheter and to avoid us from making a second incision in his lower leg, we cut down on his right femoral artery. Placing the appropriate tapes around the vessel, we opened it, slipped the three-foot-long Fogarty catheter through the small incision and—nope, it went all the way down to Eric's ankle.

"Take another film," I barked, "and this time label the damn thing right and left." She returned clearly showing the bullet again in the now labeled left leg. We had the circulating nurse prep and drape his lower extremity and made the appropriate incision below his knee, exposed the area at the trifurcation of the popliteal artery, opened the vessel. and behold—a .22 caliber bullet.

I don't know how much blood and other fluids Eric had received from the head of the table, but his vital signs were stable. We had repaired everything and we sent him to the ICU.

When Eric was out of the woods we transferred him to the Doctor's Infirmary. Other than a prolonged ileus (his intestines not working for a while) he did extremely well. Both Martin and I found ourselves just stopping by to talk with him when we had idle time. He was only a few years younger than me and we had formed a bond. He could have just as easily been a Tulane student or someone we knew.

Eric was a huge basketball fan. Being from New York, his favorite team was the Nets and his favorite player none other than "Dr." Julius Irving. Dr. J. was a phenomenon. He developed the art of flying through the air to dunk the ball from the free throw line before Michael Jordan did and led his team to multiple championships. He also garnered multiple scoring and MVP titles. As Eric would have it, he started calling me Dr. J, certainly not because of any ability to play basketball.

After he was discharged I started seeing him in my weekly clinic and at the appropriate time I let him go back to his favorite exercise, playing basketball. He was involved with a league that met a couple of nights a week.

Later that month, one of the major drug companies sponsored a drug seminar for chief residents. I was invited along with Ken Falterman, the LSU chief. Ken had a strong interest in pediatric surgery. We were flown to Dallas along with chief residents from major programs all over the country, basically to hear their drug propaganda. These conferences were mainly held to promote their line of antibiotics, which at that time was one of the most often used drugs by surgeons.

After a morning of talks and lectures, a lunch was provided. Ken and I had not had a chance to talk so we shared a large round table with eight other chief residents. The major surgery programs in Boston, New York, Philadelphia, etc. were all represented. During the meal I asked Ken what cases he had been doing the past few weeks. "Pediatric inguinal hernias, biliary atresia, Soave pull through, T-E fistula," he replied, to name a few. He then asked me what I had been doing. I hadn't noticed at the time, but the other residents at the table had stopped eating and talking and were just listening.

I told him about a couple of pulmonary resections I had done, as well as an abdominal aneurysm, carotid endarterectomy, femoral-popliteal bypass and Eric's bullet embolus. A female resident from across the table spoke up, "Excuse me, what hospital are you all on the staff at?" thinking we were professors. I replied to her that Ken was chief resident in surgery at LSU and I was chief at Tulane, both of us at Charity Hospital of New Orleans. She replied, "You all do cases like that? We don't even see cases like that."

Back at Charity one afternoon Eric showed back up in clinic. He was complaining about getting severe leg cramping when running down the basketball court. When I examined him he had bounding pedal pulses. I was hesitant to do any tests on him because of his age and what appeared to be normal circulation. After seeing him a couple more times he begged for me to check into it.

I ordered an arteriogram (the radiologists were doing them now) and to my surprise it showed that his popliteal artery was completely occluded.

He had already developed a huge set of collateral vessels going around the blockage which were responsible for his positive pulses. I brought the films out to have Dr. John look at them with me. I was very hesitant to reoperate on Eric unless I had an experienced eye and mind giving me an opinion based on experience.

"Look," Dr. John said, "this guy loves to play basketball. He doesn't make his living from it, but it's a quality of life thing. Tell him his risks and do a short-segment vein interposition graft to his popliteal artery. He'll be fine." Once again John Ochsner had given me not only sound advice but his time. And again he volunteered to come and help me.

After discussing the options with Eric, I operated on him on June 14. I'd harvested some saphenous vein from his ankle and had him face down in order to approach his popliteal artery from the back. As I was sewing in the distal anastomosis Dr. Watts Webb walked into the OR.

After an almost two-year hiatus Tulane had hired a new chairman for the surgery department. I hadn't met Webb. He asked what I was doing, so I presented the case to him. After telling him all about Eric, the embolus, and his late problem, I then asked if he would like to scrub in. He shook his head, turned and walked out.

The rest of the case went fine. Eric recovered and was discharged

After I left Charity, Martin told me about a case he did involving a shot-gun wound to the abdomen. He was up to his elbows in blood and BB holes one evening when Webb walked in on him. After being presented the case and being invited to scrub in, again he declined and walked out.

Butch Knoepp had served his mandatory two years in the military service in Germany. When he came back to Tulane in 1978, he met with Webb to resume his place in his residency. Webb told him he could "stay or go." This was an unheard-of response. In the late 1950s, the Board of Directors of Charity Hospital had passed a rule with regard to any house officer who left their training to serve in the military. The rule stated that their place had to be reserved for them when they got out. Certainly Knoepp had no way of knowing this, Webb should have known. Knoepp stayed.

Sometimes in the early nineties I received an urgent call from my old friend and co-intern Jim Dowling. Jim had stayed on the staff of the Tulane Department of Surgery before he left the school to join Dr. Walter Becker at the Mahorner Clinic. What he wanted to tell me was that he and other members of the staff had gotten paged to return to the school for an urgent meeting in the Tulane Surgery Library one afternoon. In the same room where the weekly D&C conferences were held and the same room that contained the formaldehyde preserved brain of Dr. Rudolph Matas, Webb proceeded to give them a presentation on Amway. I wonder what Dr. Matas' brain thought about that.

It was too much to think that a "Drapanas" could be duplicated. Everyone has a different intellect, a different amount of knowledge, personality and manner of teaching. However, these differences were too great in a lot of resident's minds. I'm sure Webb did a lot of positive things during his stay at Tulane. I know that his dismissing Collins was one of them. When Webb left Tulane he joined the LSU staff and later when he retired, ironically he moved to Alexandria, Louisiana, Knoepp's hometown.

On June 23 I did an exploratory thoracotomy on a sixty-one-year-old-male (FH) for carcinoma of the lung. It was unresectable. It had been nine years since I had graduated from Tulane Medical School.

Tulane surgery faculty and staff, 1977.

I had been trained under the influence of Creech and four other acting or full-time chairmen. A surgeon's technique is usually not attributable to any one person. The first person to show you or teach you how to do a particular procedure is generally on what you are going to base anything else you do. Ideally, you then modify and improve each technique as to how it bests suits you.

My father had taught me how to tie surgical knots when I was in high school. Glenn Kokame had shown me how to do cut downs. A.D. Smith, Robichaux, Woolverton, Gage, and many along the way had all contributed in some way to try, knowingly or unknowingly, to make me a better physician and a good surgeon. Above all, it was the unwritten program ethos passed down from Gus through all of them: the right way to do things you absorbed and perfected because you had to—patients' lives depended on it. It was "Iron Man" training.

I loved doing abdominal aneurysms when I was in private practice and I changed very little in the technique I had learned from the way John Ochsner had done them. I also learned how to do coronaries the way John and Noel did them. Over the years as the methods of stopping the heart and protecting the myocardium improved, I was able to modify different steps in my procedure. You have to be flexible enough to adapt to new technological advances and procedures as they benefit the patient. In CV surgery changes don't come often and they aren't accepted as quickly in other specialties. There is too much at stake.

To that point, in 1995, I attended a meeting of the Society of Thoracic Surgeons in San Diego. A surgeon from South America presented a paper with reference to a series of patients he had operated on for congestive heart failure. He had developed a radical new heart operation with amazing results. The whole place was abuzz and everyone wanted to go back home and do one. The schedule for these meetings is prepared one year in advance, nothing is added on.

Because of all the commotion about this new "lifesaving operation," a special session was fit in during a noon break with the presenter and a distinguished panel of known surgeons. Several surgeons gave anecdotal reports of one or two of the new procedures they had done. The fervor increased. Then, I'll never forget it, Dr. Denton Cooley slowly rose from his chair and, with that long Texas stride, approached the podium. He said a few words and then stuck out his arm and forefinger as if pointing to each and every one of the assembled surgeons in that huge hall and said, "Don't you dare go back to your hospitals and practices and think you can do this procedure and replicate these results. Give it some time." I listened to his advice, I know of some who didn't. The procedure was soon abandoned.

One of Dr. Drapanas' favorite philosophies to come out of the Friday D&C conference had to do with how you would take your board exams. Time and time again he would say, "Remember, when asked how you would treat a patient or take care of a problem, you tell them how we do it here. Do not tell them what you read in some journal last week, you tell them how we do it here."

This came home in spades to me in the winter of 1978 when I sat for the oral portion of the American Board of General Surgery exam. It was in Denver and I had just left one room being quizzed by Dr. Seymour Schwartz, the Seymour Schwartz who wrote the textbook on surgery I had virtually memorized to prepare for these very boards. On entering the next room, I was greeted by two people seated behind a desk. One was a board examiner from Boston; the second, a local female surgeon board examiner.

After some minor discussion she presented to me the case of a young man who had been in an automobile accident and had hit a telephone pole. He was conscious, alert, vital signs were stable and he had no visible signs of trauma. On physical exam, however, she admitted that I had found abdominal tenderness, direct and rebound. Rebound tenderness is a definite sign of intraabdominal irritation or injury. She asked me what my course of treatment would be. Reflecting on what Dr. Drapanas had repeatedly told us, I told her I would start an IV, insert a nasogastric tube, Foley catheter, draw some blood for a type and match and bring him to surgery.

"What!" she said. "You're going to operate on him just like that?"

I answered in the affirmative.

"You can't do that," she said, "What else can you do?" Since she wasn't going to let me operate on him, I then went through a list of esoteric tests that not only were not available to us at Charity, but we wouldn't have done anyway.

She told me those were all negative so I told her I would put him in the ICU for overnight observation. She allowed me to do that. She then told me that I got a call at 2 a.m. telling me the patient was in shock. What would I do now? I replied, "Well, if you had let me operate on him earlier he wouldn't be in shock. Can I take him to the operating room now?" Now that's being damn cocky with an examiner who was holding your fate and no telling what else in her hands.

She allowed me, but still quizzed me on what type of incision, what to look for and other details. There was no blood in his abdomen, his spleen was intact and whichever organ I asked about was normal.

She had a smirk on her face I wanted to see disappear. It came to me what he had and I told her the maneuver I would perform. I then told her that he had a blowout of the duodenum at the head of his pancreas. "You're right!" she exclaimed, almost in disbelief. Thank you Dr. D.

Epilogue

"The Day the Music Died"

On July 2, 1977 I hooked up my 1973 yellow Volkswagen station wagon to a large U-Haul rental truck containing all of our worldly possessions and got behind the wheel. Warren Hillel, one of Charity's few orderlies joined me in the cab. His wife, Pam, an LPN at Charity, babysat for us on numerous occasions. I had approached Warren and offered him a trip to Rochester, Minnesota, and a return airplane trip back home if he would help me with the driving and troubleshoot any problems with the truck. Warren had never been out of the city limits of New Orleans, and I had never driven a big truck on a long trip. He jumped at the opportunity.

The first night after dinner and back in our motel room in St. Louis, I told him he could call home. I'll never forget the expression on his face while talking with his wife, his looking around the motel room and his expression, "You will not believe where I am."

The next afternoon we pulled into Rochester and parked in front of the house Len and I and the kids would be living in for the next twelve months.

The next-door neighbor came out to welcome us followed by another one from across the street carrying a six pack of cold beer. The four of us sat on the curb. Four guys drinking some beer.

Warren was on an adventure in a land he had never been to and probably would never come to again.

I was on an adventure to a new hospital and clinic that would further shape my life almost as much as Charity Hospital had. It would open doors and add to a resume that I did not think could be improved on.

I spent three months at a time on the service of four different cardiac surgeons.

For the better part of the year I spent every other night in St. Mary's Hospital. There were small sleeping rooms right next to one of the two cardiac ICUs. There were six cardiac operating rooms, two-story amphitheater types similar to the Delgado Amphitheater at Charity. The main exception was a huge ten- to fifteen-foot-tall window. During those winter months I would find myself watching Canadian geese fly by with a royal blue sky as a backdrop.

Even though my fellowship in Rochester exposed me mainly to the correction of congenital heart defects coronary arteries and valves were also operated on. There were tidbits of technique I took away from whomever I operated with, no matter what the case was.

Dr. Dwight McGoon was a master in the correction of the most complicated congenital heart defects you would ever see or read about. He had been a resident at Hopkins when Rowena Spencer was an intern.

His patients were from all over the world and quite often when making rounds I had to do so with one or two interpreters. His technique and mannerisms were precise and replicated from procedure to procedure even to the exact number of stitches he placed in each part of the heart. He was a physician's physician and a surgeon's surgeon.

Besides being able to operate with the masters and being able to take away the positive things, you also put in your surgical computer the things you don't want to remember or change. If it ain't broke don't fix it. I was surprised that the Mayo surgeons were still putting in Starr-Edwards valves and not doing internal mammary artery grafts.

We survived the snow and minus degrees of the Rochester winter. Although I was not the primary surgeon on most of the cases I scrubbed on, I regained my confidence in being able to do cardiac surgery.

I passed both parts of my general surgery boards with ease.

Our third child, Nickolas, was born in late April when there was fresh powdery snow on the ground.

The calls started coming in for a cardiac surgeon to go to different areas to join a practice or start a cardiac program. Although Charity was in the rearview mirror, I would never forget it and would always be one of its children.

I interviewed at the Children's Hospital in Washington, D.C. It would be an incredible position doing solely pediatric heart surgery with an appointment as an assistant professor on the staff of George Washington University Medical School. On returning from the interview, I had a conversation with Dr. McGoon. "What are your plans, Jim?" he asked. Was this going to be like the talk I had with Dr. John?

He continued, "You know sometimes we ask one of the fellows like yourself to stay on at the Clinic. Have you given that some thought?" I was honored to have been given that consideration, but also embarrassed in having to tell him of my plans and that I was committed to going to Washington. I felt a twinge of guilt. He wished me good luck and told me what a good position that was. He was the most gracious, humble, and generous man I think I ever experienced.

A year later he presented a seminar on congenital heart disease in Bethesda for the American College of Cardiology. I attended the seminar at the Heart House. In front of a group of approximately 150 other physicians he acknowledged one of the papers I had written while in Rochester.

During my second year on the staff at Children's Hospital National Medical Center in Washington, DC a young girl I had previously operated on for a very complex congenital cardiac condition was readmitted. She needed emergency surgery that afternoon to repair an intracardiac baffle. I rapidly told her nurse a list of instruments and materials I needed to do a cut down. I then went to my office to review her chart.

After a few minutes I returned and everything I had wanted was laid out perfectly on a sterile drape on a Mayo stand. At first I couldn't believe it. Probably for the first time, I looked at the nurse.

On her white uniform was a gold pin with scalloped corners. A silver pelican was in the center surrounded by the initials CHNO. She was a Charity Hospital-trained nurse. "I should have known," I told her.

Charity Hospital of Louisiana nurse's pin.

In Rochester, and occasionally in D.C., I would receive a note from Eric Ross. His girlfriend's sister had developed a serious illness and she had moved back to Florida. Eric moved back to his native New York, went to law school and became an attorney. We continued to correspond. When we moved to the D.C. area we occasionally talked with each other.

One day he drove down to Bethesda to see us and have dinner. We talked and reminisced. His leg was doing well and he was still playing a little basketball. He still called me "Dr. J."

Later that year I was asked to interview at LSU Medical School for the position of head of the section of pediatric heart surgery. I spent two days interviewing with LSU faculty members, going to cardiac conferences and visiting with some people I had known when I was a resident. During a small break between interviews, I decided to walk over to Charity and hang out in the main lobby. I wanted to see if I recognized anyone. I wanted to see if anything had changed; take the pulse of the place.

Unlike private practice where you sometimes become friends with your patients or your friends become your patient, in residency there is very little to no contact with a patient after their surgery. What's more you rarely receive a follow-up.

I had finished a short conversation and while leaning against a wall, a middle-aged gentleman came over and said, "Aren't you Dr. Ciaravella?" I answered and he said, "Yes, I knew it, you took out my lung for cancer a few years ago." I asked him his name—it was him, WL, the man we had done the pneumonectomy on for oat cell carcinoma. He was alive and well five years post-op. Dr. Drapanas would have been relieved, and I was as grateful as the patient.

In the spring, I was being interviewed for a position at a private hospital in Metairie, Louisiana. They were showing me around the hospital, and as we went through the cardiac catherization lab, I was introduced to the technicians and lab personnel. A young lady called out, "Dr. Ciaravella you operated on my brother at Charity Hospital." "Oh, what did I do to him?" I replied. "He was in a motorcycle accident with a badly broken leg and torn blood vessels. You saved his leg," she said. It was RG's sister. I asked her if he was still riding motorcycles. She said he'd given those up. Another lesson learned.

In August 2005, Hurricane Katrina filled up the Gulf of Mexico with its 100-plus mph winds, torrential rain, and swollen seas on its deadly march to New Orleans and the Mississippi Gulf Coast. As a kid growing up in below-sea-level New Orleans, during hurricane season, often the *Times-Picayune* newspaper would print on its front page an artist's rendering of what would happen to the city when "the big one" hit. Quite literally, they showed a bowl flooded with water and buildings sticking out of it.

It was proposed that a counterclockwise-spinning hurricane would come up the mouth of the Mississippi from the Gulf or into Lake Borne, through the Rigolets into Lake Pontchartrain. It would then dump the contents of Lake Pontchartrain into the bowl that was and is New Orleans.

Katrina pretty much followed the script. However, although the end result was the same, the water didn't come over the concrete steps and sea walls along Lakeshore Drive at the lakefront. The surge of water and pressure coming into New Orleans drainage canals was too much for the levees to stand and many of them were breached or gave way and flooded the city.

The day after Katrina hit, it was thought that New Orleans had weathered the storm and lucked out. Although trees were down, power was out and there was some flooding, it was not worse than had happened with Hurricane

Betsy years before. Windows were knocked out of some high-rises, such as the Hyatt Regency next to the Super Dome, but there was no massive flooding.

Hyatt Regency Hotel, New Orleans, post-Hurricane Katrina, 2005.

The water then crept in hours later, filling everything, including the basement of Charity Hospital, its stair wells and the first floor. All patients who could be evacuated (the walking wounded) had been transferred out prior to the eleventh hour. The remaining patients were cared for by a highly dedicated staff of doctors and nurses who stayed. And they stayed through it all, took care of ventilator patients with no electricity, ran IVs with manual adjustment and wrapped the dead.

It was Katrina and politics that literally signed Charity's death certificate. They closed a hospital and put an end to one of the greatest teaching institutions this country has ever seen.

Just as the plane crash that took the lives of Buddy Holly, the Big Bopper, and Richie Valens—and inspired the song *American Pie*—didn't kill rock and roll, the death of Charity didn't kill medicine. The medicine that was learned and practiced at Charity lives on in the thousands of doctors and nurses who were trained there, and the doctors who became teaching staff and even department chairmen at major medical schools. And don't forget a Cajun-speaking vascular surgeon who became chancellor of a leading medical center, or a cop's son who became president of the American Medical Association. Physicians who provide care to people of every walk of life, from farmers and the indigent to professional people, mayors' and governors' families, irrespective of race, color, or creed, are still practicing.

Bob Thornton, a junior resident when I was a third-year, wanted the busiest, dirtiest program he could train at when he finished medical school in Arkansas. He applied to Cook County, Grady, Jackson Memorial in Miami, and Big Charity and was accepted to all four. He realized he didn't have the funds to get him anywhere but down to New Orleans.

After his internship he served his two years in the Navy. Although he'd been accepted back into Charity's ENT program, he opted for what he thought was greener grass, Atlanta's Grady. On arriving for duty he found out that their "ENT program" was actually under the direction of the head of plastic surgery. He was told, "You can do ENT, but you're not going to be making any incisions on the face."

Bob then called Dr. Harold Tabb, the head of Tulane's ENT program whom he'd previously worked under. "Doctor Tabb, I've made a mistake." Tabb had a place for him. As great a program as Grady's was, it was medically oriented. Charity, because of its heritage, was surgically weighted.

The reflections by Charity Hospital-trained surgery residents and staffers George Barnes and Bob Hewitt on when they saw action in the military during the Vietnam War are just two examples of the superior training they received compared to surgeons from other noted programs. My non-medically oriented base commander in Guam knew of Tulane and Charity.

A slightly exaggerated statement was made to Jane Todd by a chief resident at the end of her first year: "When you finish your training here, you will be able to do any procedure with a flashlight and a screwdriver in the trunk of a car." Years later, while in private practice in Center, Texas, she wasn't deterred a bit when the lights went out one day while she was doing surgery. "Get me a flashlight."

In further thinking about Dr. Drapanas, it is interesting how life has come full circle. As a promising protégée and budding transplant surgeon, he was brought to Tulane for the purpose of not only leading a famed surgery program and training future surgeons, but to transplant the human liver and pancreas. As best as I can determine he was not able to accomplish that goal.

Time and fate have filled that legacy with the appointment of Tulane's first surgery chairwoman, Dr. Mary Killackey. At our first meeting, I asked her what her specialty was. Nonchalantly, she responded, "Oh, I transplant pancreases and livers." I certainly think the Boss would be pleased and approve.

During Russell Woo's last day as a resident, before he went into private practice in San Francisco, he had a talk with Dr. Drapanas. He asked Drapanas how to be a good teacher. "In all of the years of residency we did," Russell continued, "There was never instruction on how to teach, how to pass on to others what we had learned." Drapanas told Woo that teaching was secondary. "Always be a good surgeon and foremost knowing how to carry yourself and treat people is most important. Don't forget to have heart."

Looking back, the seven years at Charity seem in many ways like they never existed; in others they seem like yesterday. I have never forgotten that first day as an intern. No matter how smart or talented you are or think you are, you have to have some luck along the way. If you are lucky, you evolve from the bottom of the totem pole to the top.

I went from the basics of how to open an infected thigh to resecting co-arctations of the aorta, replacing heart valves and assisting my junior residents in taking out stomachs and parts of intestine. I went from the student to the teacher. As unfortunate as I was to lose my chairman during the heart of my training, I was lucky to have another mentor pick up my baton, carry it, and speak up for me. "Tell John to send in his letter," Bob Wallace said. What if he hadn't? Each step gave me an advantage over the one before it.

The famous philosopher and poet Yogi Berra is quoted as saying, "When you come to a fork in the road take it." How many roads did I take and travel, figuratively and literally? How many times did I select left or right?

At times we felt like the gypsies I had encountered under the bed in C400A during one of the first days of my internship, traveling from one out-of-town hospital to another. The decision to march down to the bookstore and then virtually memorize Schwartz's two-volume surgery text, the decision to move to Rochester, the decision not to take any number of jobs and not stay in Rochester, and when we left the D.C. area I had even more choices.

Around 1987 I received a call from Dr. Jim Pluth, head of the section of cardiac surgery at the Mayo. We had developed a friendship when I was there and he did me some major favors when I left Children's Hospital. After the normal hello's, etc. he asked me, "Jim, are you happy?" Interesting question. Had he called about three years prior I would have said no. He explained how Mayo was opening up two major satellite hospitals, one in Florida and one in Arizona. I could have my choice as to which one I wanted to be chief of cardiac surgery. "When you come to a fork ... "

There are three sayings operating room nurses and others have heard me often say: First, get on the green. You golfers can relate to that. Second, never say never and always say sometimes. Be careful of superlatives. They'll come back to bite you in the butt. And lastly, the only bad decision is indecision.

After several hours of more phone calls I decided to decline his incredible offer.

I have no regrets about the path I have taken. We have been unbelievably fortunate in the people we have met along the way, the friends we have made and the successes we have had. Maybe the whole of Charity Hospital was a miracle and just as likely this thing we call life is a miracle.

I have often reflected back on what A.D. Smith told me that first day of my internship. Would I be an Iron Man? At times you feel like you can solve any problem, handle any challenge. Unfortunately, there are also humbling moments around every corner.

I often think about my patient with the successful repair of a descending aortic aneurysm who subsequently succumbed to an abdominal aneurysm I delayed repairing. I've had a child with a complicated congenital heart defect fail to survive, yet have seen an eighty-year-old heart-surgery patient walk out the same day.

To be able to talk again with those I had not talked with in such a long time was very special. I enjoyed catching up with their lives.

My old roommate, Ron Swartz, is still practicing urology in New Orleans.

Bill Browder is chairman of the East Tennessee State University Department of Surgery and still an operating surgeon.

Bill Blackshear lives in Florida and, after practicing vascular surgery, is advising on the nutritional aspects of health care.

Ruary O'Connell is still a practicing general surgeon.

Ken Falterman, my LSU counterpart my chief year and lunchmate in Dallas, is still enjoying practicing pediatric surgery. He holds Rowena Spencer in as high regard as I do.

Jane Todd married a cowboy and wound up in Center, Texas. She still practices medicine.

Liz Hilliker is still doing emergency room medicine in Missouri.

Steve Harkness's patients are fortunate to have him as their surgeon in south Louisiana.

Mo Bethea, who practiced cardiac surgery with three other Charity's children, is retired and living in New Orleans. He has written a successful book on nutrition.

Sonny Trammel retired from a surgery practice in West Virginia with another of Charity's children and moved back to Louisiana to live with his artist wife.

Butch Knoepp went from being a successful cardiac surgeon in his hometown to being one of those intensivist types, and is married to another of Charity's children.

John Church still has a great sense of humor and retired from his plastic surgery practice.

Mark Kappleman retired from teaching and surgery and lives in the New Orleans area.

Steve Golladay retired from a very successful career as an academic pediatric surgeon and lives in Texas.

Martin Evans just retired from a successful vascular surgery practice in Virginia.

Tommy Hawke is retired from surgery in Augusta, Georgia. Tommy and Martin's friendship continued to the point that their sons practice law together in Georgia.

Akio Kitahama, my "human retractor" on the first internal mammary artery graft at Charity Hospital, has moved back to his home country of Japan after Hurricane Katrina. We had a great conversation.

Jan McClanahan practiced general surgery with two more of Charity's children. He also left New Orleans after Katrina and moved back to Mississippi.

My chiefs, John Gage and Bill Woolverton, both practiced at the same clinic in the Florida panhandle, John general surgery and Bill cardiac surgery. They're both retired.

Larry Cohen retired in Texas after becoming a hospital administrator. He had no pictures of him being Santa.

Gus Wetzel returned to his family-run surgical clinic in Missouri and is still in practice.

Al Guynes retired from cardiac surgery and lives in New Mexico. He was able to find his A&M senior boots that his mother gave away. He was the second hardest to find.

Mathis Becker was the most difficult to get in touch with and is retired from thoracic and vascular surgery in central Florida.

Russell Woo retired in San Francisco and his good buddy Glenn Pennington has retired from an academic life and practice of cardiac surgery in Tennessee.

George Barnes retired from cardiac surgery and lives in south Louisiana.

Phil Brewer, who was able to joust one-on-one with the great Christiaan Barnard, is retired from cardiac surgery in Georgia.

Larry Hollier started the first vascular surgery program at the Mayo Clinic. He is dean of the LSU Medical School and chancellor of the LSU Health Science System and still doing major vascular surgery.

Don Palmisano, my chief at Lallie Kemp when I was a student, is the only one who may be more type A than me. He has become an attorney, served as president of the American Medical Association, is still writing books, doing speaking engagements and championing the cause of defending physicians.

Bob Hewitt returned to Tulane as chair of the surgery department and is now retired.

And the Banty Rooster is retired and making custom violins from exotic woods.

I do not know if I qualified to be an Iron Man. Only those who came behind me would be able to say that. I do know that I did train under Iron Men. No one taught them how to teach, specifically, but they sure did teach us how to operate. What was once one of the greatest teaching programs in this country is gone. There will never be an institution like that or a program like that again. Charity Hospital of Louisiana was an institution, a way of life, it was a culture, and it had soul.

Even though in the sixties most of the MEN, WOMEN, and COLORED ONLY signs were gone from the bathrooms at filling stations and the hand-painted COLORED and WHITE signs were removed from the water fountains, New Orleans was still a segregated city, except in the "city" that was Charity. Alec Gifford announced over the TV on that January Sunday in 1973: "They are attacking your hospital, go defend it."

It was a hospital for everyone—all races and ethnicities—and that was what they wanted to defend. Every gunshot or stabbing victim got the same level of care despite their background.

For the most part in many teaching institutions, unfortunately, the personal approach to medicine is being replaced by computerized robots that can simulate a disease process and procedures. It is almost the norm to go into a physician's office and have the physician's nurse or equivalent come into the patient's room and spend more time on a computer than examining the patient or even looking at the patient. The Mayo Clinic now allots fifteen minutes for a patient consultation.

Technology cannot replace the hands-on approach of patient care. In the 1960s that technology might have been as simple as a stethoscope or nasogastric tube. Dr. Oscar Creech often said that it was more important for a surgeon to carry a nasogastric tube than a stethoscope—he could save more lives with it.

I fear the days of the Iron Men are gone.

Glossary of Medical Terms

"hernion" (hernia): a weakened area, usually in the abdomen; can be congenital or acquired

aminophylline drip: medication given in the vein to open constricted air passages in the lungs

aneurysm: an abnormal enlargement and thinning of a blood vessel; the larger they are the more prone to rupture

aorta: the major blood vessel in the body that arises from the heart and continues down approximately to the level of the navel

atelectasis: non-expansion of areas of lung that can lead to infection, usually post-surgery

atrial septal defect (ASD): a hole in the wall between the upper two pumping chambers of the heart

Babcock clamp: surgical instrument used to grasp tissues without damaging them

Balfour retractor: an adjustable stainless steel retractor used in abdominal operations to keep the sides of the incision (the abdominal wall) open

biliary atresia, Soave pull-through, T-E fistula: very complex congenital conditions and operations performed on the liver, trachea, and colon in young children

brachial artery: the major artery in the upper part of the arm

coarctation of the aorta: a congenital narrowing of the aorta in the chest that prevents normal blood flow to the lower part of the body

collateral blood vessels: extra blood vessels that naturally form in the body to provide blood flow and oxygen around a blockage, most commonly seen in the legs and heart

colon interposition: an operation that replaces the esophagus with a segment of colon

colostomy: a portion of opened large intestine that is placed on the abdominal wall such that bowel contents have to be collected in a bag

common bile duct exploration: an operation to remove gallstones from the main tube that drains bile from the liver

cul-de-sac abscess: an abscess deep in the pelvis

cut-down: usually an incision over a blood vessel

dermatome: a broad surgical knife for taking skin grafts

empyema: an abscess in the chest cavity outside of the lung

femur: the major long bone in the thigh

fistula: an abnormal area of drainage, usually from an area of intestine, can be postoperative, from infection or cancer

gastrectomy: removal of all or a part of the stomach

hemostats: small surgical clamps used to clamp blood vessels

hyperbaric oxygenation: high pressure oxygen given in a chamber to enhance oxygen delivery to the body

inferior vena cava (IVC): the major vein that brings all the blood back to the heart from the lower half of the body

intracardiac baffle: a wall created in the heart to correct a congenital heart condition, usually for transposition of the great vessels

Marlex mesh: a synthetic material sewn into wounds, mainly hernia repairs, to strengthen the repair

Mayo stand: a stainless-steel table in the operating room; when covered with a sterile covering, it is used to place sterile instruments on

McBurney's point: a point of reference in the lower right quadrant of the abdomen where an incision is made to remove an appendix

mediastinoscopy: examination of the area in the middle of the chest between the lungs, in front of the trachea and behind the ascending aorta

medical admit and ER: unlike most hospitals, Charity had two entirely separate areas to take care of medical emergencies and trauma

outflow area: the amount of blood that can get out of the heart in a specific time; the larger the outflow area the less the strain on the heart

pacemaker: a battery-operated electrical device implanted in a patient's body to keep the heart rate from getting too slow

pericardiocentesis: a procedure in which blood or fluid is drawn from around the heart

pulmonary edema: fluid in the tissues of the lungs

purse-string suture: a suture placed in a circular fashion that can be tied, securing an area

regional perfusion: a procedure whereby an extremity is isolated to allow anticancer agents to be given just to that area

residency: that period of specialty training for a physician

retractor: a metal surgical instrument used in surgery to gain exposure

Roux-en-Y pancreaticojejunostomy: a procedure joining the open end of the pancreas to a loop of small intestine. Done for trauma to the head of the pancreas or cancer of the pancreas

running the bowel: manually examining the entire length of the small intestine at the time of an operation looking for abnormalities or, in the case of trauma-holes.

Seldinger technique: a method whereby a special needle is introduced into a blood vessel (usually the femoral artery) and a catheter directed to the area in question; dye is then injected directly into the area rather than sticking each vessel separately to place dye in it

stoma: the opening of the trachea in the neck after a tracheostomy

Stryker bed: a special bed on rollers that allows for the patient to be rotated from his back to his abdomen without being physically turned

subphrenic abscess: an abscess under the diaphragm

tapping an organ: using a needle and syringe to remove fluid from an organ or body space

Unna boot: a calamine lotion-impregnated, wrapped gauze that came sterile in a roll. Wrapped around an extremity, it would harden like a cast but not as hard. It was usually left on about a week and then changed.

Whipple procedure: an operation done for cancer of the head of the pancreas

Index of Physicians and Other Important People

Resources

Allured, Janet and Judith F. Gentry, eds. *Louisiana Women, Their Lives and Times*. University of Georgia Press, 2009.

Cochran, Bambi L. Ray, "Rowena Spencer: a study of changing gender roles in Twentieth-century Louisiana Medicine," *Louisiana Women: Their Lives and Times*, 286. University of Georgia Press, 2009.

Cohn, Isidore, M.D. *Rudolph Matas*, Doubleday & Company, 1960.

Duffy, John, *The Tulane University Medical Center*. Louisiana State University Press, 1984.

Fishkin, C. A. "Remembering Dr. Rowena Spencer (1922–2014)." *Journal of Pediatric Surgery*, 2019:09.004.

Gregory, Roger T., James S.T. Yao, Rich M. Norman. "The First Gore-Tex Femoral-Popliteal Bypass." *Journal of Vascular Surgery*, 2013: 58, 266–69.

Keese, Parton, "S.O.R.C. Series Victory Unofficially Munequita's." Special to *The New York Times*, March 3, 1973, 22.

Leighninger, Robert. *Big Charity: The History of Charity Hospital*. 64.Parishes. org/the-history-of-charity-hospital. 1–9, March 10, 2020.

Lindsey, Edward S. "In Memoriam-Oscar Creech, Jr, MD." *Synapse*, 2(4), January 1968.

Nance, Francis C., Martin H. Wennar, Lester Johnson, et al. "Surgical Judgment in the Management of Penetrating Wounds of the Abdomen." *Annals of Surgery*, 179(5): 639, 1974.

Null, Donald M., Bradley A. Yoder, and Robert J. DiGeronimo. "Early Neonatal Research at Wilford Hall US Air Force Medical Center." *Pediatrics* 2012:129;S20.

O'Leary, Patrick J. "Isidore Cohn." *American Surgical Association-Transactions*, 1–2; April 4, 2020.

Thomas, Mack A. "Anesthesiology—The John Adriani Story." *The Ochsner Journal* 11(1); Spring, 2011.

Wilds, John and Ira Harkey. *Alton Ochsner: Surgeon of the South*, Louisiana State University Press, 1990.

Wikipedia, Mark Essex, Last modified January 1, 2020

Wikipedia, Upstairs Lounge Arson Attack, Last modified February 2, 2020

Wikipedia, Desire Projects, Last modified February 7, 2020

Wikipedia, Bolivar E. Kemp, Last modified October 9, 2019

Wikipedia, Francis Xavier Seelos, Last modified September 20, 2019

Oral History Miss Emily Alessci 1967

Oral History Miss Felicie Anzalone 1950s

Oral History Mrs. Jerry Cangelosi 1990s

Oral History Dr. James Ciaravella Sr. 1950s

Dr. James Ciaravella.

About the Author

James Ciaravella Jr. was born in New Orleans, Louisiana. He received a Bachelor of Science degree in zoology from Tulane University in 1964 and his MD from Tulane Medical School in 1968. Following a straight surgery internship at Charity Hospital (1968–1969), he completed his general and cardiovascular surgical residency in 1977. He served two years' active duty in the US Air Force (1970–1972), finishing with the rank of major. He served as chief resident on the Tulane Surgical Service and as Assistant Clinical Director at Charity from 1976 to 1977. Following training at Charity

Hospital he was accepted to a special fellowship in cardiac surgery at the Mayo Clinic. In 1978 he was appointed assistant professor of surgery and pediatrics at Children's Hospital National Medical Center in Washington, D.C. In 1980 he moved to Shreveport, Louisiana, where he practiced cardiovascular and thoracic surgery until his retirement in 2003. He then started Dr. C's Designs, making custom Western furnishings, and subsequently began oil painting and sculpting. He has been a juried artist to the Western Design Conference in Jackson Hole, Wyoming, for sixteen years, and has twice served as a judge in that event. His art has served as the cover on three editions of the *Journal of the Louisiana State Medical Society.* His bronze sculpture of the noted Crow chief and historian Dr. Joseph Medicine Crow, the only authorized sculpture of Dr. Medicine Crow, is in the collections of two museums. In 2009 Dr. Ciaravella designed, sculpted, and donated to the city of Shreveport the US Navy SEAL Memorial honoring two of Shreveport's fallen heroes: Lieutenant Commander Jonas Kelsall and Chief Petty Officer Robert Reeves. Dr. Ciaravella and Len, his wife of forty-nine years, live in Shreveport, Louisiana, for half the year and in Alpine, Wyoming, for the other half.

CPSIA information can be obtained
at www.ICGtesting.com
Printed in the USA
BVHW041643160621
609642BV00001B/127

9 781736 154908